STANFORD'S

Geological Atlas
of
Great Britain

T. EASTWOOD

A.R.C.S., M.I.N.N., F.G.S.

Formerly Assistant Director
of the Geological Survey

LONDON
EDWARD STANFORD LIMITED
12–14 LONG ACRE WC2

Stanford's Geological Atlas

was first published in 1904. The present edition
has been entirely re-written and re-drawn.

PRINTED IN GREAT BRITAIN

CONTENTS

CONTENTS

LIST OF ILLUSTRATIONS

Front endpaper Index map to sheets in this atlas
Back endpaper Index and explanation of symbols and delineations employed

PREFACE

THE first edition of Stanford's *Geological Atlas* appeared in 1904 and dealt only with Great Britain. It was modelled on Reynolds's *Geological Atlas*, an excellent work of its time, of which two editions appeared, in 1860 and in 1889. A second edition of Stanford's was published in 1907 and included maps and description of Ireland. A third and still further enlarged edition by H. B. Woodward appeared in 1914; it included an account of the geology of the Channel Islands, amplified descriptions of geological features observable during railway journeys and was accompanied by a *Photographic Supplement*—all excellent material but very unequal in treatment. For example, England was dealt with by counties or groups of counties, Wales, Scotland and Ireland respectively in two north and south portions and the Channel Islands as a unit. English counties vary in size and to accommodate them to the pages the maps varied in scale while grouping upset the alphabetical arrangement; the map of Oxfordshire and Berkshire, for example, preceded that of Cambridgeshire and Huntingdonshire which immediately preceded Cheshire and that of Cornwall. These factors combined with the irregular shapes of our counties made reference across the county border awkward and difficult, for geology bears little or no relation to such boundaries. For these reasons while realizing that certain aspects may call for county treatment, it was decided to abandon that basis and to arrange the maps as a sequence of rectangular sheets all on the same scale with a certain amount of overlap to permit easy reference to neighbouring sheets. Wherever possible the sheet boundaries are chosen to include geological entities even when that requires considerable overlap and the same is true of the accompanying text.

Since Ireland is now a divided country it was felt desirable to revert to the original plan of the Atlas and to omit that country from the present edition. The Channel Islands are also omitted as being nearer to the shores of France than to Britain.

Moreover, since passenger transport today is no longer dominantly by rail, the portions dealing with what may be observed from trains are also omitted, for whether the user travels by rail, by car, by air or on foot the route and the geology may be followed from the maps. Any other course would have required for road users at least similar treatment to that accorded to railway passengers with consequent great increase in volume.

There are fewer figures of fossils in this than in the Woodward edition and this is to be regretted to some extent especially so from the 'collector angle'. From the broader aspect of stratigraphy, however, it is believed that the selection of the principal zonal forms for illustration will more than compensate for this even though the number of such fossils from Jurassic rocks has been sadly reduced in order to retain something like balance between formations.

The figures of fossils, inspired by H. B. Woodward's illustrations, are largely based on those of the Geological Survey Regional Handbooks supplemented by

some from such text-books as Zittel's *Palaeontology*, Kayser-Lake's *Comparative Geology*, Jukes Browne's *Stratigraphical Geology* and Archibald Geikie's *Text Book of Geology*.

The sheets of maps are based primarily on the 'Ten Mile' Map of Great Britain, with the production of which the author was much concerned, though maps of other scales have been laid under contribution.

The maps in the first instance were designed to be on the scale of 8 miles to an inch: they were to be colour printed and were to occupy a pair of facing pages at the beginning of each sheet account. At a late stage, however, colour printing was abandoned by the publishers for economic reasons, the scale reduced to 12 miles to an inch giving single page maps, and for the same reasons photographs of geological interest were discarded. The maps, however, are still perfectly readable geologically and at least will serve as a useful index to the 10 mile maps of the Geological Survey.

The maps are reproduced from the Ordnance Survey and Geological Survey map with the sanction of the Controller of H.M. Stationery Office, and both writer and publisher gratefully acknowledge permission to use this material.

While the horizontal or longitudinal and vertical sections are new in some respects many are based on Geological Survey material, i.e. modified, extended or curtailed from sections published on maps or in memoirs. The sources of these are also acknowledged with thanks.

To his many one-time colleagues on the Geological Survey the writer also tenders his thanks for help, especially to Sheila Warner who is mainly responsible for disentangling many of his drawings and producing such excellent results therefrom. Last but not least to his wife who has patiently read through manuscripts and tolerated much disorder from overwhelming masses of notes and sketches during recent years.

T. EASTWOOD

INTRODUCTION

THIS work purports to be a geological atlas and not a text-book of geology but in order that it may serve a fairly wide public not too familiar with geology some introduction to the science may be desirable. In the first place what is geology? Literally it is the science of the earth but while some geologists speculate as to the interior of the earth the majority are concerned with the investigation of the outer portion or crust. The thickness of this crust, available for examination in some form or other, is equal to the height of the highest mountain (Everest 29,000 ft.) added to the greatest depth of the ocean (34,440 ft. in Philippine Trench of the Pacific) and so amounts to about a dozen miles. The information derived from deep mines (South Africa 9,000 ft.) and borings (25,000 ft. in U.S.A.) though relating to a somewhat less thickness of crust is, however, of greater practical value than the sounding of a colossal sea-depth.

Everyone is conversant with some aspects of geology though he may not be conscious of the fact that geology is involved. This applies equally to the savage using stone implements and to modern man in the atomic-bomb age living in houses of stone, brick (baked clay), concrete (stones and cement), roofed with slates, walking on roadways also of geological origin or travelling by bus or rail, and so dependent on metals dug out of the earth's crust as ores and smelted and refined, using minerals such as fluor or rocks such as limestone for flux and so on. He lives on crops, animal or vegetable, nurtured by geological soils and drinks water in some form or other derived or stored in reservoirs, wells or rivers.

The shape of the ground he traverses is dependent on geological processes or factors. Flat ground may be the alluvium of a river now concealed by buildings or be due to a belt of clay or to a hard band of rock lying horizontally. A hill may be due to the actual hardness of the rock of which it is composed, such as granite, or the shape may be original, such as a volcanic cone or a glacial moraine, but is much more likely to be due to the relative hardnesses of a series of rocks forming the district or to their resistance to weathering processes which depend largely on the presence or absence of cracks. The Downs and the Chilterns, for example, are sculptured out of chalk which though not a hard rock is more resistant to weathering than the underlying clays and sands though hard cemented bands in otherwise soft sands will often produce a steep hill by providing a protective capping, as, for example, Leith Hill in Surrey or the ferruginous band at the top of Edge Hill near Banbury.

Geology then is not only on everyone's doorstep but is encountered everywhere and the object of this atlas is to provide geological data relative to Great Britain in a simple form.

KINDS OF ROCKS

Mention has been made of rocks. To the layman a rock is something hard; to the geologist it is any naturally formed inanimate constituent of the earth's crust

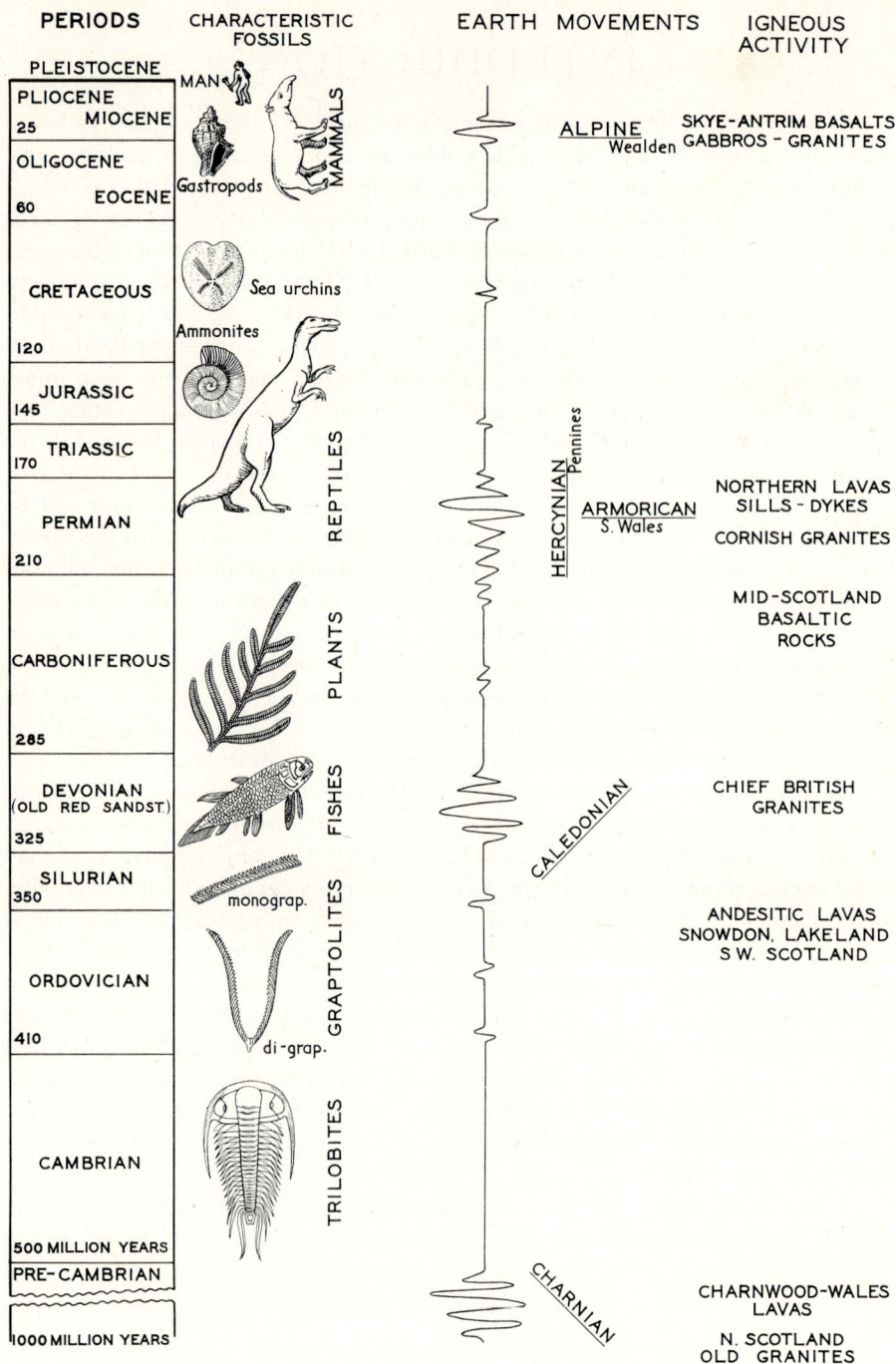

Figure 1. The age of the Earth and its principal events

CHIEF PRODUCTS   FORMATIONS

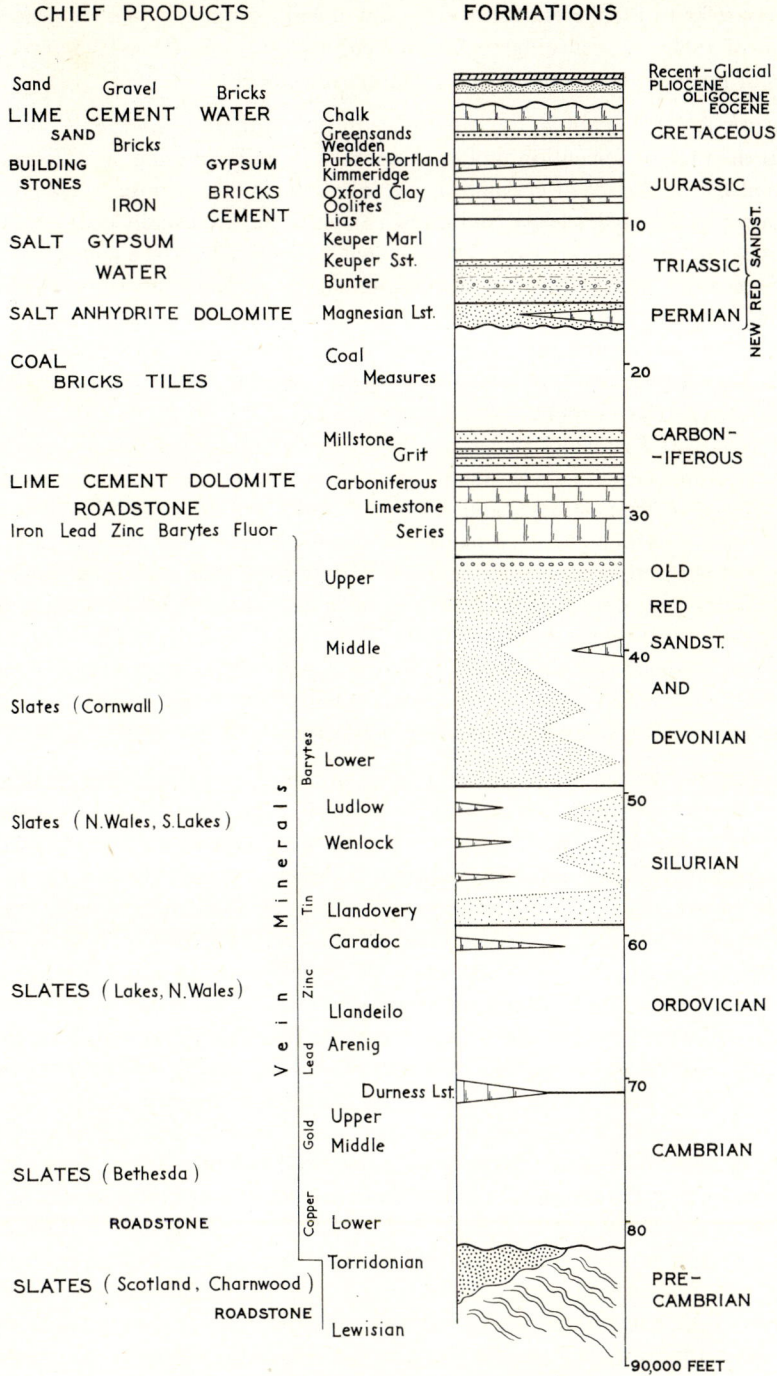

Sand   Gravel   Bricks
LIME CEMENT   WATER   Chalk   Recent–Glacial
   SAND   Bricks   Greensands   PLIOCENE
                                 Wealden   OLIGOCENE
BUILDING   GYPSUM Purbeck–Portland   EOCENE
   STONES   Kimmeridge   CRETACEOUS
                  IRON   BRICKS Oxford Clay   JURASSIC
                        CEMENT   Oolites
                                 Lias   10
SALT GYPSUM   Keuper Marl
                                 Keuper Sst.   TRIASSIC
       WATER   Bunter
                                                          PERMIAN
SALT ANHYDRITE DOLOMITE   Magnesian Lst.

COAL   Coal
     BRICKS TILES   Measures   20

                                 Millstone   CARBON–
                                       Grit   –IFEROUS
LIME   CEMENT DOLOMITE   Carboniferous
     ROADSTONE   Limestone   30
Iron Lead Zinc Barytes Fluor   Series

                                 Upper   OLD

                                                          RED

                                 Middle   SANDST.   40

                                                          AND
Slates (Cornwall)
                                 Lower   DEVONIAN

                                 Ludlow   50
Slates (N.Wales, S.Lakes)
                                 Wenlock

                                 Llandovery   SILURIAN

                                 Caradoc   60
SLATES (Lakes, N.Wales)
                                 Llandeilo   ORDOVICIAN
                                 Arenig

                                 Durness Lst.   70
                                 Upper
                                 Middle   CAMBRIAN

SLATES (Bethesda)
                                 Lower   80
     ROADSTONE
                                 Torridonian

SLATES (Scotland, Charnwood)   PRE–
     ROADSTONE   CAMBRIAN
                                 Lewisian

                                                          90,000 FEET

NEW RED SANDST.

Barytes Tin Zinc Lead Gold Copper

Vein Minerals

Figure 2. Stratal Grouping and Products
(For vein minerals see figures 25 and 26)

3

and may refer to incoherent sand, soft clay or hard granite. A convenient classification of rocks is according to their origin and this results in the three main classes of igneous, sedimentary and metamorphic rocks.

IGNEOUS ROCKS Though not due to fire in the ordinary sense the igneous rocks were at the time of formation molten; they then froze by cooling, at different rates indicated by the degree of crystallization, into solid rocks. Those which solidified deep down in the earth's crust, and known as plutonic, are usually coarsely crystalline masses of considerable size. Those which reached the surface and were poured out of volcanoes as lava flows or blown into the air as fragments to form what are now tuffs, though they may have large crystals are seldom crystalline throughout; these are known as volcanic rocks. An intermediate class filling the cracks or tunnels between the plutonic masses at depth and the volcanoes at surface are known as hyperbyssal rocks.

The above are further classified according to the amount of silica they contain but as rock analyses are costly their composition is estimated as a rule from thin slices ground to transparency and examined under the microscope. This reveals the minerals of which they are made and whose composition is known. On this basis those with much silica or free quartz are termed acid rocks and these range from granites (plutonic) to rhyolites (volcanic lavas). Those with little silica and no free quartz constitute the basic and ultra basic rocks—usually darker and heavier than the acid rocks—ranging respectively from gabbros and serpentines to basalts. Between the two main classes are the intermediate rocks ranging from the plutonic diorites and syenites to andesite, trachyte and rhyolitic lavas.

SEDIMENTARY ROCKS The primeval crust of the newly formed world must have been of igneous origin due to the solidification of molten and gaseous matter such as now forms the sun. The effect of weather on that crust would be to break down the rocks mechanically into fragments and these into pebbles and sand, while chemical weathering of certain constituents, such as the feldspars, would give clays and limestones by setting free silicate of alumina and lime. These would be deposited in the ancient seas which arose by condensation of water vapour and so give rise to the first of the sedimentary rocks. Those we see today may be second-, third-, fourth-hand (or more) for they are made over from existing rocks to form sediments or precipitates and as such are laid down, usually in water, in regular layers, bands or beds—hence their name of stratified or bedded rocks.

Since they are laid down layer by layer in water the sedimentary rocks are liable to entomb animals or plants living at the time. The remains of such organisms are known as fossils. It follows that unless there has been disturbance the lowest layer of a stratified rock should be the oldest and the same will be true of the included fossils. By studying the fossils and sediments it is possible to arrange them in a relative time scale which constitutes the major basis for classification for it must be remembered that the same lithological types of sediments recur in rocks of various ages. Thus, for example, sandstones made from consolidated sand in the Barmouth area of Wales and belonging to some of the oldest stratified rocks with fossils, the

Cambrian, are not markedly different in appearance from much younger sandstones in the Coal Measures of South Wales or indeed from some of the relatively recent sandstones in southern England and the same is true of the compacted clays we know as mudstones and shales. Their fossils on the other hand are markedly different.

On the basis of relative age as indicated by their stratigraphical order and by their fossils the stratified rocks are grouped into systems with subdivisions known as series and so on each characterized by its own rocks and fossils. These are illustrated in very general fashion by Figs. 1 and 2 which also gives some indication of conditions prevailing at the time.

METAMORPHIC ROCKS   As their name implies these rocks are believed to have changed their form and this change usually involves a rearrangement of the chemical constituents so that new minerals appear. Heat is the chief agent and may be provided by the intrusion of a mass of igneous material, as in contact metamorphism, or heat engendered by large-scale movements of the crust where large masses of rock override one another, as in regional metamorphism. In both cases the grade of alteration varies considerably but the nearer to the source of heat the greater the alteration. In extreme cases there is undoubtedly addition or exchange of constituents between the rocks involved giving rise to rocks which otherwise would be regarded as of igneous origin. As an example of contact metamorphism the Skiddaw region of the Lake District may be quoted from many others. Here the invasion of slates by granite has resulted in a wide aureole of metamorphism ranging from little-altered spotted and chiastolite slates through much altered and hardened cordierite hornfels to a narrow band of mica schist at the granite contact. Regional metamorphism is magnificently displayed in the Highlands of Scotland where large tracts of country originally composed of sedimentary and igneous rocks have been altered into a great new series of foliated rocks known as gneisses and schists according to their mineral content and arrangement.

GEOLOGICAL STRUCTURES

Mention has been made of earth movements and of rocks being 'made over'. The original emplacement usually requires some movement of the crust: thus for great thicknesses of strata to accumulate one part of the crust must be sinking while another is rising, so bringing material within the effect of weather and producing the raw materials to be brought down by rivers, wind and so on into the sea as sediments. Most sedimentary rocks accumulated in the sea but some were deposited on land—screes which are now breccias or as dunes of blown sand—and some in lakes and rivers.

These earth movements may be gentle and prolonged or violent. The former are likely to give smooth folds of which the downfolds are known as synclines or basins and the upfolds as anticlines or domes according to shape. The coalfields and the London basin, for example, owe their preservation to downfolds while inter-coalfield areas such as the Pennines and also the Weald are due to upfolds (see

Figs. 32, 37, 39). There are also crust dislocations known as faults; of these the commonest and termed normal faults show more or less vertical displacement or 'throw' of the strata on the two sides of the fracture (see Figs. 50, 53). Complementary pairs of such faults may therefore give similar effects to folds by producing troughs or the upraised portions known as horsts. Faults vary in size from fractions of an inch, such as may be seen for example displacing bands in slates, or with throws of several thousand feet as, for example, in the Central Valley of Scotland. Irrespective of throw they may extend for miles as, for example, some of the mineral veins (which occupy the fault fissures) with throws of 10–50 ft. in the Alston–Weardale area or with large throws restricted in lateral extent as in some of the Cornish lodes and in parts of the Cumberland and Lancashire coalfields (see Figs. 46, 49).

More intense movements give rise to sharp folds such as, for example, in parts of the Lake District or by excess pass into overfolds which by the stretch of the middle limb lose continuity and are then known as reverse faults or thrusts. The latter are common in the Highlands but are not unknown in the coalfields of South Wales and Bristol (see Figs. 34, 35).

Periods of marine deposition followed by periods of uplift, folding, igneous activity and general continental conditions giving red rocks tend to run in cycles. For example the red Torridonian and Old and New Red Sandstones are followed by Cambro–Silurian, Carboniferous, Jurassic–Cretaceous marine sediments though these are not free from interruptions as will be noted in the sequel. An attempt to epitomize some of these major episodes is made in Fig. 2.

Uplifts followed by erosion and then by subsidence and deposition gives rise to unconformity; here some beds are missing and the younger strata do not conform to the older members. Examples are to be seen in many districts as, for instance, in the Settle area of Yorkshire where flat lying Carboniferous Limestone rests on folded lower Palaeozoic slaty rocks, but in many cases the unconformity has to be inferred since no actual sections may be visible. On many of the geological maps, as for example Sheet 3, Trias and Cretaceous strata may be noted in juxtaposition with older rocks of various ages.

From the foregoing it follows that not all members of the geological sequence are present in any one place. For example, tilting of the crust giving a dip or inclination of the strata may be noted in the various members from the oldest to nearly the youngest in passing from the slaty rocks of Wales to London. First on to the red rocks of the Welsh Marches then to the creamy limestones of the Cotswolds (Sheet 7) followed by the clay vales and the Chalk of the Chilterns to the clay of the London Basin (Sheet 6) yet borings almost anywhere along that route will reveal unconformities. Beneath London, for example, (Fig. 32) Lower Greensand well developed just north and south is missing along with strata as far down the scale as the Devonian. For a similar but less complete interruption in the rock sequence the Market Weighton axis between York and Hull may be quoted for its effects on Jurassic strata which thin towards that ridge which was finally overwhelmed by the Chalk sea (see Sheet 15).

The geological map therefore gives what may be expected to occur at the surface

or beneath superficial deposits. What may be present at depth depends on the structure which is really a picture of the geological history. Some of the main events in that history are treated in the sequel but for many the reader must consult text-books, detailed works and memoirs of the Geological Survey.

GEOLOGICAL MAPS AND MEMOIRS

Here attention may be drawn to Geological Survey publications in general.

The One-inch Geological Maps of England and Wales are in two series: an older set of hand-coloured maps, known as Old Series, and the New Series of later date and mostly colour printed. The latter measure 12×18 inches and cover an area of 216 square miles; the former are issued partly as whole sheets and partly as quarter sheets—some of the latter are slightly smaller in size than the New Series sheets.

For Scotland the maps correspond to the English New Series save that they are twice the size.

Prior to 1940 there were one-inch geological maps for the whole of England and Wales and more than half were New Series. During the war stocks were destroyed by enemy action but some are available for reference in college and other libraries. It is unlikely that Old Series will be revived whereas New Series are gradually being reprinted and supplemented by new maps as geological field-work in specific areas is completed. The index of the New Series (Fig. 3b) shows what sheets were available for Great Britain at the end of 1963.

For certain districts special one-inch geological maps are available; they include Isle of Wight, Isle of Man, Anglesey, Bristol, London, Nottingham, Oxford, Glasgow, Assynt and Isle of Arran.

For many parts of Great Britain horizontal (longitudinal) and vertical sections are published to illustrate structure and sequence; these are in addition to those on the margins of recent maps.

For both countries there are quarter-mile maps available save for parts of Scotland.

There are also six-inch maps for many areas—some in manuscript only but available for inspection at the London and Edinburgh offices of the Geological Survey, while others, chiefly of mining regions but also including the London area, are published.

In both England and Wales and in Scotland there are explanatory memoirs mostly either referring to a particular sheet of Old or New Series, and known by that number and by the principal town, or to a district covering several sheets or parts of sheets, especially those of Coalfield areas. There are others, however referring to a particular subject as, for example, that on the Silurian Rocks of Britain of which one volume covers much of the Southern Uplands or the Special Reports on Mineral Resources, now partly superseded by district memoirs such as that on the Northern Pennines and that covering South-west England; while another set of memoirs and pamphlets deal with water supplies from underground sources.

7

All these publications are listed in the Regional Handbooks of the Geological Survey to which attention is frequently drawn in this Atlas.

The geological maps forming this atlas are based on those of the Geological Survey particularly the two sheets of the new 'Ten-Mile' Map but others ranging from the quarter-mile and the one-mile to those on the six-inch scale have been laid under contribution. The individual sheets have been chosen to represent as far as possible individual geological areas. In all cases sufficient overlap has been given to preserve this individuality.

The explanations of the sheets are largely based on the Geological Survey Handbooks of British Regional Geology and on the various sheet, district and special memoirs. To these the reader is referred for further details as well as to such works as *The Jurassic System in Britain* by Arkell, the *Handbook of the Geology of Great Britain*, edited by Evans and Stubblefield, *Geology in the Field* (Geol. Assoc.), the *Journal of the Geological Society of London* and the *Proceedings of the Geologists Association*. The Proceedings also furnish accounts of various excursions to well-known areas as do also the Excursion Guides of the International Congress of 1948. The reader is also recommended to study the exhibits in geological museums such as that of the Geological Survey in South Kensington, those with geological departments such as the Natural History Museum, South Kensington in London, the Royal Scottish Museum in Edinburgh, the National Museum of Wales in Cardiff and the many provincial museums.

REFERENCES

A detailed bibliography would be out of place in a work such as this but in the accounts of the various sheets of the Atlas the reader is referred to the appropriate Geological Survey Handbooks of Regional Geology which in addition to further geological data also give fairly adequate references. Attention, however, is occasionally drawn to particular publications germane to an area as well as to published accounts of excursions in order to further the study of geology in the field. Of major importance are the Proceedings and Pamphlets of the Geologists Association; and this body to mark its centenary is publishing a series of 'Guides' to the geology around university towns, to areas of particular interest and to coastal regions.

Several kindred associations and societies outside London also arrange field meetings for members, notably the Yorkshire Geological Society and those of Edinburgh and Glasgow. There are also 'Excursion Guides' issued in connection with the International Geological Congress held in 1948; of these, 'B' are day trips based on London.

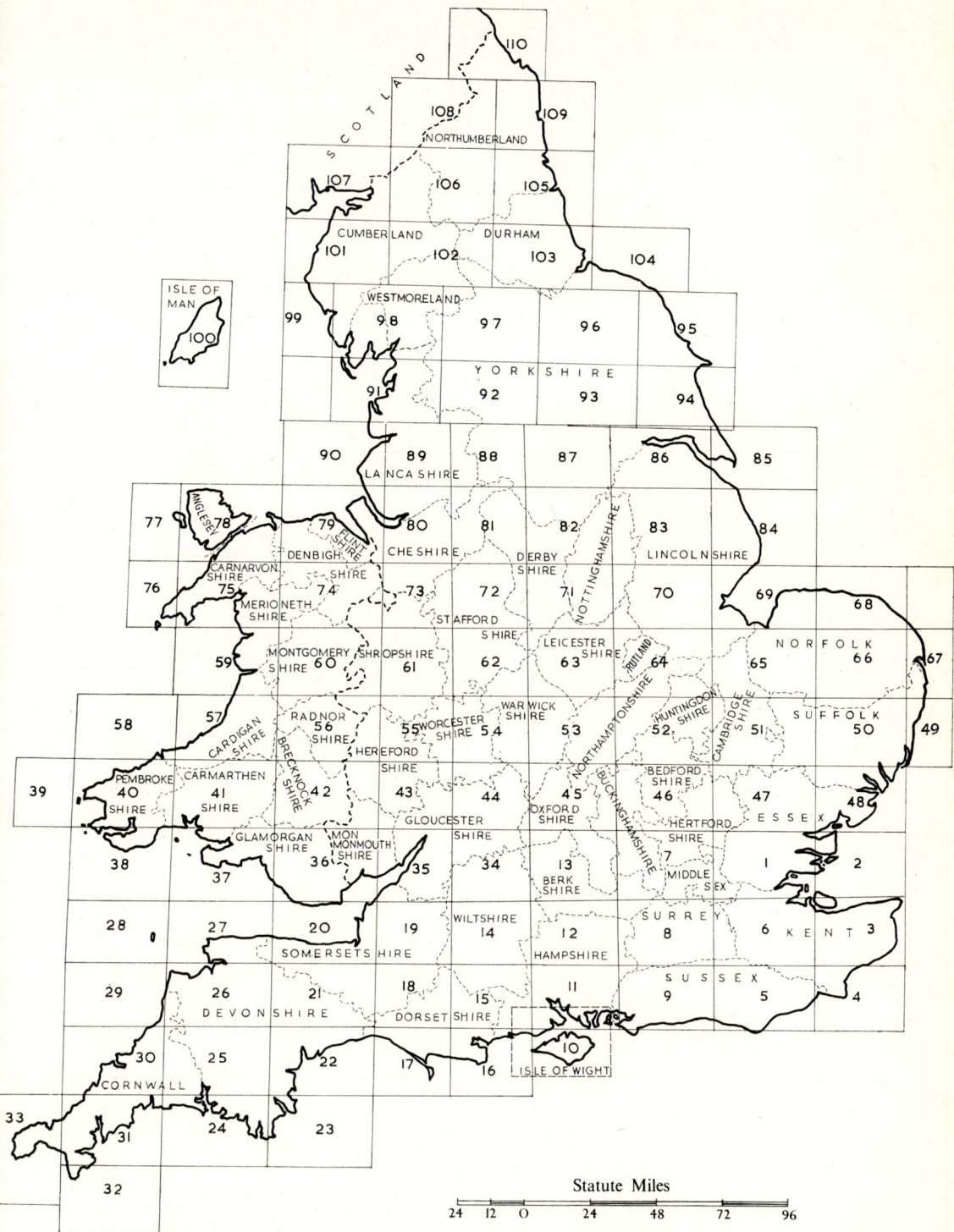

Figure 3a. Index to the Old Series One-inch Geological Map
This series is now out of print, but may be consulted in some old-established libraries

9

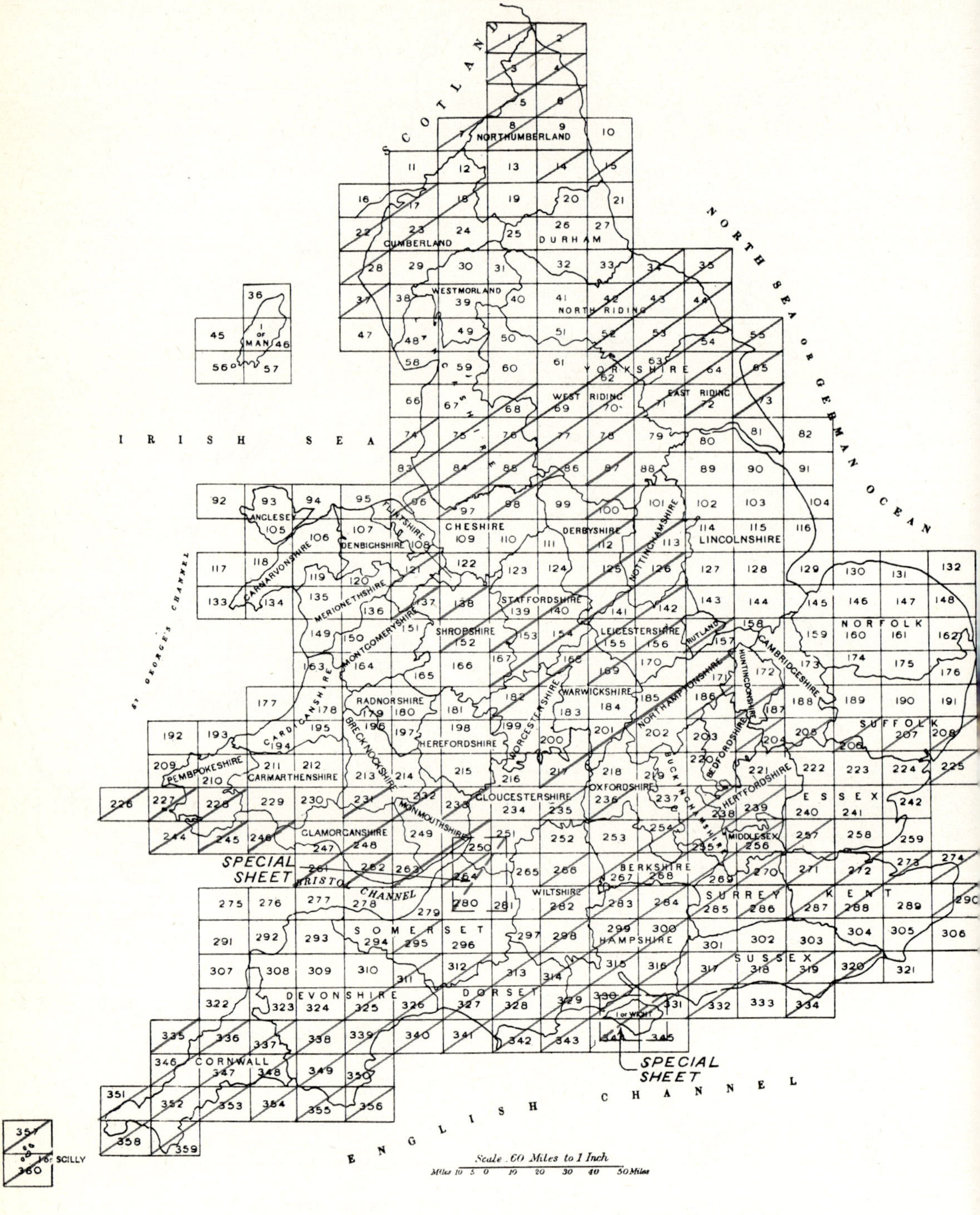

Figure 3b. Index to the New Series One-inch Geological Map
Sheets available at the end of 1963 shown by diagonal lines; some are published as
'Solid', some as 'Drift', others combined 'Solid and Drift'

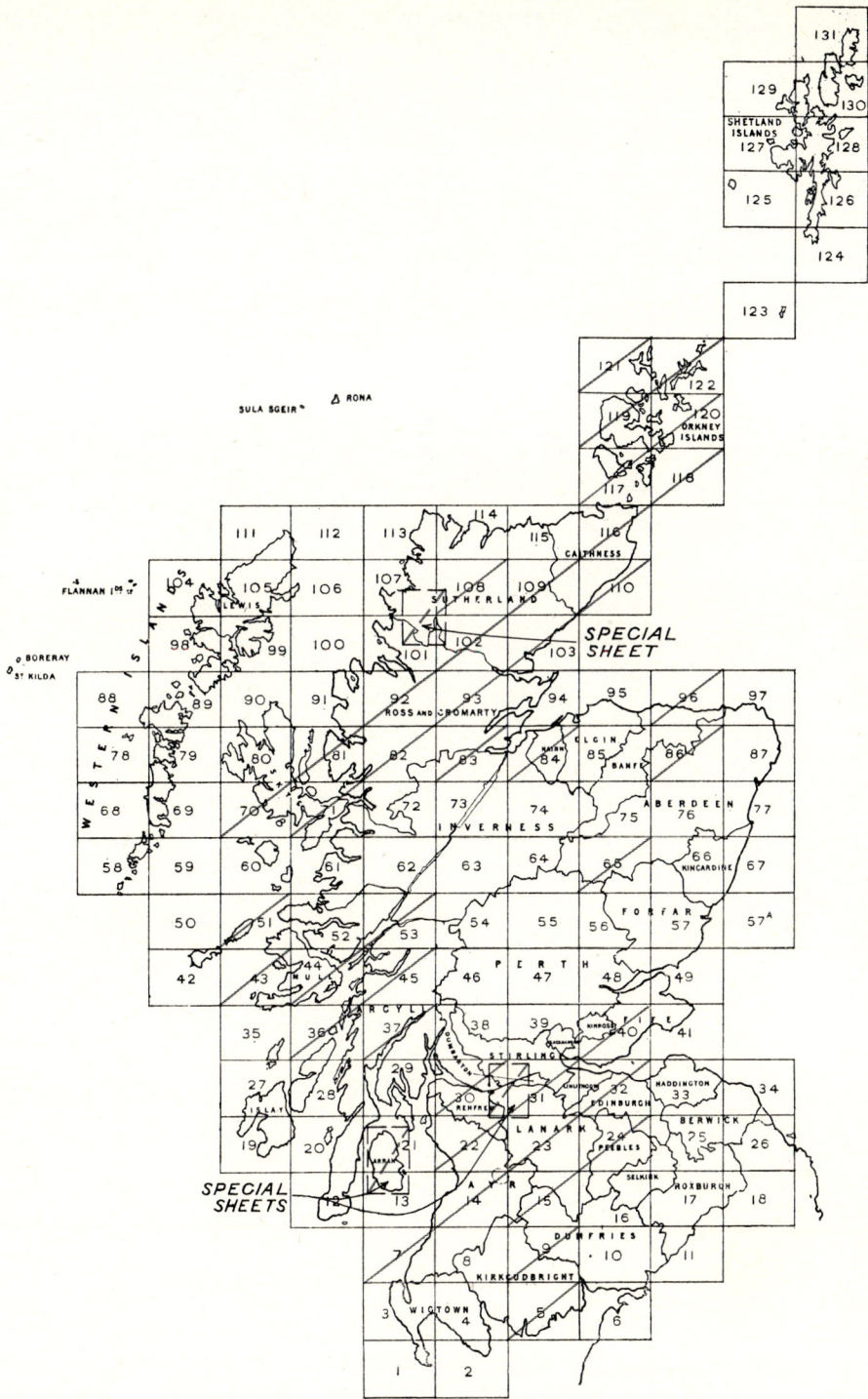

SULA SGEIR○ △ RONA

131

129
130

SHETLAND
ISLANDS
127   128

○   125   126

124

123 &

121
122
119   120
ORKNEY
ISLANDS
117   118

111   112   113   114
                              115   CAITHNESS   116

104
105   106   107   108   109   110
LEWIS   SUTHERLAND

FLANNAN I○○   *SPECIAL*
                                                SHEET

98   99   100   101   102   103

○ BORERAY
○ ST KILDA

88   89   90   91   92   93   94   95   96   97
                              ROSS AND CROMARTY

78   79   80   81   82   83   84   85   86   87
                                        NAIRN ELGIN BANFF

68   69   70   71   72   73   74   75   76   77
W E S T E R N   I N V E R N E S S   A B E R D E E N

58   59   60   61   62   63   64   65   66   67
                                                      KINCARDINE

50   51   52   53   54   55   56   57   57ᴬ
                                                F O R F A R

42   43   44   45   46   47   48   49
            MULL   P E R T H

35   36   37   38   39   40   41
A R G Y L L   KINROSS F I F E

27   28   29   30   31   32   33   34
ISLAY   DUMBARTON RENFREW EDINBURGH HADDINGTON
                  STIRLING LINLITHGOW   BERWICK

19   20   21   22   23   24   25   26
            ARRAN   L A N A R K PEEBLES SELKIRK

SPECIAL   12   13   14   15   16   17   18
SHEETS   A Y R   ROXBURGH

                  7   8   9   10   11
                        DUMFRIES
                  KIRKCUDBRIGHT

3   4   5   6
WIGTOWN

1   2

Scale :— 60 Miles to 1 Inch

11

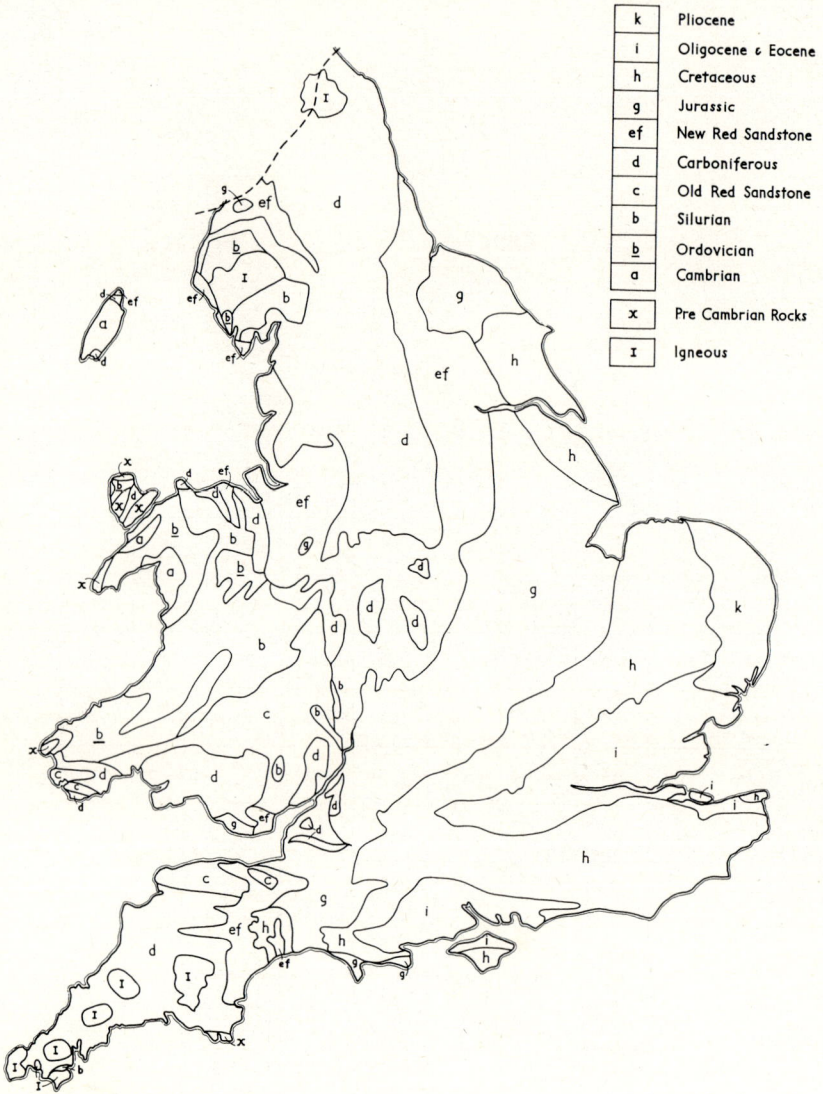

k	Pliocene
i	Oligocene & Eocene
h	Cretaceous
g	Jurassic
ef	New Red Sandstone
d	Carboniferous
c	Old Red Sandstone
b	Silurian
<u>b</u>	Ordovician
a	Cambrian
x	Pre Cambrian Rocks
I	Igneous

Figure 4. Simplified Geological Map of England and Wales

STRATIGRAPHY

It is now possible to discuss the various formations occurring in Great Britain. For convenience distribution of the major outcrop of the rocks comprising the systems dealt with below are indicated on the small scale generalized geological maps of England and Wales and of Scotland on pages 12 and 14. They are treated in more detail on the Sheet Maps and in the descriptive accounts of those sheets.

PRE-CAMBRIAN The rocks of the pre-Cambrian include little-altered sedimentary and igneous types but metamorphosed foliated rocks derived from them, such as gneisses and schists, predominate especially in Scotland. There, north of the Highland Boundary Fault, which extends from Stonehaven to the Firth of Clyde, they cover extensive tracts of country as well as forming much of the Hebrides. In Britain relatively small patches emerge from beneath Cambrian and later rocks in Wales, the Midlands and in Cornwall but these also include contrasting types.

In the absence of fossils and in the presence of varying lithology emphasized by folding and metamorphism and with rocks displaced by gigantic thrusts it is difficult to determine relative ages of many of the rock masses but the coarse Lewisian gneisses are usually regarded as the oldest with a mixed series of rocks in various stages of alteration, that are classed as Moine and Dalradian, intervening between the Lewisian and the little altered or disturbed Torridonian red sandstones and conglomerates.

Igneous rocks, both volcanic and intrusive, predominate in the Midlands—Charnwood Forest, Nuneaton, South Staffordshire and eastern Shropshire—but grits and shales appear in the Longmynd of Shropshire. A mixed series of gneisses, quartzites and other altered sediments with volcanic and plutonic igneous rocks make up much of Anglesey, western Caernarvonshire and Cornwall whereas those in the intervening area of South Wales are mainly volcanic.

In addition to occupying part of the surface pre-Cambrian rocks form the platform on which later rocks rest. They have been found, for example, in various parts of the English Midlands and as far east as Norfolk.

Economic products—Road metal, Charnwood; slates, Charnwood and Scotland. Mineral deposits: lead, zinc, barytes of Islay, Strontian and Tyndrum in western Scotland.

CAMBRIAN As the name indicates rocks of the Cambrian system are well developed in Wales, particularly north of Barmouth, but isolated outcrops of them appear in the Midlands—near Church Stretton, Malvern, Birmingham and Nuneaton—and they have been located beneath Mesozoic rocks in boring north of London at Calvert. Farther north the lower unexposed portion of the Skiddaw Slates of Lakeland and part of the Manx Slates may perhaps belong to the Cambrian but it is not until the north-west Highlands are reached that the rocks are again developed in force and carry diagnostic fossils.

g	Jurassic
ef	New Red Sandstone
d	Carboniferous
c	Old Red Sandstone
b	Silurian
<u>b</u>	Ordovician
a	Cambrian
x	Schists & Pre-Cambrian
I	Igneous

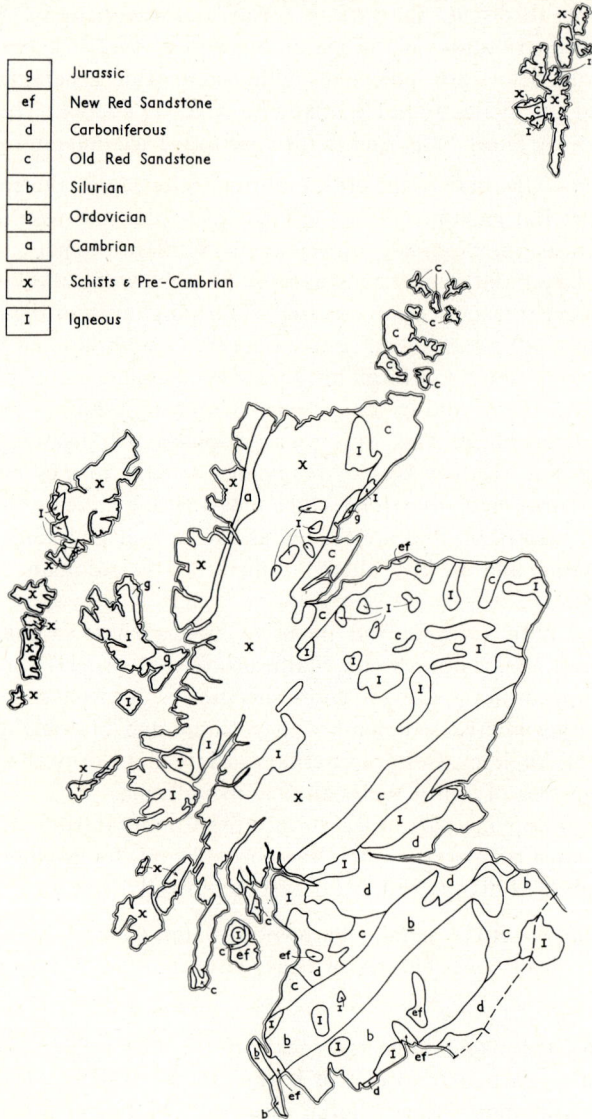

Figure 5. Simplified Geological Map of Scotland

In most areas sandstones and grits (or quartzites as in the Midlands) tend to predominate in the lower part of the system whereas shaly beds are more abundant at higher levels. It is only in Scotland that there is a marked development of limestone—the Durness Limestone—and that high in the sequence with some fossils suggestive of Ordovician age, though thin limestones are present in the Midland sequences.

Trilobites are the characteristic fossils though other forms are present, especially brachiopods, and in the uppermost beds with a shaly sequence the many-branched graptolite *Dictyonema*. The trilobites form the basis of the stratigraphical-palaeontological subdivisions, see Fig. 6.

Economic products—Slates, Snowdon area; road metal, Midlands; gold, Dolgelly, manganese, Barmouth.

ORDOVICIAN   The name was proposed by Lapworth to cover the then debatable strata between the Cambrian of Sedgwick and the Silurian of Murchison, and is taken from the Ordovices an ancient tribe occupying that stratal territory.

The rocks are of two marine facies: (*a*) a shallow water one comprising sandstones and shales with occasional limestones and (*b*) deep water shales and mudstones. The latter carry graptolites as characteristic fossils; these though less common in the shallow water facies serve to correlate the two; the chief fossils, however, in the shallow type are trilobites and brachiopods. On the basis of fossils the system is divided into the following ascending series: Arenig, Llanvirn, Llandeilo, Caradoc, Ashgill. The first three names are derived from type localities in Wales; Caradoc from the Church Stretton area and Ashgill from Lakeland. Fossils are illustrated in Fig. 7.

The deep water facies as a whole is confined to the Moffat area of Southern Scotland; farther west, at Girvan, shallow water types appear at intervals. In England (Lake District and Shropshire), Isle of Man and Wales, the shallow water types predominate. The strata are more restricted in occurrence than the Cambrian and Silurian.

With the sediments of both facies are associated volcanic rocks; these include lavas ranging chiefly from andesites to rhyolites and tuffs and agglomerates of similar composition. While volcanic activity is represented throughout the system it reached its peak about the middle of the succession as, for example, the Borrowdale Series of Lakeland and in Snowdonia.

Economic products—Slates, as cleaved tuffs of the Borrowdale Series, in Lake District; ordinary slates, Blaenau Ffestiniog; bricks and tiles, Caernarvonshire; lead, zinc, barytes, formerly graphite and copper, Lake District; lead, Conway Valley of Wales, Shropshire, Leadhills and Wanlockhead of south-west Scotland.

SILURIAN   The name was given by Murchison in 1835 to strata in Wales and its borders in territory formerly occupied by the Silures. The rocks, however, extend through the Lake District into southern Scotland and underlie more recent strata over much of Britain from which they emerge in several places in the Midlands though deeply buried elsewhere as at Ware and at Harwich.

The main area of sedimentation was in a depression, ranging from south Scotland and the Lake District to North Wales, in which sinking and deposition kept pace (geosyncline). Here thick deposits of ill-sorted and ill-graded sands and muds have given rise to sandstones, shales and mudstones; these are deficient in lime but carry pyrite. On the flanks conditions were more stable, sorting was better giving cleaner shales, mudstones and sandstones, and lime was abundant enough to provide massive limestones as, for example, in south Staffordshire and Shropshire.

Fossils are chiefly graptolites and brachiopods. The former are single-branched as opposed to the tuning-fork and extended double-tined forms of the Ordovician and are more especially characteristic of the deeper water sediments, while the shells dominate the marginal facies though both are sufficiently widespread to act as links in correlation. Fossils of other types are fairly common and include trilobites, lamellibranchs, starfish and corals; some of the limestones are particularly rich in corals. The following series in ascending order are characterized by the shells and graptolites mentioned though the list is not complete. Llandovery or Valentian: *Pentamerus oblongus*, *Monograptus sedgwicki* and *M. crenulatus*, *Rastrites maximus*. Wenlock: *Cardiola interrupta* and the trilobites *Phacops* and *Calymene; Cyrtograptus*. Ludlow: *Chonetes striatella* and *Conchidium knighti; Monograptus leintwardinensis*. See Fig. 8.

Igneous activity was nowhere marked if the emplacement of some of the large granite masses of Scotland ascribed to this period be excepted.

Economic products—Slates (Burlington Blue) of southern Lake District; lead and zinc deposits of Central Wales and Newton Stewart; copper of Anglesey; lime, Midlands and Shropshire.

DEVONIAN During the Devonian period two contrasting types of sedimentation took place: (*a*) the Devonian confined to Devonshire and neighbouring counties, consisting of grey sandstones and shales with, in places, thick limestones, and containing a variety of marine fossils and (*b*) the Old Red Sandstone so named to distinguish it from the New Red Sandstone; these formations respectively precede and follow the Carboniferous rocks. The Old Red Sandstone consists of sandstones, conglomerates and marls, dominantly red in colour though in part grey or green, with occasional peculiar limestone bands known as cornstones. These red rocks indicate that continental if not actual desert conditions prevailed at the time; the chief fossils are the remains of non-marine fishes and the period is sometimes known as the age of fishes though shells such as *Lingula* occur and some lowly plants. The Old Red Sandstone extends from north of the Bristol Channel to the west Midlands covering much of Herefordshire; northwards it does not reappear until the Cheviots are reached though some basal Carboniferous conglomerates and other rocks are claimed by some authors as Old Red Sandstone. In Scotland it forms much of the ground bordering the Midland Valley and there are large areas of it north of the Highland Boundary Fault in Aberdeenshire, around Inverness and in Caithness and extending still farther north to cover most of the Orkneys and part of Shetland. Although the rocks of the two facies are usually markedly

different some resemblance is claimed between those of South Wales and those of North Devon. Moreover, *Pteraspis* occurs in both Lower Old Red Sandstone and Lower Devonian. The plane of division between the Silurian and Devonian or Old Red Sandstone is a matter of opinion. Some authors wish to include as uppermost Silurian great thicknesses of red mostly argillaceous strata from the conformable sequence through grey then red Downtonian strata.

The dying out of graptolites below the Ludlow Bone Bed and the incoming of fish there, together with change in colour and lithology, suggests the use of that bed as the boundary and it is so used here. Apart from lithology the threefold subdivision of the Old Red Sandstone is based on fishes; that of the Devonian on brachiopods, corals and trilobites, see Fig. 9. Lower Old Red Sandstone is characterized by *Pteraspis* and *Cephalaspis*; the Middle by *Pterichthys* and *Coccosteus*; the Upper by *Holoptychius* and *Bothriolepis*. See Fig. 10.

The sequence appears to be complete in Scotland though over great tracts of country one or other subdivision is absent. In England and Wales most of the middle of the formation is missing and Upper Old Red Sandstone is markedly transgressive. On the other hand there is an upward passage into the Carboniferous.

The Old Red Sandstone was a period of folding; uplift permitted denudation and the provision of conglomerates, sandstones and marls which now constitute the formation. Folding is particularly marked along south-west—north-east lines (Caledonian). It was accompanied or followed by great igneous activity resulting in the emplacement of large masses of granite, gabbros and allied rocks in Scotland, the Cheviots and the Lake District, by dyke intrusions, and in the widespread eruptions of lavas and tuffs mostly in Scotland though represented in Devon.

Economic products—Brick-making on limited scale from clayey beds of Old Red Sandstone. Building stones, flags and tilestones from sandstones; pebbly sandstones provide millstones for cider presses. Lime, building stone and marble from Devonian limestone. Delabole Slates from Cornish Devonian. Road metal from igneous rocks. Mineral deposits include tungsten ores of Carrock, barytes in south-west Scotland and Arran.

CARBONIFEROUS The strata are so named because they include most of the deposits of coal. They fall into three main subdivisions. In the lowest, the Carboniferous Limestone Series, limestone predominates over most of England and Wales but in northern England beds of limestone are separated by considerable thicknesses of shale and sandstone (Yoredale facies) often with a coal seam between an upper limestone and a lower sandstone. At lower horizons these thick sandstones (Fell Sandstones) and alternations of thin limestones and shales (Cementstones) appear and continue into Scotland. The base of the formation is not always at the same horizon; in the Bristol area, for example, there is a transition from Old Red Sandstone whereas in North Wales and parts of northern England limestones much higher in the sequence rest on older rocks, usually with the intervention of conglomerate.

Millstone Grit, the middle member, when typically developed, as in Lancashire and Yorkshire, consists of thick sandstones and grits (formerly used for millstones) separated by shales. North and south of these counties, however, the measures are often thin and insignificant and apart from fossils would be classed with the lower part of the Coal Measures. The latter carry the main coal seams amidst rocks, predominantly grey, of shales, mudstones and sandstones. These productive measures are succeeded by a very variable series of rocks, largely red or purple in colour, included in the Upper Coal Measures.

The fossils of the Carboniferous include representatives of most groups of animals and, as might be expected, many plants though not of the flowering kinds. Fossils indicate that marine conditions predominated in the Carboniferous Limestone Series, are less prevalent in the Millstone Grit and mere episodes in the Coal Measures. For zonal classification and correlation brachiopods and corals are used in the Limestone Series with goniatites forming links with those of the Millstone Grit and the Coal Measures. Zoning in the Coal Measures, however, is largely based on non-marine lamellibranchs and on plants.

In Devon and Cornwall Carboniferous strata are of shales, with thin dark limestones and radiolarian cherts and sandstones, known as the Culm Series from the occurrence of occasional seams of sooty coal locally called culm. The beds are much folded and dislocated by thrusts so that true structure and sequence is not obvious but fossils, including goniatites, lamellibranchs and plants, indicate that the Culm embraces strata of Coal Measures, Millstone Grit and Carboniferous Limestone ages.

Igneous activity during Carboniferous times is mainly volcanic with subsidiary dykes; there are no large intrusive masses. Activity was marked on the site of the Midland Valley of Scotland and of the Border country. There are small areas in Cumberland, Isle of Man, Derbyshire, Midlands and south-west England. The rocks are dominantly of basaltic types.

Economic products—Coal is the most important and is mainly derived from the grey Coal Measures though some is obtained from the Millstone Grit of the Pennines and from the Limestone Series of northern England and Scotland. Iron ore in the form of carbonate nodules was until recently of importance from the Coal Measures; the more valuable red oxide, haematite, is restricted to the limestone of West Cumberland, Furness, North Wales, Forest of Dean and Cardiff areas. Lead, zinc, barytes, witherite, fluorspar are or have been important ores from veins chiefly in the limestones of the Pennines, north-east Wales and Mendips. The limestones also furnish lime, building stone and marble, fluxes, cement and roadstone. Sandstones provide building and paving stones, flags, tilestones, grindstones and roadstones; the shales and clays both of the grey and red measures bricks and tiles, and the fireclays refractory and sanitary ware. In Ayrshire bauxitic clays from the decay of Millstone Grit lavas provide refractory material.

PERMIAN   The system takes its name from Perm in Russia where it was established by Murchison. In Britain it and the succeeding Trias constitute the New Red Sandstone.

From Northumberland to Nottingham the Permian consists largely of the Magnesian Limestone resting on thin Marl Slate and basal Yellow Sands and divided and succeeded by Permian Marls. West of the Pennines there is very little limestone and the bulk of the strata assigned to the Permian consists of the windblown Penrith Sandstone and/or breccia representing washed out scree material; these are followed by the red St. Bees Shales and St. Bees Sandstone—the latter being regarded as Trias and largely of Bunter age. Some breccias in the Midlands and breccias and sandstones in Devon are also referred to the Permian. In southern Scotland a bright coloured aeolian sandstone represents Penrith Sandstone; it is accompanied by breccias and by thick lavas and some tuffs. There are some volcanic rocks in Devon but of greater importance are the large granite masses and associated dykes of Devon and Cornwall emplaced during this period. About the same time the Whin Sill of Northern England was intruded into the Carboniferous strata.

The Permian rests unconformably on earlier rocks and between its formation and that of the Coal Measures the latter were consolidated, folded into basins and partly denuded. The folding was on north-south, east-west lines as exemplified by the Pennines and by the South Wales Coalfield.

A tendency towards aridity shown by the red Upper Coal Measures became more pronounced and the seas in which the dolomitic limestones and the associated salt and gypsum deposits were laid down became ultra saline with the result that such animals as survived were stunted. Many, including trilobites and goniatites, did not survive the upheaval. Typical fossils are shown in Fig. 14. Plants are known from certain horizons—usually grey beds such as those of Hilton near Penrith.

Economic products—The Magnesian Limestone yields lime, refractories and building stones. Interbedded with the marls are the salt of Hartlepool and the anhydrite of Billingham, the gypsum of the Eden Valley and north-west coast.

Roadstones are provided by the igneous rocks. The granites of Cornwall and Devon and associated slaty rocks carry veins of tin, wolfram, copper, lead and zinc etc., and the chemical decay of the granites provides china clay.

TRIAS This, the upper part of the New Red Sandstone, is so named from its tripartite arrangement of Bunter, Muschelkalk and Keuper on the continent of Europe but in Britain the middle series is not recognizable.

The Bunter consists of red and variegated sandstones often of windblown grains and of dune form (Lower and Upper Mottled Sandstones) with, in the middle part, conglomerates (Bunter Pebble Beds) in which the pebbles are predominantly of quartzite. The Keuper has a basal red or buff sandstone of variable grain (Lower Keuper Sandstone) followed by a thick series of red mudstones and shales (Keuper Marl) with beds of salt and of gypsum, thin dolomitic sandstones (skerries) and in places a sandstone known as the Upper Keuper or Arden Sandstone. The topmost beds, interleaved with green shales or wholly green in colour are styled the Tea-green Marls.

The whole formation bespeaks desert conditions. Fossils are few but include small reptiles, as at Elgin, spiders and water fleas.

In Scotland there are only scattered patches of Triassic rocks but in England the outcrop has the form of a Y flanking the Pennines with a stalk reaching to Devonshire. Trias also extends a considerable distance beneath newer rocks.

Economic products—Building stones (especially Keuper). Moulding sands (Bunter). Gravel (Pebble Beds). Salt (Isle of Man, Lancashire, Cheshire, Stafford, Worcester, Somerset). Gypsum (Newark and Tutbury, Somerset–Gloucester). Celestine (Yate, Gloucestershire). Copper (Cheshire). Bricks and tiles from Keuper Marl. The sandstones yield large supplies of water usually of excellent quality; that in the Burton area carries gypsum in solution and is particularly suitable for brewing.

RHAETIC   An abrupt change in lithology occurs at the summit of the Keuper with the appearance of black and grey shales with thin limestones and sandstones and abundant fossils. These are known as the Rhaetic Beds and mark a definite marine transgression. By some authors they are included with the Trias; others prefer to regard them as Jurassic. They usually total about 40 feet in thickness and extend from Devon to the Yorkshire coast with patches still farther north in East Sutherland and in Mull. Characteristic fossils are the oyster *Pteria contorta* and various pectens but the most important are the vertebrate remains in the bone beds and the earliest British mammal *Microlestes*.

JURASSIC   This system of rocks, named after the Jura Mountains, is composed of clays or shales and limestones; sandstones are not much in evidence but in some districts there are great developments of bedded ironstones.

The Lias forms the lowest part of the Jurassic strata; argillaceous sediments predominate though these are interspersed with thin limestones. In the next group oolitic limestones alternate with thick belts of clay which serve as a rough means of subdivision. The basal Inferior Oolite and the succeeding Great Oolite limestones are of considerable thickness and importance in the Cotswolds but diminish north-eastwards from Oxfordshire though part of the Inferior Oolite formation farther north thickens to become the Lincolnshire Limestone. The other limestones are thin except those of Portland and Purbeck which as such are confined to the southern counties. One, the Corallian, fails abruptly east of Oxford and is replaced by the Ampthill Clay with the result that the three clays of Oxford, Ampthill and Kimmeridge form one clay belt.

Although the total thickness of the Jurassic is far less than that of the Carboniferous its subdivisions are much more numerous. This is due to the alternations of well marked beds with characteristic fossils and to the gentle dips. This combination gives a terraced effect easy to follow so that it is not surprising that the early mapping of the pioneer William Smith was of these beds. Although many of the individual formations may be traced for miles there are, as already indicated, considerable changes in crossing the country from Dorset to North Yorkshire. Some of the most startling changes take place in the vicinity of the Humber and are attributed to the influence of the Market Weighton Anticline, for this upfold continued to move until the time when the Chalk was laid down. In Yorkshire many

of the formations of the south are not recognizable as such. Farther north, in Scotland, patches of Jurassic rocks are restricted to the west coastal tract and its neighbouring islands and to the vicinity of the Moray Firth.

The Jurassic period has been called the age of reptiles and complete skeletons of large beasts have been found in the argillaceous formations; of more importance, however, from a stratigraphical standpoint, are the ammonites on which the zoning of the strata depends though there is a wealth of other shells many of which characterize certain beds. Plants, hitherto largely gymnosperms, now include true flowering species. (See Figs. 15, 16, 17).

The period was one of quiescence; earth movements were slight and igneous activity dormant. Most of the sediments are marine though some are deltaic in origin. Borings reveal that over much of eastern and south-east England land conditions frequently prevailed during Jurassic times with the result that many formations are absent there.

Economic products—The oolites furnish excellent freestones for building, as, for example, the Bath and Portland Oolites and the Lincolnshire Limestone; some parts of the limestones are sufficiently fissile to provide roofing material such as the Stonesfield Slate of the Witney area and Collyweston Slate near Stamford; most furnish lime and some of the argillaceous limestones and clays are used in cement manufacture, as in the Lias near Rugby and the Inferior Oolite at Ketton. Most of the clays are used for brick-making, but from the Oxford Clay between Bicester and Peterborough more bricks are made than from any other formation in Britain, and the ironstones of the Lias and the Inferior Oolite formation from Yorkshire to Banbury provide the bulk of home ore. The Lias of Raasay also has a bed of iron ore. Whitby, famous for its jet, was at one time the seat of alum manufacture. In north-east Scotland a Jurassic coal is worked at Brora and some of the thin coals of the Estuarine Series in Yorkshire were workable about Coxwold. At Robertsbridge near Hastings beds of gypsum in the Purbeck are mined extensively.

CRETACEOUS The Cretaceous system takes its name from the Chalk though that formation only forms the upper half of the strata included in the system; the lower half is a variable series of clays and sands, with occasional limestones, interrupted by many unconformities. The scientific division between Upper and Lower Cretaceous, however, is placed below the Chalk at the base of a clay bed known as the Gault which normally separates two Greensand formations. In the south of England the system begins with a belt of sandrock with minor clays (Hastings Sands, Tunbridge Wells Sand) followed by the Weald Clay and this in turn by the Lower Greensand. In Lincolnshire the beds include limestone and ironstone and on the Yorkshire coast are represented by the marine Speeton Clays; north of Yorkshire no Lower Cretaceous beds are known. They are absent even beneath London and elsewhere are often transgressed.

The Gault and Upper Greensand are followed by the Chalk, a formation over 1,000 feet thick which exhibits only minor differences across country from the south coast to Flamboro' Head. No Chalk has been found *in situ* in Scotland

though fragments of it occur in glacial drift and in volcanic agglomerates. Upper Greensand is present in patches in Mull and Morven.

Ammonites so prolific in the Jurassic develop uncoiled shells before they die out in the Chalk though beautiful coiled specimens may be got from the Gault. Lamellibranchs, brachiopods, sea urchins and sea lilies are relatively common and some of them are used for zoning purposes (see Fig. 19). Fish teeth are by no means rare and some of the Wealden strata yield bones of giant reptiles such as *Iguanodon*, while others are rich in plants.

Economic products—Common bricks are made from the clays and some of the sands furnish bricks and tiles of high quality as well as providing sands for building, moulding, refractory ware and glass making. Some of the harder and also the limy sandrocks are used for building but the use of chalk faced with flint is commoner. Some of the thin limestones of the Weald were polished as marble (Paludina Limestone). The Wealden iron ores and the phosphatic coprolites of Cambridge once important are no longer used. Fuller's earth is worked near Nutfield in Surrey. Chalk furnishes lime and when mixed with clay, cement. Horsham Stone a fissile sandstone of the Wealden provided much roofing material.

TERTIARY The clear seas of the Chalk were shallowed by uplift but the record is incomplete in Britain where the Tertiary strata are not only unconformable but of restricted occurrence and thickness. The systems into which the Tertiary is subdivided bear little comparison with those of the older strata of Britain and for that reason are here dealt with as a whole.

In the Eocene the London Clay, a dull blue-grey clay of marine origin, is the most important subdivision. Through it most of London's underground railways are tunnelled. Above and below it come a mixed series of sands, loams and clays. The marine Thanet Sand at the base is followed by mottled clays, sands and pebble beds, partly marine partly freshwater, classed as Woolwich and Reading Beds and Oldhaven and Blackheath Beds. Above the London Clay come the Bagshot Sands interleaved with the clayey Bracklesham Beds. There are outliers of these capping London Clay on Highgate, Hampstead and Harrow hills but they are more widespread about Woking and Bagshot and cover large areas in the New Forest and the Isle of Wight.

The only Eocene in Scotland is furnished by the leaf beds amidst the lava flows of Mull and Skye.

The fossils of the Eocene include a small proportion of forms now living and the rest are not dissimilar though many are of tropical and subtropical forms especially amongst the plants. The change from the Cretaceous is emphasized by the great unconformity between them and the contrast in the sediments. This change prevented the survival of many forms; for example corals, sea urchins and brachiopods are almost entirely replaced by gastropods and lamellibranchs. See Fig. 20.

Oligocene strata are mostly confined to the Hampshire Basin and there consists of clays, sands and thin limestones, but in Devon include the pottery clays and lignites of Bovey Tracey. Fauna and flora show an increasing resemblance to modern forms. See Fig. 21.

No beds of undoubted Miocene age are known in Britain largely because of earth movement at that time.

On the other hand deposits hitherto classed as Pliocene cover wide areas in East Anglia where the shelly sands are known as White or Coralline Crag, Red Crag and so on. These Crag deposits are followed by the Cromer Forest Bed Series that contain many arctic forms of plants and shells and thus provide a link with glacial conditions. The boundary between Pliocene and the more recent Pleistocene is debatable, however, and has been successively lowered until now only the lowest or White Crag, restricted to the vicinity of Orford Ness, is referred to the Pliocene. Outside East Anglia there are remnants of probable Pliocene as far apart as Lenham in Kent and St. Erth in Cornwall.

Mention has been made of earth movement during Tertiary time, and to this period the downfold which has preserved the London Clay in the London basin and the upfold of the Weald which led to the formation of the North and South Downs by denudation is ascribed, as well as the doming of the Lake District with its consequent radial drainage (see page 195). Earth movements are often accompanied by igneous action and the profound igneous activity in Western Scotland, particularly between the Outer Hebrides and the mainland (and also in Antrim) is related to this phase. Apart, however, from restricted occurrences of associated leaf beds of Eocene age there are no other sediments useful for fixing the period of activity. In England on the other hand, where Tertiary strata are widespread in the area south-east of a line from Cromer to Weymouth there are no igneous rocks.

In Scotland there are three successive phases of activity (a) volcanic, (b) plutonic, (c) minor intrusions. In the volcanic phase basaltic lavas predominate; the plutonic phase ranges from ultrabasic peridotites through gabbros to granites and the minor intrusions also include several types. South of the Border the Cleveland Dyke of northern England, the Butterton Dyke of the Midlands and the Wolf Rock in the Channel are believed to belong to the same period.

Economic products—London Clay provides some bricks but of greater value are the ceramic and pipe clays of Bovey Tracey and Poole. Sands and gravels have been worked for building purposes but today the 'second-hand' deposits of terraces etc. are more important.

PLEISTOCENE AND RECENT With these deposits which range from the Pliocene to the present day this atlas is not much concerned. It is necessary, however, to point out that these modern and as a rule unconsolidated deposits mask, to varying extents, the outcrops of the so-called solid rocks so far described.

Under Pleistocene are included boulder clay, glacial sands and gravels, some of the high level terraces of rivers and so on. It is difficult in places to differentiate between Glacial or Pleistocene and recent deposits of terraces, alluvium, raised beaches, peats, blown sand and the like but the former contain many types of plants and amimals extinct or no longer living in the region; for example, the mastodon, mammoth, cave-bear, tiger, etc. In the latter the works of man in the form of implements, ornaments, pottery and the like serve as zone fossils to some extent

but it should be remembered that southern England remained free of ice when the region farther north suffered at least two major glaciations. There were periods of considerable but indeterminate length when the climate ameliorated to leave nearly the whole of the lower ground of Britain free of ice and with but local glaciers in the mountains. During such times man probably wandered northwards as the ice retreated but no remains of Palaeolithic man have been found in northern England whereas Neolithic remains are common there.

Glaciation reached about as far south as the Thames but even north of that line the incidence of glacial deposits is extremely varied; for example, the Cleveland Hills of Yorkshire were not overridden by ice though higher hills not only to the north but also to the west and south of Cleveland were buried by ice which has left behind far-travelled erratics as well as boulder clay, mounds of sand and gravel and laminated clays. Boulder clay represents the rock debris picked up, carried and deposited unsorted under the ice; often over 100 feet thick it may exceed even twice that thickness as in parts of the Midlands, and may descend to well below present sea level, as in Cheshire. The sands and gravels are mostly outwash from the melting ice either directly on land, as eskers and moraines, or as deltas into temporary lakes in which the laminated clays settled down. Beyond the range of the glaciers products of ordinary weathering remain though even these have been affected by freezing and thawing, as, for example, many of the muddy gravels of southern England, as well as the high level clay-with-flints so widespread on southern Chalk.

Examples of fluviatile alluvium and terraces at various heights may be seen along most rivers. Dungeness is an extensive old beach and there are raised beaches and marine terraces of mud along the Solway and elsewhere. Peat may be in low level bogs associated with alluvium, as for example, Chat Moss west of Manchester, or hill peat, such as occurs on the Pennines and other high ground. As examples of low-lying peat associated with alluvial and marine deposits and glacial drift the Fens and the Vale of York may be quoted, but many parts of western Scotland and the Isles show similar features. Blown sand is probably more widespread on our western than on our eastern coasts. In some places, as in the Hebrides, it contains much shell debris. An old blown sand in the Liverpool area (Shirdley Hill Sand) has been much used for glass making.

As mentioned previously the thicknesses of superficial or Drift Deposits, particularly those of glacial origin, vary considerably within small areas. For example, at Sydney near Crewe a boring revealed glacial deposits to be over 320 feet thick and to extend more than 160 feet below sea level yet within 2 miles to the west Keuper Marl crops out. Near Warrington beneath the present Mersey a drift-filled hollow extends to over 140 feet below O.D. and there is a similar one 284 feet deep at Talargoch Mine in the Vale of Clwyd. At Whittleford, south of Cambridge, drift is recorded to be over 455 feet thick and more than 335 feet B.O.D., to be 200 to 300 feet thick about Cromer, and to reach more than 150 feet below sea level at Yarmouth (see 'Thicknesses of Strata' *Mem. Geol. Surv.*).

Post glacial deposits, as may be expected, are less variable in thickness. In

Lincolnshire, for example, where they cover much of that county, they are commonly 20 feet thick though over 60 feet in the lower Trent Valley; in the Fens of Cambridge and Huntingdon they are usually between 20 and 30 feet thick.

If the superficial deposits were removed eastern Britain in particular would present a very different picture from the present one. The sea would sweep inland from Bridlington across Holderness to Hull and thence by the wolds of Lincolnshire into the great inlet of the Fens.

Economic products—Boulder clay, muddy alluvium and the silt grade (known as brickearth and possibly partly windblown in origin) have been extensively used for brick and tile making. Glacial sands and gravels, marine and terrace gravels provide sand and concrete aggregates. Blown sand is used for moulding and when shelly as a dressing for land. Peat is still cut for fuel but more for moss litter and agriculture. Turf from low level silt terraces is in great demand for golf, tennis and bowling greens as, for example, from the Solway area.

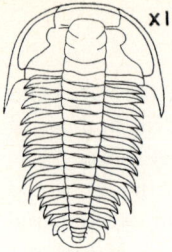

Olenus catactes
a³

Linguella davisi
a³

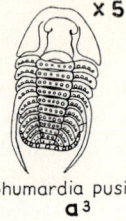

Shumardia pusilla
a³

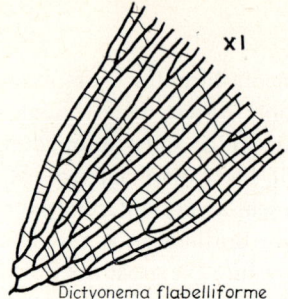

Dictyonema flabelliforme
a³

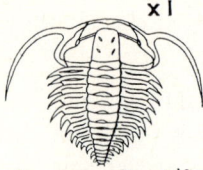

Ctenopyge flagellifera
a³

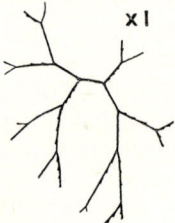

Clonograptus tenellus
a³

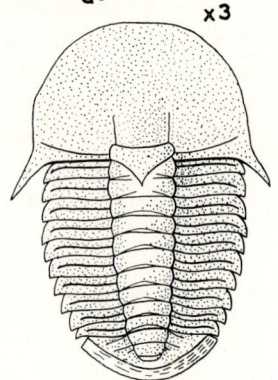

Hartshillia inflata
a²

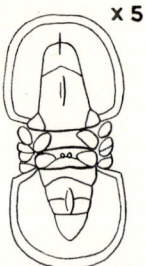

Agnostus fissus
a²

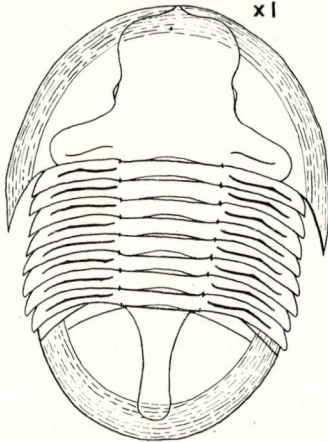

Asaphellus homfrayi
a³

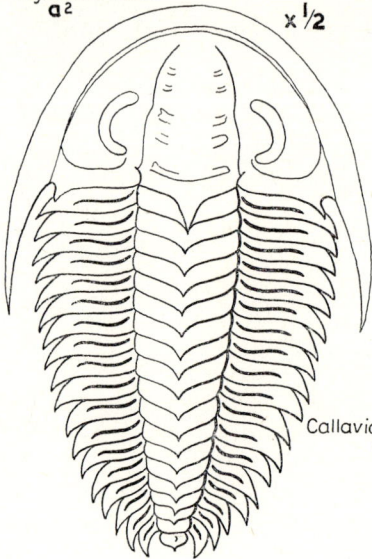

Callavia callavei
a¹

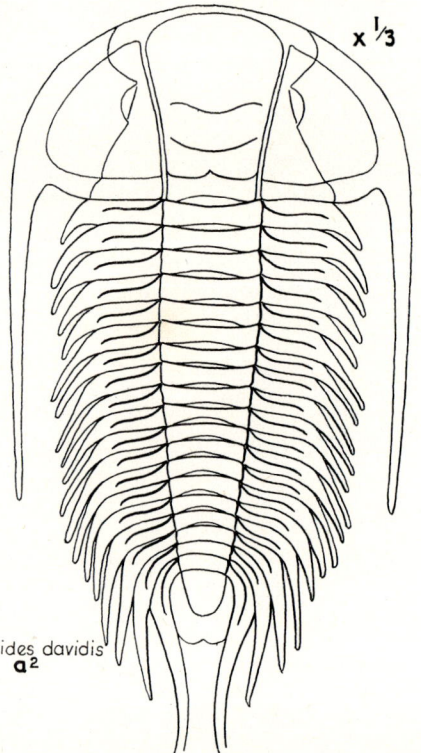

Paradoxides davidis
a²

Figure 6. CAMBRIAN FOSSILS Upper, a³; Middle, a²; Lower, a¹

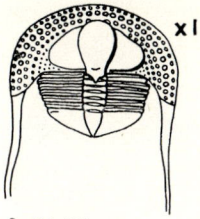

Cryptolithus concentricus

Staurocephalus murchisoni

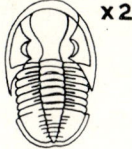

Phillipsinella parabola

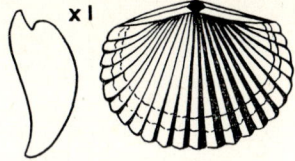

Orthis flabellulum

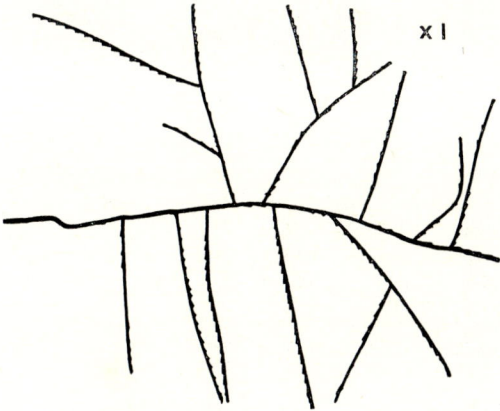

Sowerbyella sladensis

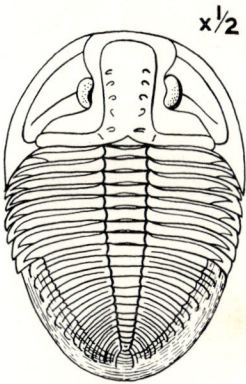

Pleurograptus linearis

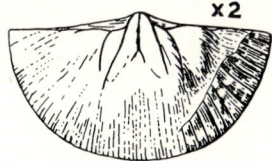

D. murchisoni

Diplograptus multidens

Orthograptus truncatus

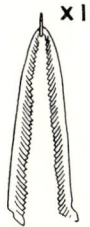

Ogygiocaris buchi

Dicranograptus brevicaulis

Didymograptus bifidis

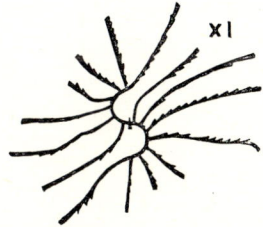

Nemagraptus gracilis

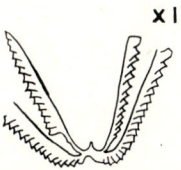

Tetragraptus serra

Didymograptus hirundo

Didymograptus extensus

Figure 7. ORDOVICIAN FOSSILS Ashgillian, top row; Caradocian, 2nd row; Llandeilo and Llanvirn, middle; Arenig, bottom

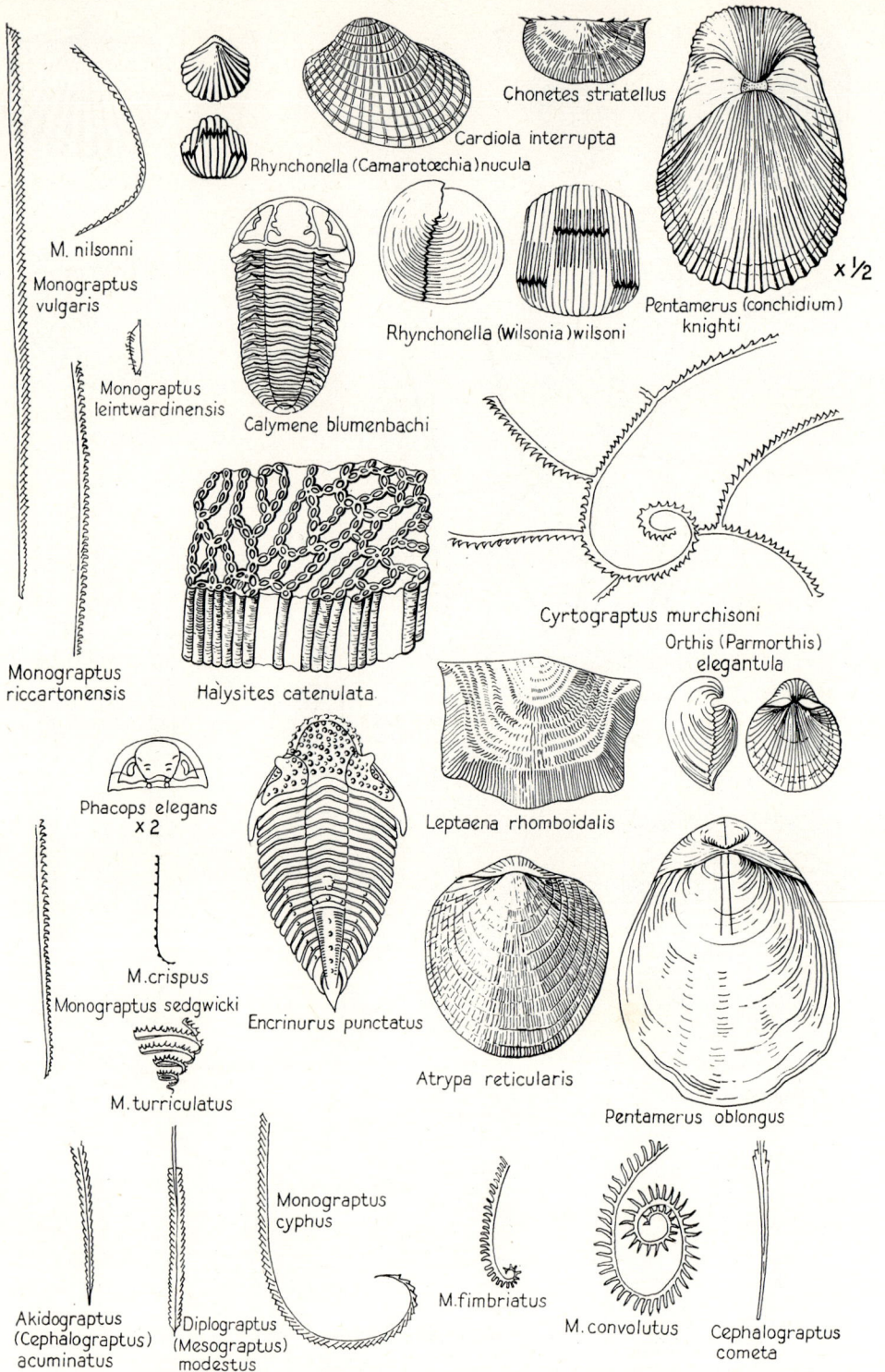

Figure 8. SILURIAN FOSSILS Ludlow, top quarter and *M. leintwardinensis*; Wenlock, middle portion and *Calymene* and *Atrypa*; Llandovery, lower third

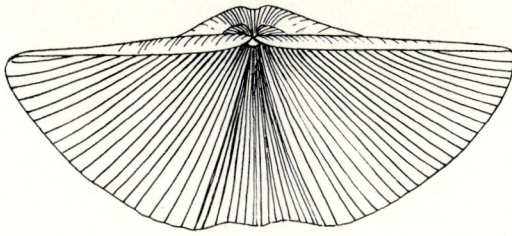

Spirifer verneuili

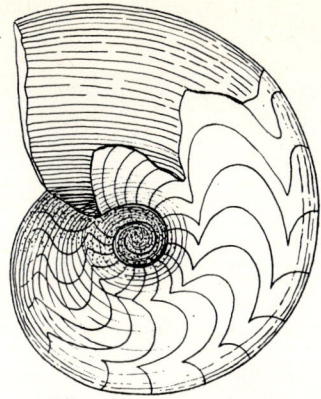

Manticoceras intumescens

Phillipsastrea hennahi

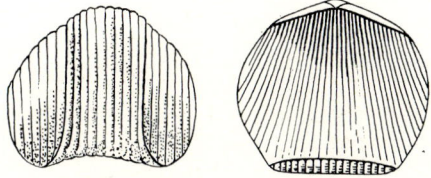

Rhynchonella cuboides

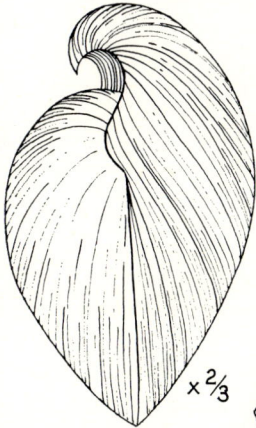

Stringocephalus burtini $\times \frac{2}{3}$

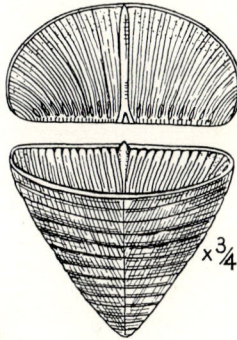

Murchisonia angulata

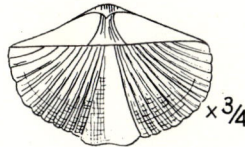

Calceola sandalina $\times \frac{3}{4}$

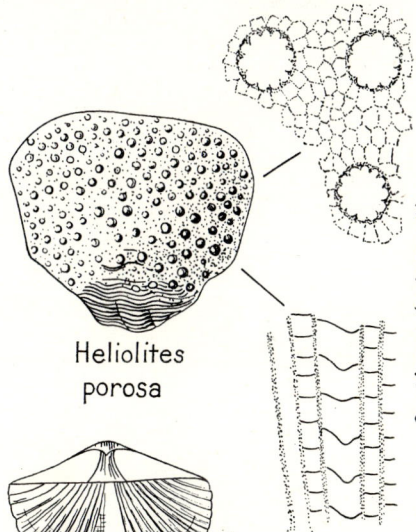

Heliolites porosa

Sections (enlarged)

Phacops latifrons

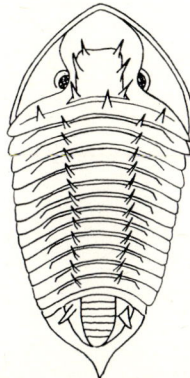

Homalonotus armatus

Spirifer subcuspidata $\times \frac{3}{4}$

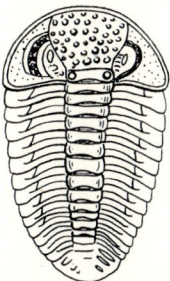

Bronteus flabellifer

Figure 9. DEVONIAN FOSSILS Upper, top row; Lower, bottom row and *Spirifer*; rest Middle Devonian

Archanodon ×¼

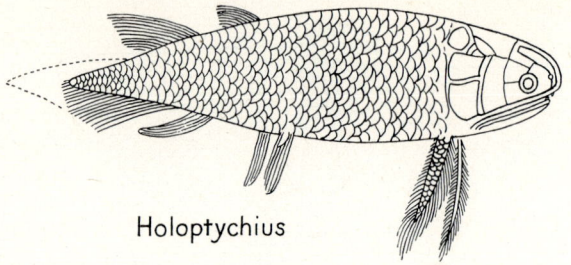

Holoptychius

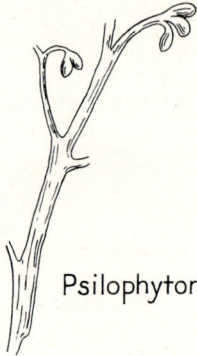

Psilophyton

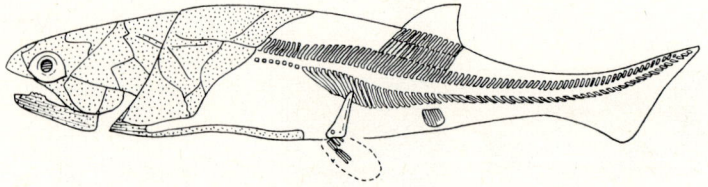

Coccosteus

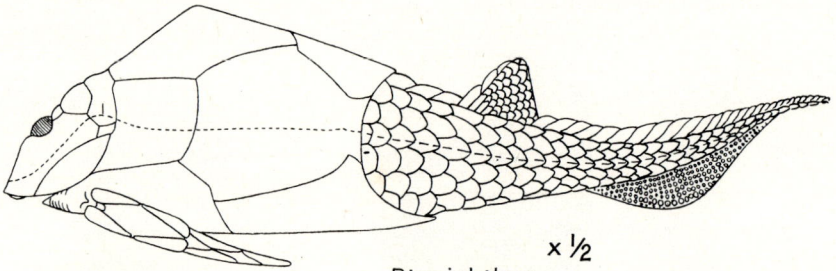

Pterichthys ×½

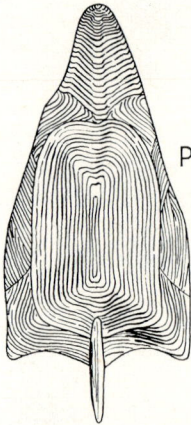

Pteraspis

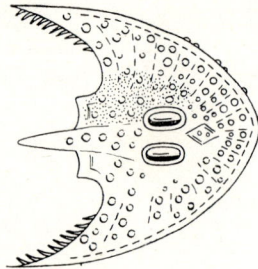

Cephalaspis

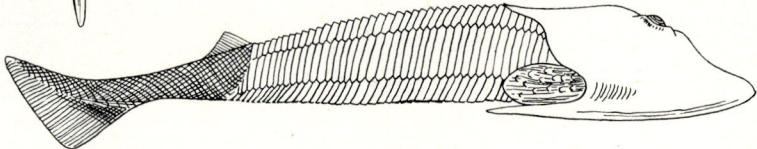

Figure 10. Old Red Sandstone Fossils Upper, top row; Lower, bottom third;
Middle, rest of page

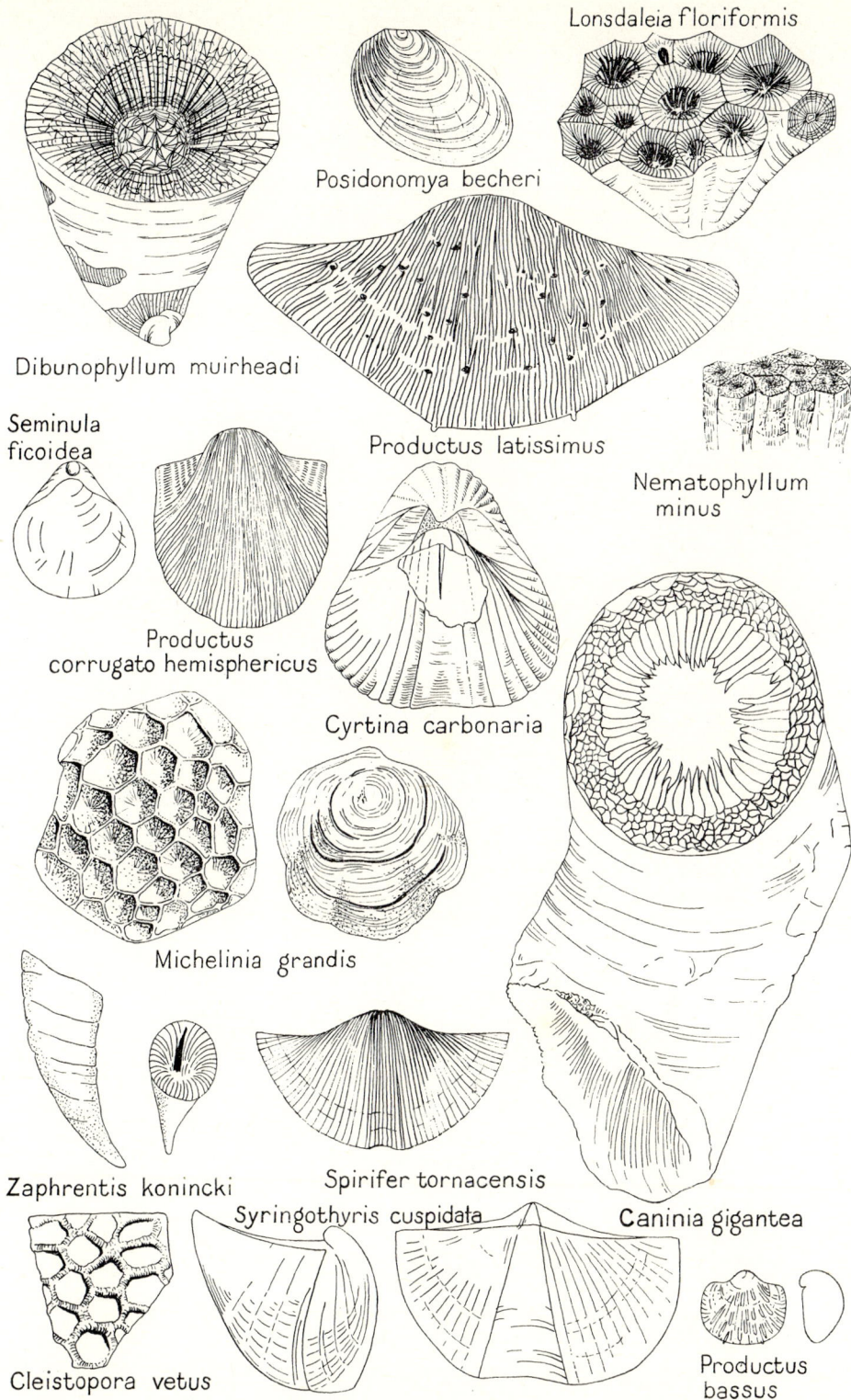

Lonsdaleia floriformis

Posidonomya becheri

Dibunophyllum muirheadi

Productus latissimus

Nematophyllum minus

Seminula ficoidea

Productus corrugato hemisphericus

Cyrtina carbonaria

Michelinia grandis

Zaphrentis konincki

Syringothyris cuspidata

Spirifer tornacensis

Caninia gigantea

Cleistopora vetus

Productus bassus

Figure 11. CARBONIFEROUS LIMESTONE ZONE FOSSILS D, top four; S, next four:
C, next two; Z, next two; K, rest

Homoceratoides
jacksoni

Anthraconauta tenuis

Anthraconauta
phillipsii

Gastrioceras
listeri

Anthraconaia
pulchra

Carbonicola
similis

Gastrioceras
cancellatum

Carbonicola
os-lancis

Anthracomya
modiolaris

Lingula
mytiloides

Reticuloceras
superbilingue

Carbonicola pseudorobusta

Dunbarella
papyracea

Homoceras
beyrichianum

Naiadites
quadratus

Carbonicola communis

Eumorphoceras
bisulcatum

Anthraconaia lenisulcata

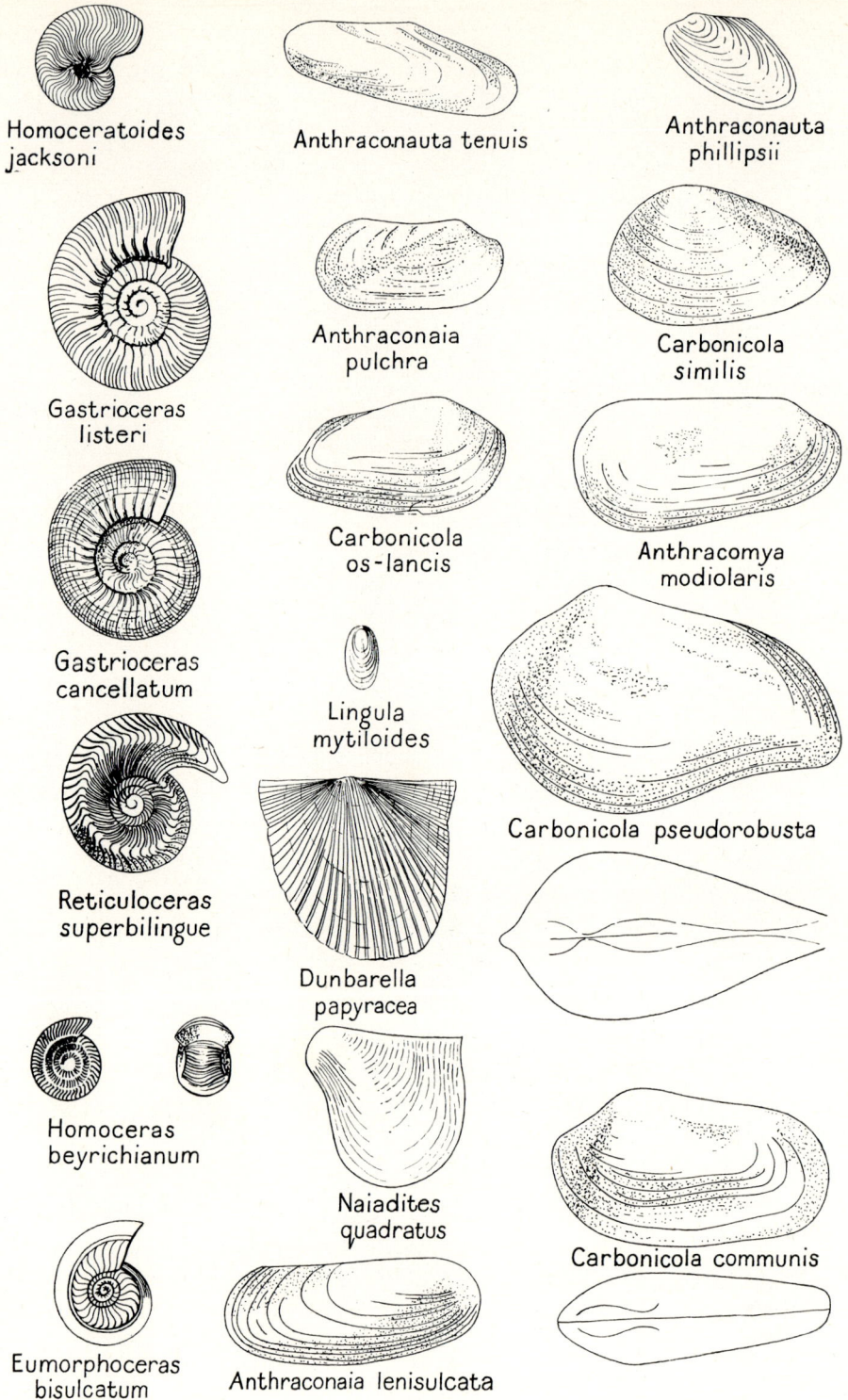

Figure 12. ZONE FOSSILS OF MILLSTONE GRIT AND COAL MEASURES   The initial
letters of the goniatites on the left mark zones E, H, R, and G. The 'mussels' are
in ascending Coal Measures sequence, with *Dunbarella* and *Lingula* indicating
marine interludes

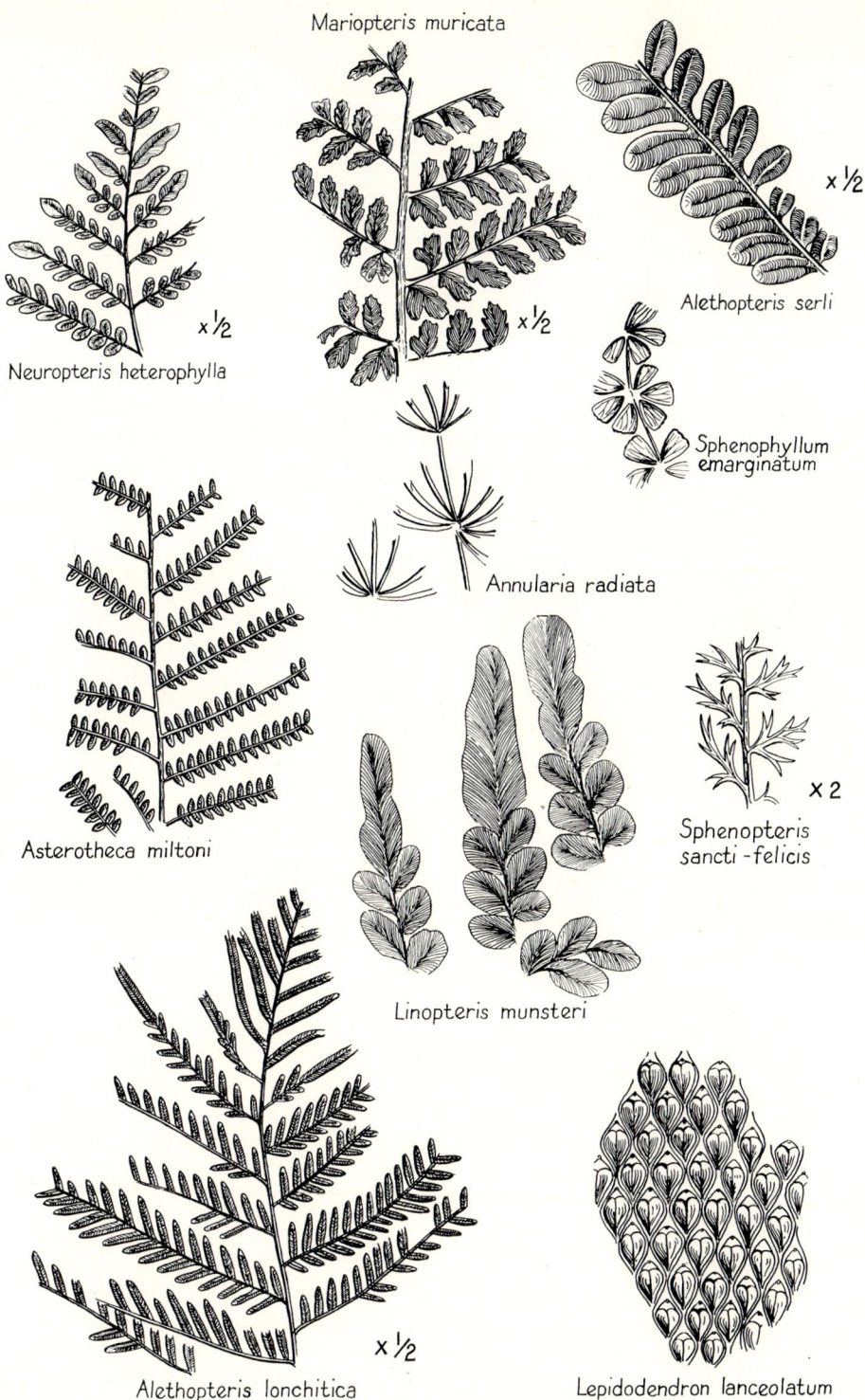

Figure 13. FOSSIL PLANTS OF COAL MEASURES

Mariopteris muricata

Neuropteris heterophylla

x ½

x ½

Alethopteris serli

x ½

Sphenophyllum emarginatum

Annularia radiata

Asterotheca miltoni

Sphenopteris sancti-felicis

x 2

Linopteris munsteri

Alethopteris lonchitica

x ½

Lepidodendron lanceolatum

2

Pteria contorta

Estheria minuta

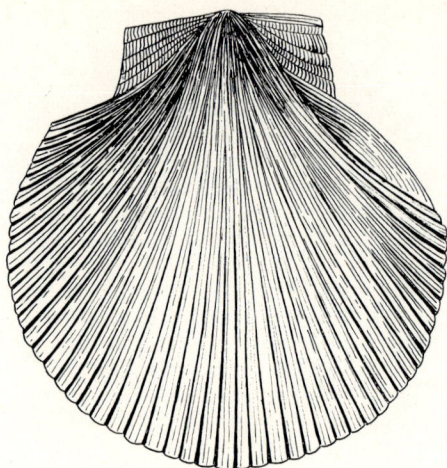

Chlamys valoniensis

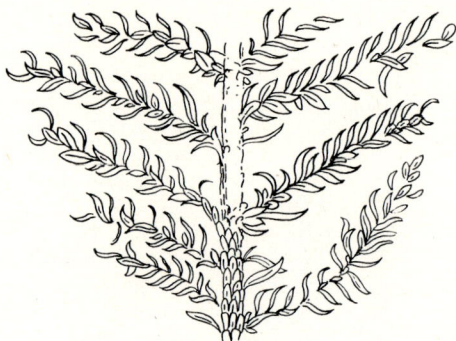

Walchia piniformis

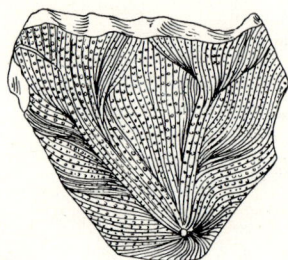

Fenestella retiformis

Camarophoria schlotheimi

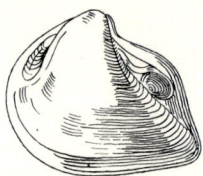

Schizodus obscurus

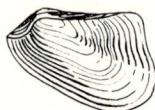

Bakevellia antiqua

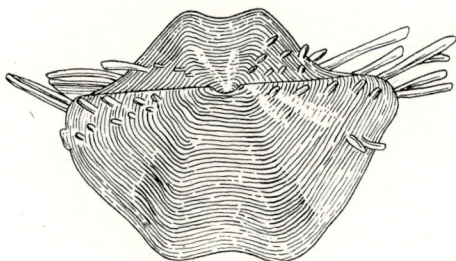

Productus horridus

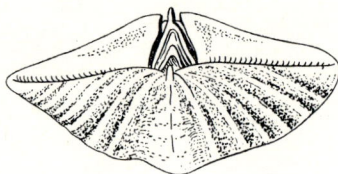

Spirifer alatus

Figure 14. NEW RED SANDSTONE FOSSILS Permian to Rhaetic

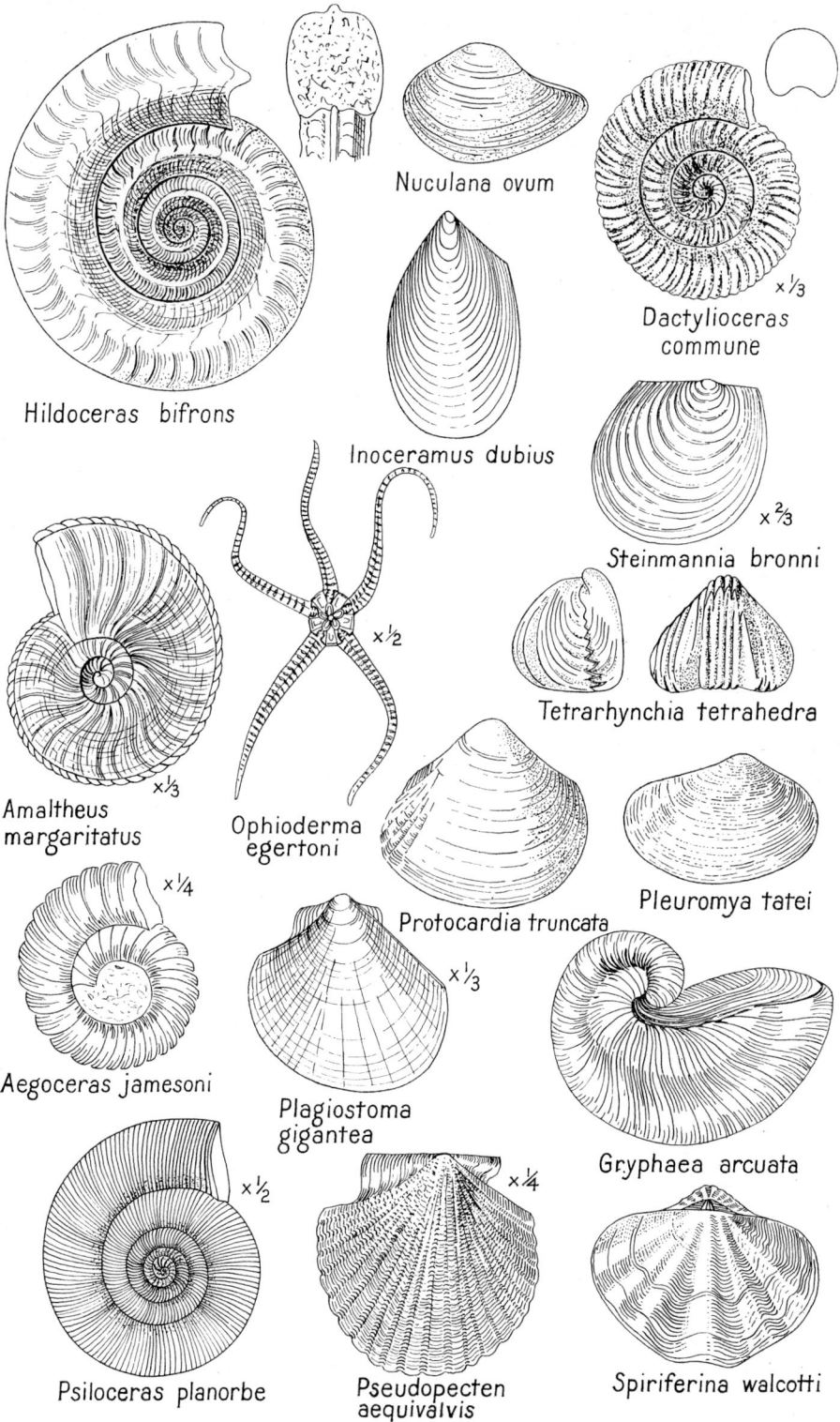

Nuculana ovum

Dactylioceras commune ×⅓

Hildoceras bifrons

Inoceramus dubius

Steinmannia bronni ×⅔

Amaltheus margaritatus ×⅓

Ophioderma egertoni ×½

Tetrarhynchia tetrahedra

Protocardia truncata

Pleuromya tatei

Aegoceras jamesoni ×¼

Plagiostoma gigantea ×⅓

Gryphaea arcuata

Psiloceras planorbe ×½

Pseudopecten aequivalvis ×¼

Spiriferina walcotti

Figure 15. LOWER JURASSIC (LIAS) FOSSILS

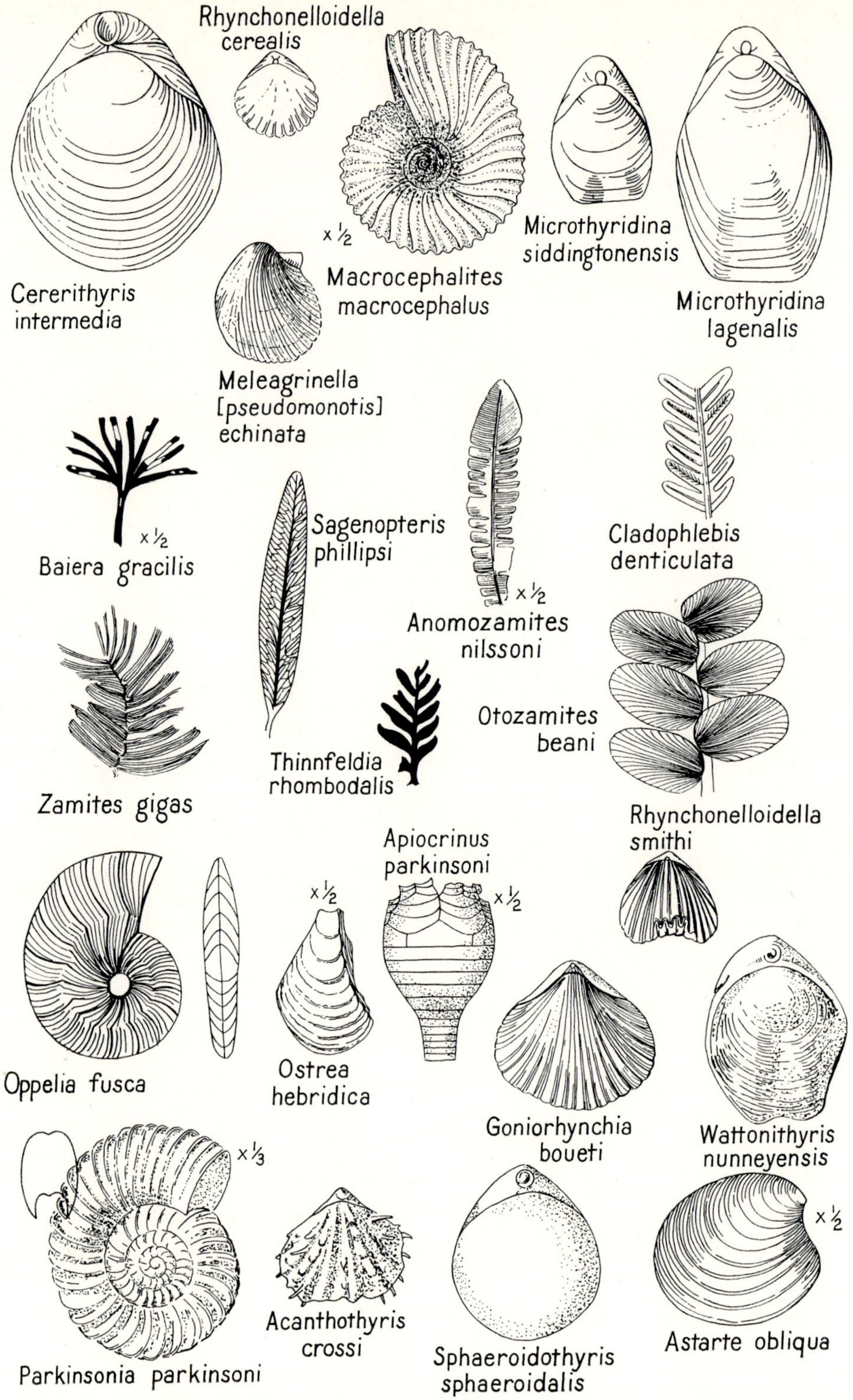

Figure 16. MIDDLE JURASSIC FOSSILS   Cornbrash, top row; Estuarine Series; Great Oolite; Inferior Oolite, bottom row

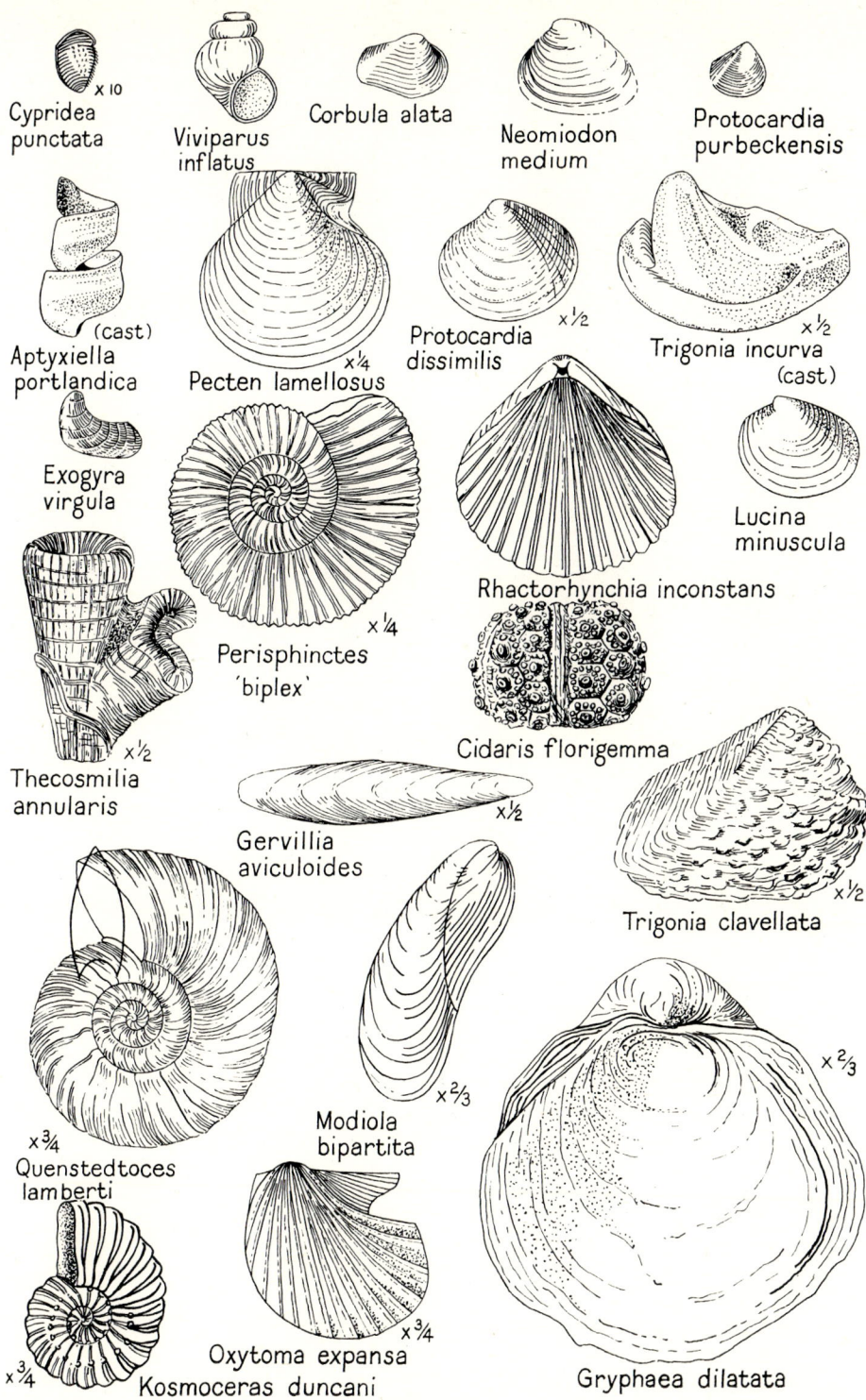

Figure 17. UPPER JURASSIC FOSSILS Purbeck, top; Portland, 2nd row; Kimmeridge, 3rd row; Corallian; Oxford Clay, bottom

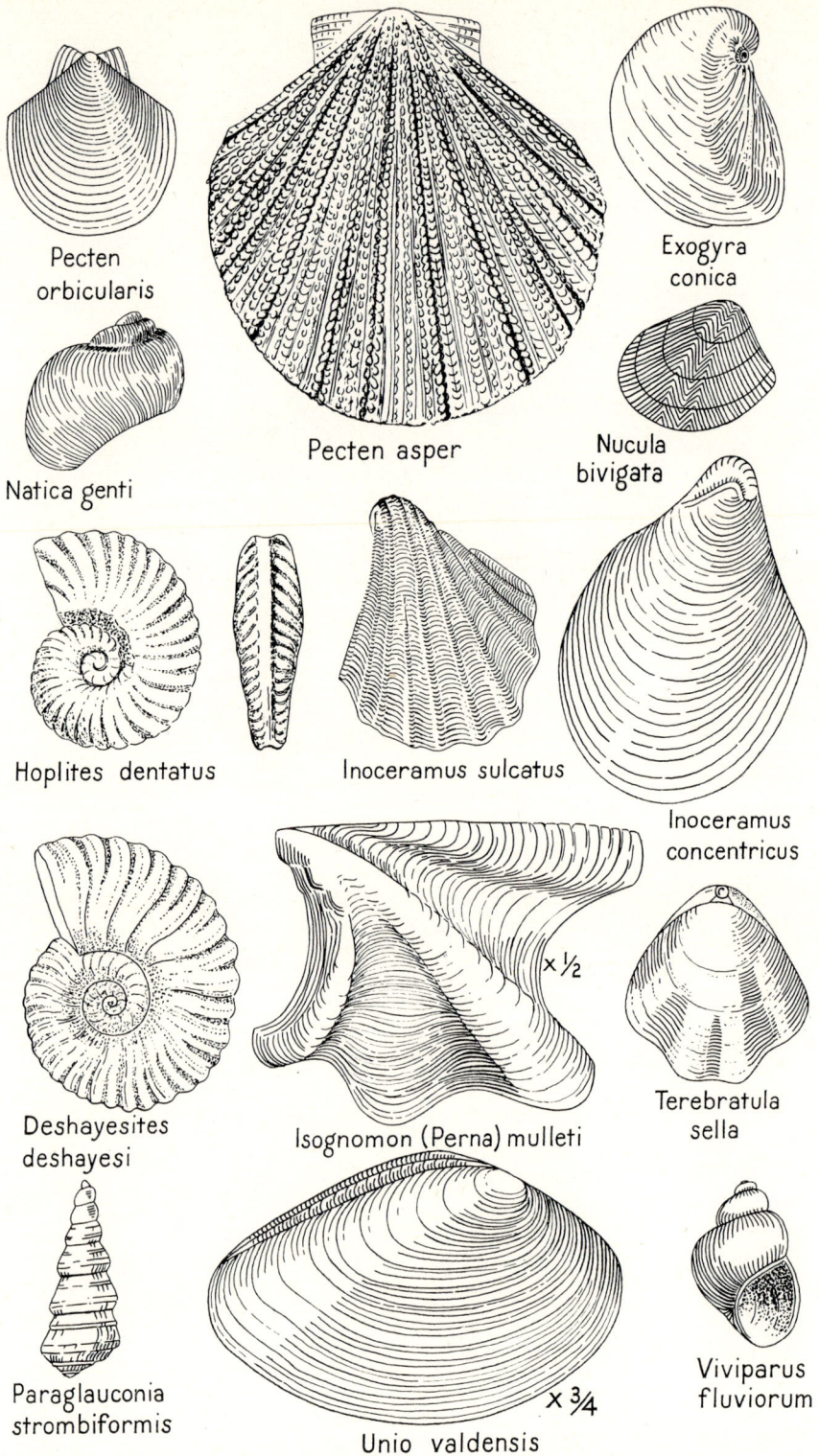

Figure 18. FOSSILS OF LOWER PART OF CRETACEOUS Upper Greensand and Gault, top half; Lower Greensand, middle; Wealden, bottom

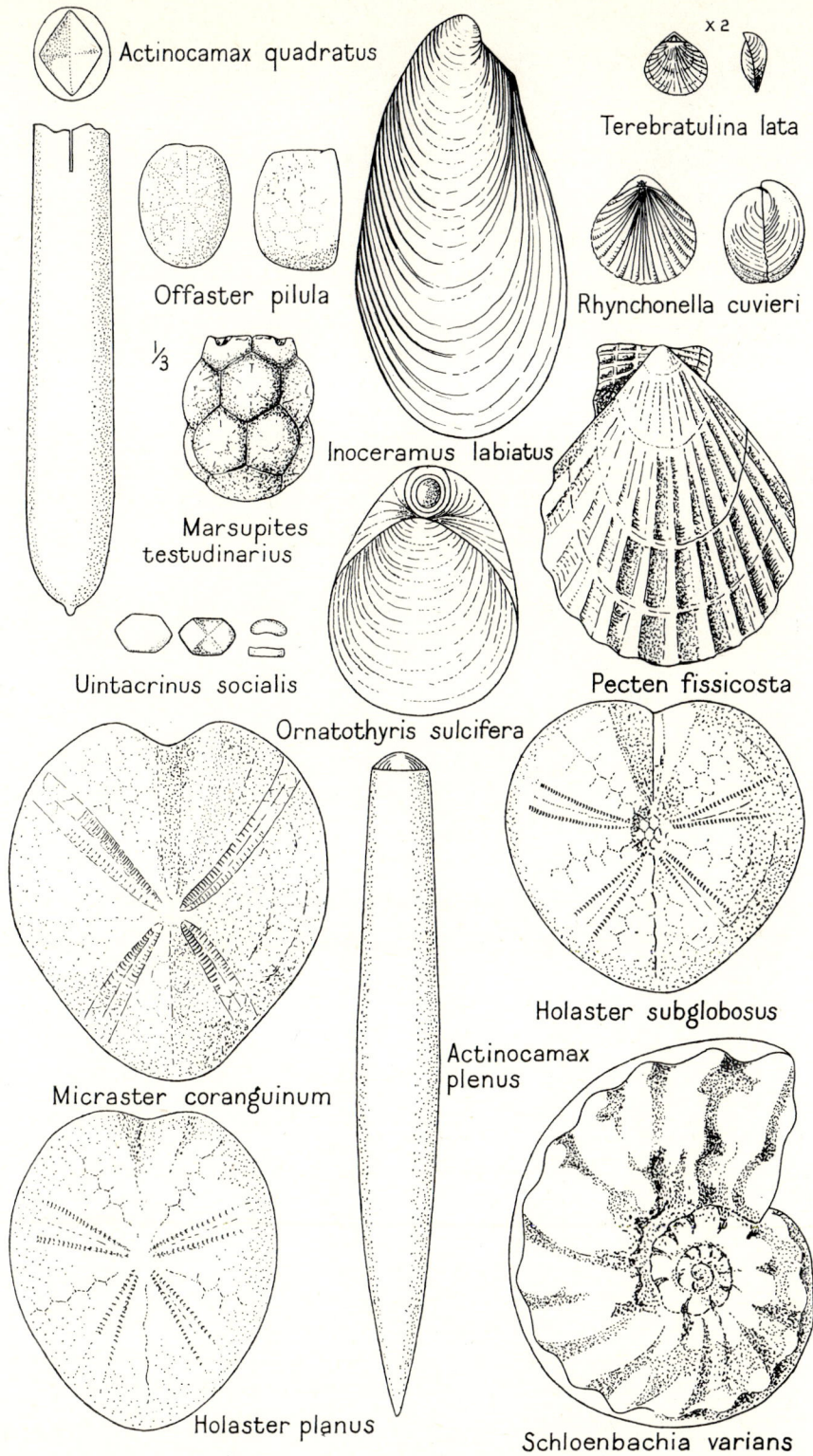

Figure 19. CHALK FOSSILS Upper Chalk, left; Middle Chalk, top right; Lower Chalk, bottom right

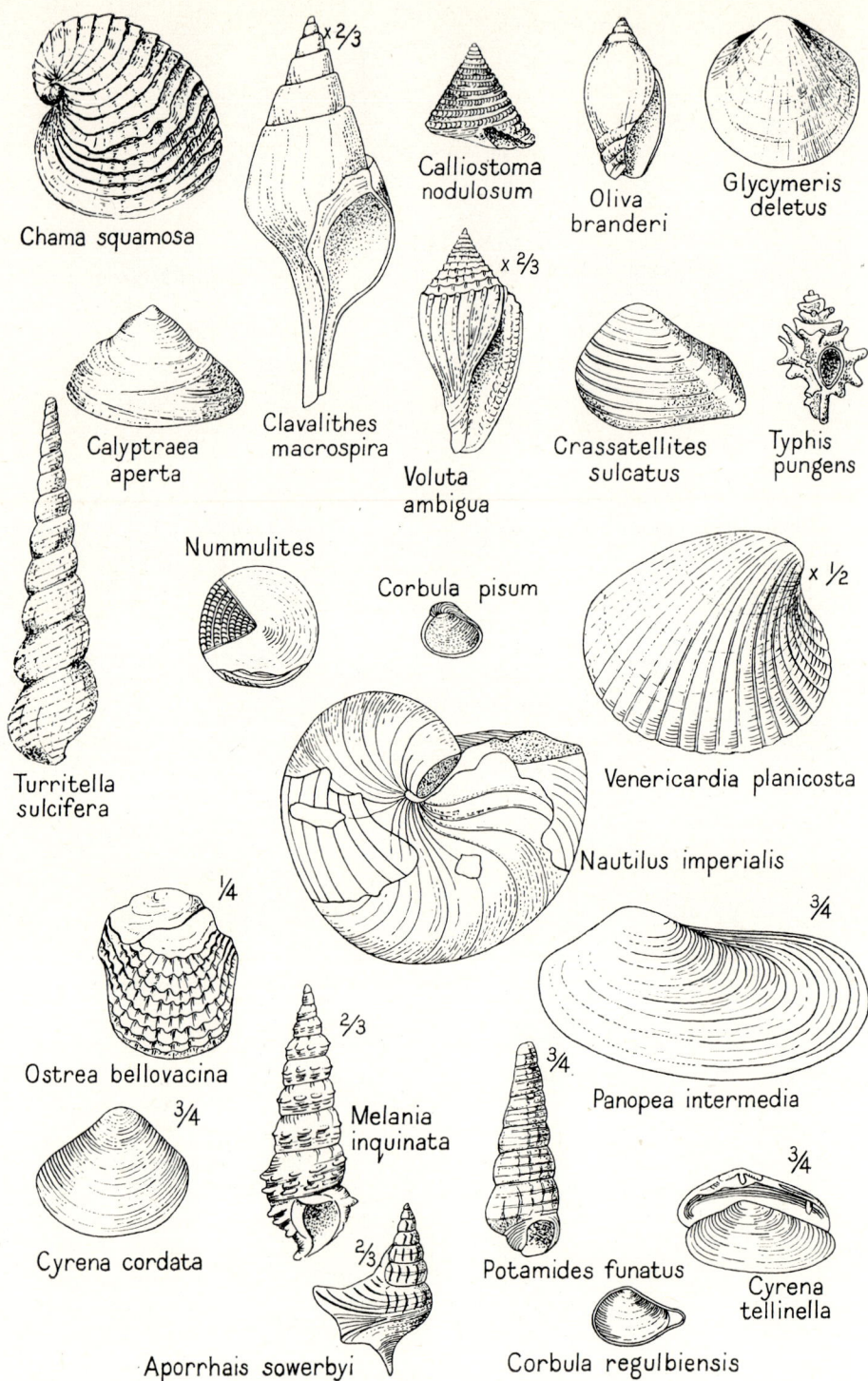

Chama squamosa

x 2/3

Calliostoma nodulosum

Oliva branderi

Glycymeris deletus

Calyptraea aperta

Clavalithes macrospira

x 2/3

Voluta ambigua

Crassatellites sulcatus

Typhis pungens

Nummulites

Corbula pisum

x 1/2

Venericardia planicosta

Turritella sulcifera

Nautilus imperialis

1/4

Ostrea bellovacina

2/3

Melania inquinata

3/4

Panopea intermedia

3/4

Cyrena cordata

3/4

Potamides funatus

3/4

Cyrena tellinella

2/3

Aporrhais sowerbyi

Corbula regulbiensis

Figure 20. EOCENE FOSSILS Barton, top two rows; Bracklesham, 3rd; London Clay, 4th; Woolwich and Reading, 5th; Thanet, bottom

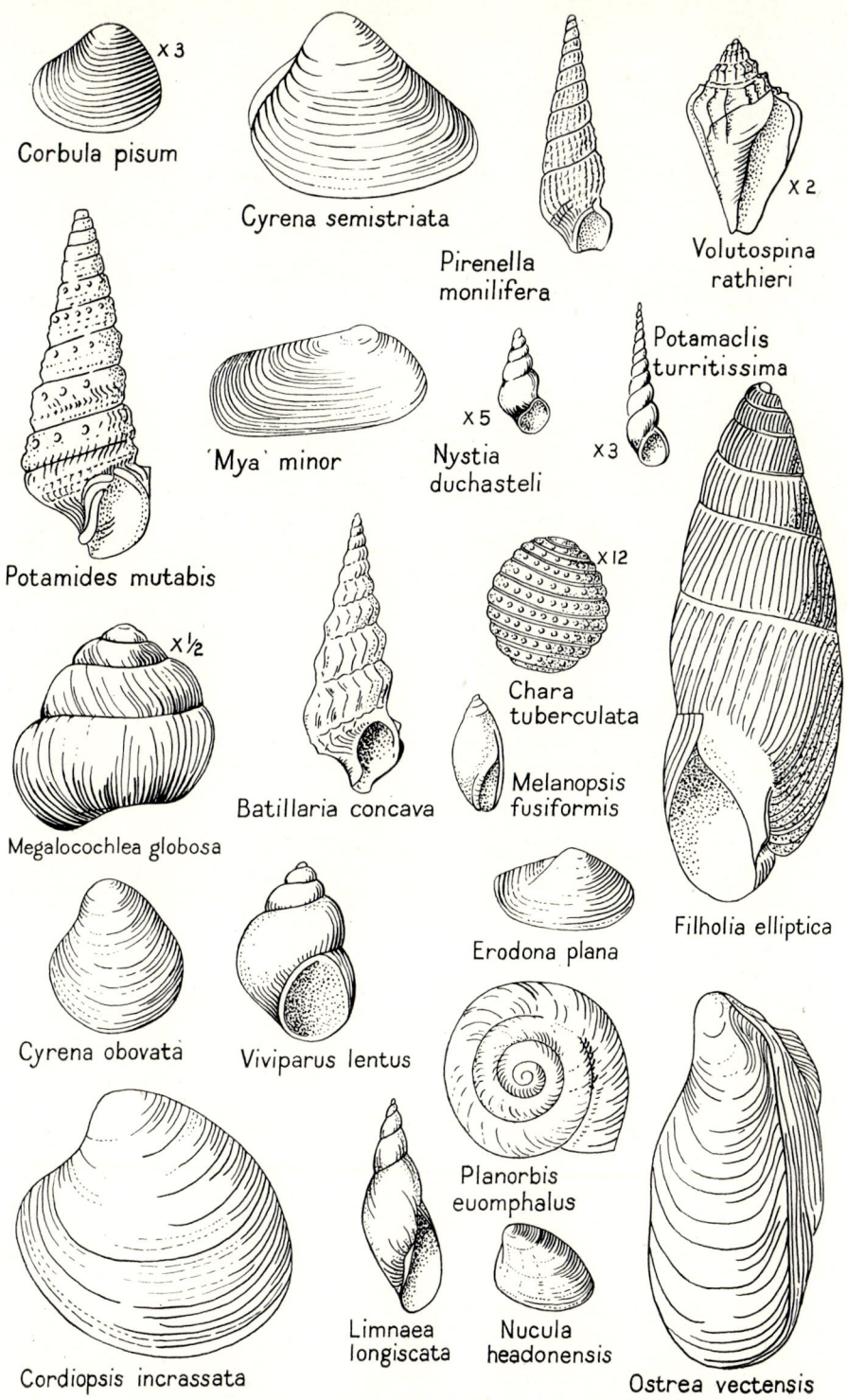

Corbula pisum ×3

Cyrena semistriata

Pirenella monilifera

Volutospina rathieri ×2

Potamides mutabis

'Mya' minor

Nystia duchasteli ×5

Potamaclis turritissima ×3

Batillaria concava

Chara tuberculata ×12

Melanopsis fusiformis

Filholia elliptica

Megalocochlea globosa ×½

Cyrena obovata

Viviparus lentus

Erodona plana

Cordiopsis incrassata

Limnaea longiscata

Nucula headonensis

Planorbis euomphalus

Ostrea vectensis

Figure 21. OLIGOCENE FOSSILS in general natural sequence

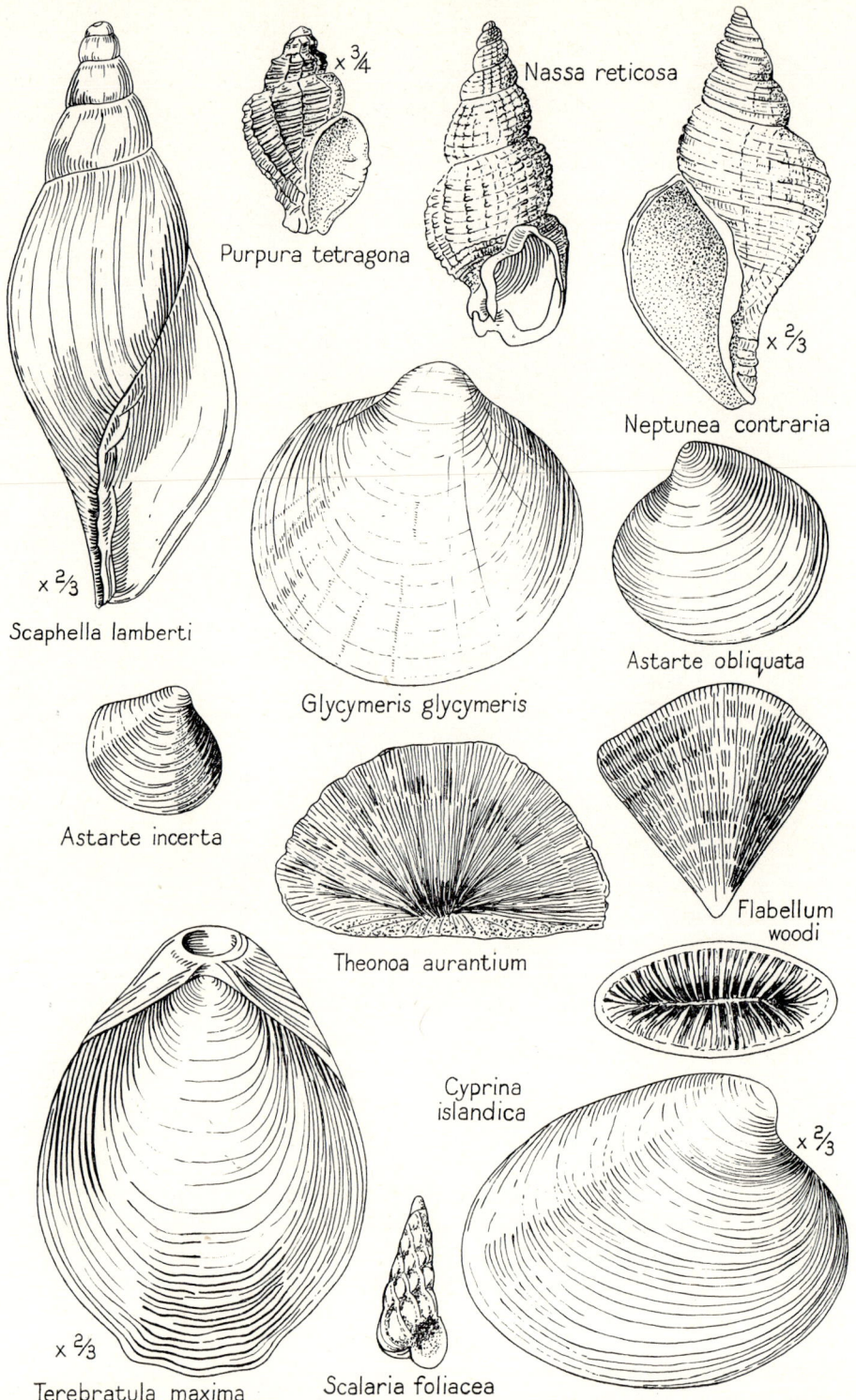

Figure 22. PLIOCENE—PLEISTOCENE FOSSILS   Red Crag, upper half; Coralline Crag (Pliocene), lower half

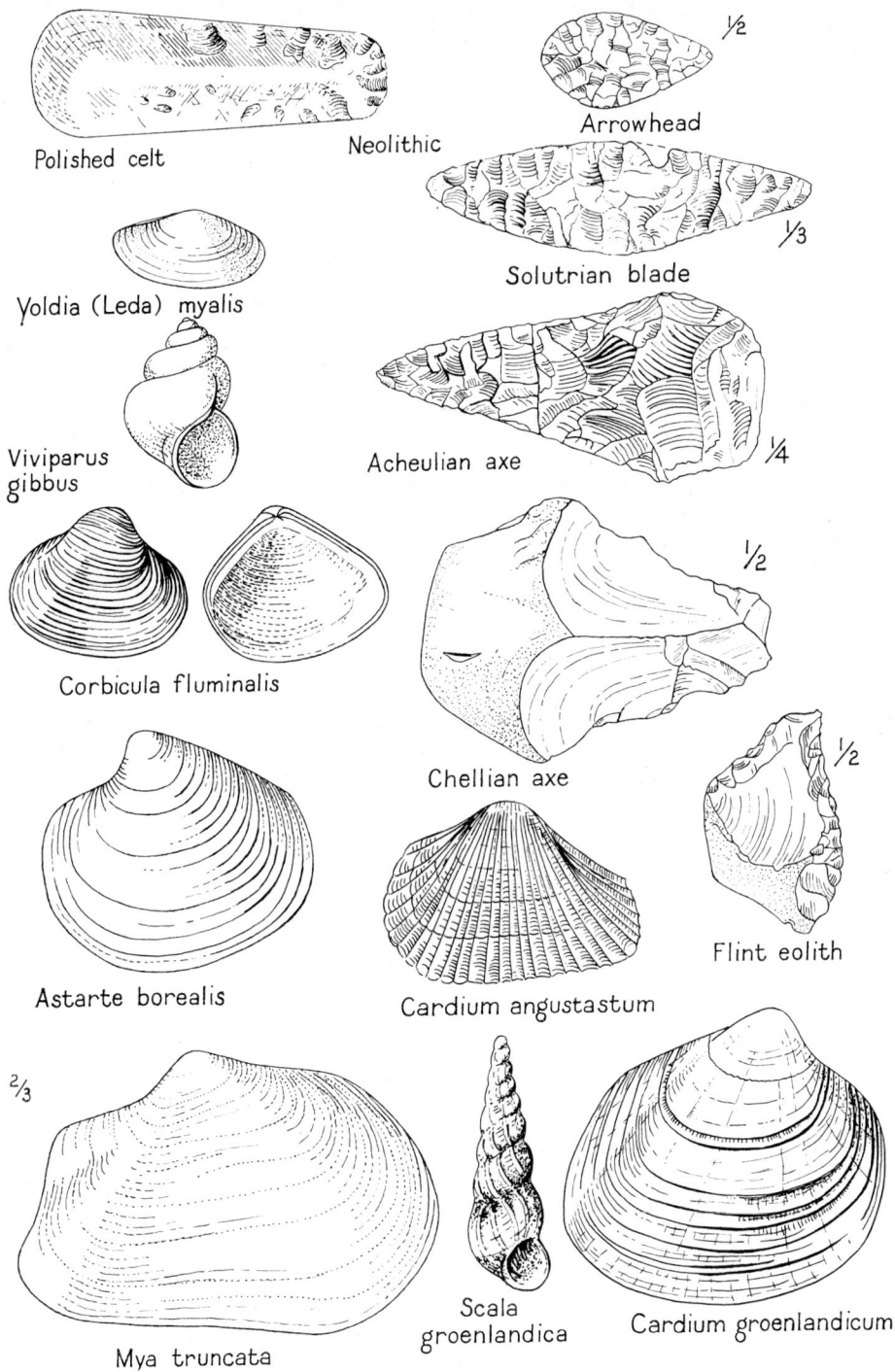

Polished celt   Neolithic

Arrowhead   ½

Solutrian blade   ⅓

Yoldia (Leda) myalis

Viviparus gibbus

Acheulian axe   ¼

Corbicula fluminalis

Chellian axe   ½

Flint eolith   ½

Astarte borealis

Cardium angustastum

⅔

Mya truncata

Scala groenlandica

Cardium groenlandicum

Figure 23. PLEISTOCENE—RECENT FOSSILS Norwich and Weybourne Crags, lower two rows

ECONOMIC PRODUCTS

As a tailpiece to each formation some mention has been made of the economic products of or associated with those rocks. At this stage the products may be dealt with collectively. In everyday language coal is spoken of as a mineral though its natural location is termed a coalfield, while mineral field is reserved for the terrain of ores of iron and other metals. In scientific terms a mineral is a naturally occurring inorganic substance of definite chemical composition and constant physical properties. On this definition neither coal nor oil are minerals, being organic, and few of the minerals mined will conform to constancy in chemical and physical properties. As for an ore, whether it be restricted to metal yielding minerals or not, since the price that it commands enters into the meaning attached to the word, a mineral may be an ore today but if the price falls or the costs rise unduly and thus render the working of the deposit unprofitable, it may not be an ore to-morrow. For general purposes then a certain latitude with respect to the word mineral must be allowed and ore should include both metallic and non-metallic substances and defined perhaps as follows: a natural aggregation of mineral substance sufficiently concentrated (or localized) to be worth working (or extracted).

The most important mineral deposits in Britain are those of coal and of iron. These will be dealt with first and others later if they are of sufficient value to warrant inclusion here.

COAL   It is generally accepted that coal is derived from plants that flourished long ago. From the fact that most coal seams rest on a seatearth of fireclay penetrated by what are obviously rootlets it is assumed that a coal seam at least in its initial stages is a result of plant growth *in situ* though some vegetable matter, often thoroughly macerated, undoubtedly drifted into position as the site slowly subsided. The shales or sandstones that succeed the coal and now form the roof are a result of quicker subsidence. Coal is a complex substance made up of carbon combined mostly with hydrogen though there are small amounts of oxygen and nitrogen. The proportion of hydrocarbons to fixed carbon, i.e., of the gases driven off by heating to the remaining coke, determines the class of fuel and the purposes for which it may be used. These are often quoted as on an ash moisture-free basis. Ash represents not only the inherent inorganic material of the plant tissues but also extraneous mud and the like incorporated with the coaly material from the waters of the coal swamp or infiltrated into a seam long after formation. Coal in the scuttle often shows banding by the alternation of layers of charcoal-like substance (fusain) with others of bright streaky coal (clarain), glistening black glassy coal (vitrain) or hard dull coal (durain). Some of these bands may predominate in a seam for example, durain in the Top Hard Seam of the Yorkshire field. There is also the dull light-weight coal with conchoidal fracture rich in gas and easily ignited known as cannel. This may occur alone or as bands.

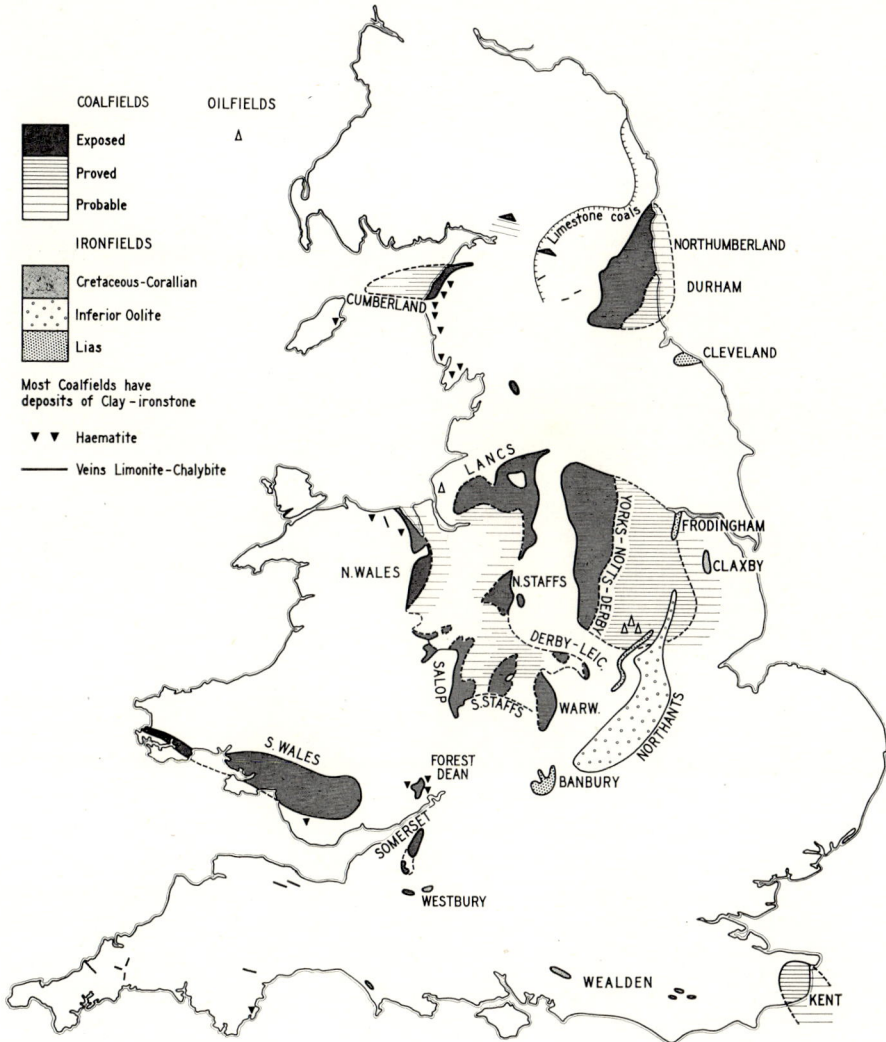

Figure 24. Coal, Iron and Oilfields of England and Wales

These coal bands differ in composition and in mode of origin. Durain is often rich in spores, the bright streaks in clarain seem to represent bark, fusain a mat of sticks, vitrain is probably a jellied plant substance, as is also cannel though not quite in the same way. Most coals belong to the so-called bituminous class with 20–40 per cent of volatile matter to 80–60 per cent of fixed carbon on an ash-free basis and thus range between domestic, manufacturing, coking and gas coals. Anthracite has over 93 per cent of fixed carbon while steam coals form an intermediate grade between anthracite and the bituminous coals. The ash content, of course, decides the value of each class. Anthracite in quantity is restricted to that part of the South Wales Coalfield west of the Vale of Neath. It is known that seams bituminous in the east have a gradually diminishing volatile content when traced westwards and that lower seams are affected before the upper ones but apart from the fact that some heating, i.e. a sort of coking *in situ*, is involved the real cause is unknown.

A coal seam represents uninterrupted accumulation of vegetable matter. If an area subsides unevenly then a seam may 'thin' in a certain direction, usually towards the area of quicker subsidence, or be split by partings of shale where coal growth has crept out over the original mud bank. For example, the famous seams the Thick Coal of South Staffordshire and of Warwickshire are formed by the union of several seams separated by considerable thicknesses of shale farther north. That of Staffordshire, 30 feet thick, is now largely exhausted but the Warwickshire seam, over 20 feet thick, is still actively exploited north of Coventry. Most coals are thinner than these and the workable seams commonly range from 2 to 5 feet.

The swamps in which the plants grew and the coal-making material accumulated were much more extensive than the present coalfields many of which were parts of one large swamp though some original barriers are known as, for example, that between the Midland fields and those of South Wales and Gloucester known as St. George's Land. In general the separation into individual coalfields is due to earth movements, the elevated portions were eroded while the downfolded portions are preserved. For a study of the ancient geography see L. J. Wills' *Concealed Coalfields*, 1956, Blackie.

Coalfields are classed as exposed and concealed. In the former the coal bearing strata crop out at the surface as, for example, in South Wales and in the Forest of Dean. In the other class the coal-bearing strata are concealed by younger rocks or by the sea. The concealing rocks may be upper barren Coal Measures, as over much of Warwickshire, or Trias, as in part of Leicestershire; in these as in many other areas the coalfields are partly exposed and partly concealed. In the case of Kent that coalfield is wholly concealed by Jurassic and Cretaceous strata. As an example of a partly submarine coalfield that of West Cumberland may be quoted. In most cases it is to the concealed portions that we must look for reserves and here mention may be made of the colossal reserves beneath the Permo-Trias on the east side of the York–Nottingham–Derby field.

The distribution of the exposed coalfields is shown on the various sheets as well

as on Fig. 24 where some attempt has been made to indicate concealed fields, and on Fig. 25.

In this account the Jurassic coals of North Yorkshire (p. 189) and of Brora (p. 275) and those of Tertiary age at Bovey (p. 87) and near London (p. 95) may be neglected.

IRON ORES   Until the latter half of the last century most of the iron of Britain was got from the clay band and black band ironstones occurring as nodules or as bands in shales accompanying the coal bearing strata. Both are carbonates of iron with some clay impurity but the latter have sufficient black carbonaceous matter (up to 10 per cent) to provide fuel for calcining. Such ores were raised in nearly all the coalfields but particularly in Scotland, West Yorkshire, Staffordshire and South Wales where ironworks originally using local ores now survive on ores from farther afield or from abroad. In North Staffordshire and in Scotland such ironstones were raised until recent years but in most other fields iron mining did not survive into the twentieth century. The ores ranged in percentage from 30 to 35 iron, 6 to 15 silica, alumina 1 to 10; lime, phosphorus and sulphur are low.

About the same time the higher grade haematite ores supported a major industry. These occur mainly as irregular deposits replacing certain favourable beds in the Carboniferous Limestone usually in the vicinity of faults which evidently permitted access to the mineralizing solutions. West Cumberland was the principal field and mines are still active there and near Cardiff but with less total output than formerly. Those of the Forest of Dean, of North Wales and of Furness are now exhausted. In the Furness area some of the ore occurred in gigantic 'sops' of funnel shape which appear to have been swallow holes in the limestone. In other areas such as near Ennerdale and in Eskdale the ore occurred in veins in Skiddaw Slates and in granite respectively.

These ores range from 45 to 60 per cent iron and are low in sulphur and phosphorus.

In the North Pennines siderite or chalybite ($FeCO_3$) ore occurs in veins and associated flats in Carboniferous Limestone. In the veins stretches of iron ore may alternate with stretches of lead ore and as these minerals were usually sought by different companies there were frequent changes of personnel. Some mining was done here during the 1939–45 war.

Chalybite ores oxydized to limonite ($2Fe_2O_3.3H_2O$) near the surface have also been raised in Cornwall from veins of which the most famous is the Perran Lode near Newquay. In Devon a variety of haematite, known as specular ore from its shining small flakes, is raised at Kelly and Great Rock mines near Bovey Tracey. Some magnetite (Fe_3O_4) was raised at Haytor.

At the present time over 90 per cent of home ores are got from the bedded deposits of Jurassic age which occur with some interruptions from Cleveland in North Yorkshire to beyond Banbury. Somewhat similar ores were worked in very early days in the Weald and also occur in Raasay.

In the Cleveland area the Main Seam 6 to 11 feet thick occurs near the top of the Middle Lias and is separated from thinner seams below by shale bands. Quarrying

47

B   Barytes   🖛   Coal Measures
Cr   Chromite   Limestone Coals
C   Copper
G   Gold
Gr   Graphite
I   Iron
L   Lead
Z   Zinc
▲D   Diatomite
▼   Haematite

BRORA COALFIELD

SKYE

L. KISHORN

BALLATER

LZ
STRONTIAN

Cr
KILLIN

TYNDRUM LZ

LOCH
C FYNE

ISLAY L

MUIRSHIELDS

HADDINGTON

B
GLEN
SANNOX

GASSWATER
B

LG
LEADHILLS

Gr

NEWTON
STEWART

LZC

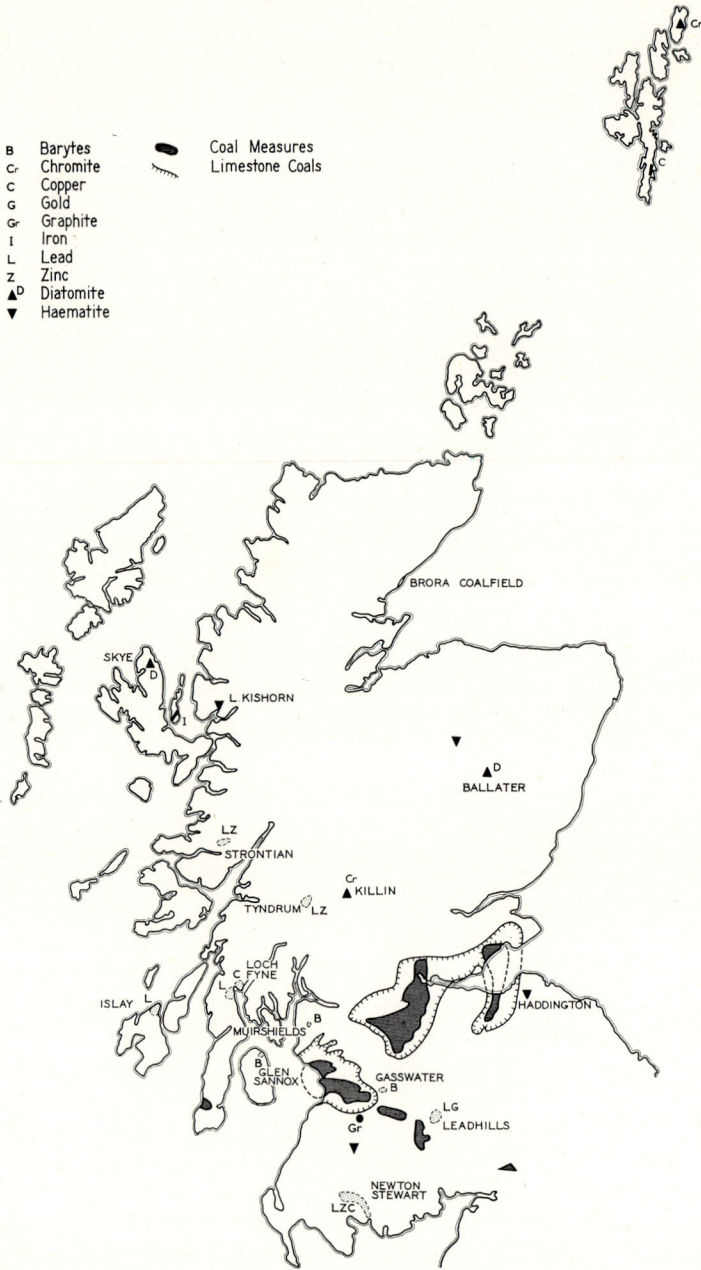

Figure 25. Mineral fields of Scotland

Black and Clay Band Ironstones are associated with the coals. Oil shales occur below the Limestone Coal Series in Fife and the Lothians.

of the ore ceased years ago and all is now got from mines. Southwards the seams fail and the next field of importance is that of Scunthorpe south of the Humber. Here the chief or Frodingham Ironstone occurs about two-thirds of the way up in the Lower Lias as a bed up to 30 feet thick. This in its turn fails southwards but ore reappears in the Middle Lias of Mid Lincolnshire and persists into Leicestershire and even more important is the appearance of the Northampton Sands Ore in the Inferior Oolite which stretches from about Lincoln to about Northampton. West of the latter area the Middle Lias ironstone gradually becomes an ore again which reaches its greatest development about Banbury but fails about Hook Norton. There is some Lower Cretaceous ore worked about Nettleton in Lincolnshire and a bed in the Corallian about Westbury in Wiltshire. All these ironstones have much in common; they are limonitic at or near surface but become greenish and more complex under cover.

NON-FERROUS ORES   Under this head are included the ores of tin, tungsten, copper, lead, zinc, arsenic etc. as well as the spars of barium, fluorine, calcite, salt, gypsum, etc. Some of these occur as bedded deposits, such as the salt and gypsum and also the manganese ore worked recently in the Lleyn peninsula and at one time near Barmouth, but most of them are found in veins or lodes. These are more or less vertical fissures, often faults, filled with mineral matter or broken rock intermixed with minerals; they are not equally rich in mineral content either laterally or vertically and the kind of rock forming the walls has a profound effect on both size of vein and contents. For example, soft rocks such as some shales do not lend themselves to open fissures and therefore hindered mineralization whereas the harder sandstones and limestones give wider veins richer in mineral. Structure also plays a part for gentle upfolds, especially if the strata there include some impervious bands such as clay or rotten lava, are particularly favourable to deposition and have evidently hindered the further uprise of mineralizing solutions (see Fig. 43). In some cases the wall rock, particularly in limestones, is replaced by minerals along the bedding and thus forms 'flats' as, for example, in the North Pennines. The payability of a deposit while affected by various factors such as difficulties in mining, separation of the desired mineral from the refuse or gangue, smelting procedure and so on is ultimately decided by world prices for the products. In general, however, lead ores require about 10 per cent of the mineral galena (PbS) whereas those of zinc-blende (ZnS) must be considerably richer say 15 per cent if that be the only ore; on the other hand one per cent of black tin or cassiterite (SnO_2) is usually considered payable in Cornwall.

Most mineral deposits show some sign of zoning either laterally or vertically though both are related to distance from the centre of mineralization. The lateral zoning is well marked in the ribbon-like lead veins in limestones. For instance, in the North Pennines there is an inner zone rich in fluorspar (CaF_2), a middle zone where lead is abundant and an outer zone mainly of barium minerals; in Derbyshire lead and fluor predominate in the east and as the veins (locally known as 'rakes') are traced to the west these give place first to barytes ($BaSO_4$) and then

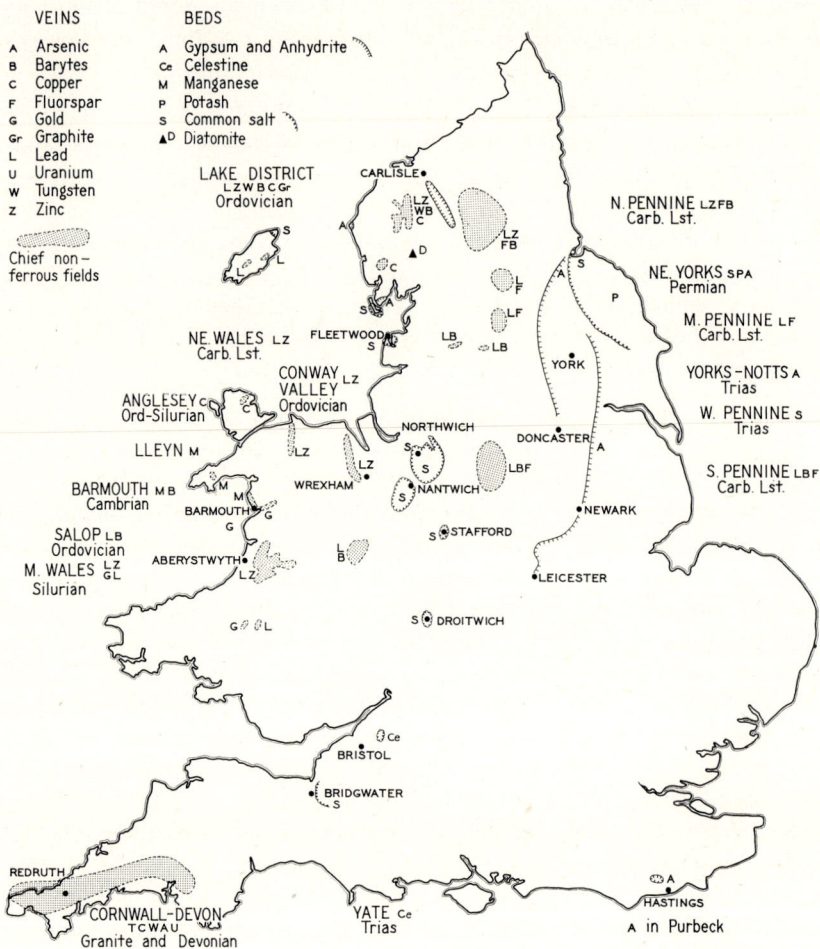

Figure 26. Mineral fields of England and Wales other than Iron and Fuel

that to calcite (CaCO$_3$). In hard rock slate or granite country where the veins are more persistent in depth than laterally a vertical zoning is usually apparent. For example, in the Keswick area the sought-after minerals range from blende in depth followed upwards by galena and then by barytes. In Cornwall copper ores lie above that of tin (see page 90 and Fig. 31) but the latter is in payable quantity only in the vicinity of mineralization centres. For example, both ores are workable about Camborne whereas no payable tin in quantity has been discovered beneath the rich copper ores of the Tamar Valley. Arsenic and tungsten ores occupy intervening or rather overlapping zones between tin and copper and the latter is followed in places by those of lead, zinc, barytes and iron.

Tin, chiefly as cassiterite, is confined to the vicinity of the granite masses in Cornwall and Devon where it is often accompanied by tungsten ore mainly as wolfram $(FeMn)WO_4$ but with some scheelite $(CaWO_4)$. It is interesting to record that these two tungsten ores occur at Carrock in Cumberland whereas no minerals of much value have been located in the widespread granites farther north. In Cornwall and Devon the tungsten deposits of Cligga Head and of Hemerdon (east of Plymouth) occur in small ramifying veins which collectively are known as a stockwork. Of the hundreds of mines formerly working in Devon and Cornwall only a handful survive.

Arsenic ore, mispickel (FeAsS) was got mainly from the Cornish tin lodes though there is some at Carrock.

The copper centres are more widely spread than those of tin with fair-sized fields about Keswick and Coniston and in Anglesey (Parys Mountain) and smaller ones in Staffordshire and Wales though Devon and Cornwall were the leaders. No copper ores are raised at present. The primary ore is copper pyrites $(Cu_2S.Fe_2S_3)$: In the superficial oxydized zone this gives place to black and red oxides and to green (malachite) and blue (azurite) carbonates and in an intermediate zone to various copper minerals enriched by downward percolating copper solutions from the oxydized zone. Uranium ores accompany copper at a few Cornish localities. A peculiar deposit of copper ore was worked at one time at Alderley Edge in Cheshire; it took the form of specks of malachite in sandstone and conglomerate of Keuper age.

Lead and zinc ores are usually associated. Some were raised in Cornwall and Devon but the larger fields lay farther north—some in slaty rocks such as in Wales, Shropshire, Lake District and south-west Scotland, others in limestone, as in the Mendips, north-east Wales and in particular the Pennines with a few north of the Highland Border. There was also considerable lead mining in the Isle of Man (Laxey and Foxdale). Of the hundreds of mines a few survive but there is a better chance for resuscitation of this industry than for copper.

The spars of barium—barytes $(BaSO_4)$ and witherite $(BaCO_3)$— and fluorspar (CaF_2) commonly associated with lead and zinc ores are still mined or got from dumps in the Pennines particularly Derbyshire, Durham and Northumberland; barytes is got in the Lake District, in Shropshire, in Arran and in south-west Scotland. Calcite is raised at Youlgreave, Derbyshire and was formerly mined in Shropshire.

Small quantities of many other minerals were formerly raised in Britain from veins or similar deposits including graphite from Seathwaite in Borrowdale, nickel and cobalt in North Wales and gold from the Barmouth–Dolgelly area and from Pumpsaint (between Carmarthen and Lampeter). Alluvial gold has been got in Scotland. Much silver, mostly from galena, has been obtained at various times and even supplied local mints.

Of the non-ferrous bedded deposits the most important are those of common salt and of gypsum $(CaSO_4.2H_2O)$ and anhydrite $(CaSO_4)$. These along with dolomite $(CaMg)CO_3$ are often spoken of as evaporites for they were formed by

the natural evaporation of sea water. The largest field of common salt is that of Cheshire with smaller fields north (Fleetwood, Walney Island) and south (Stafford, Droitwich and Bridgwater) all in the Keuper Marl and in the Middlesborough area of Permian where the salt is associated with dolomite and anhydrite. Deep borings near Whitby penetrating similar strata have revealed the presence of beds of potash salts associated with the Permian limestones and also a thick bed of Keuper salt. Rock salt is mined at Winsford near Nantwich but most of it is got as brine.

Gypsum occurs in Permo-Triassic marls in West Cumberland, Furness and the Eden Valley and in Keuper Marl about Uttoxeter and Newark. In southern England there is some in Somerset, Dorset and Gloucester but that of Robertsbridge near Hastings is more important; this occurs in grey Purbeck strata whereas in other localities the rocks are red. It is associated with celestine (strontium sulphate $SrSO_4$) about Yate in the Bristol area. Gypsum was formerly mined as ornamental stone (alabaster) but is now mainly got for plaster of paris. Where a bed of gypsum passes under considerable cover it is usually replaced by anhydrite. This was worthless until fixation of nitrogen from the air was introduced at Billingham; it also provides sulphuric acid and cement.

It is a moot point whether certain clays and slates should be classed as minerals (as they are legally) or as rocks. China clay for instance, restricted to certain areas of Devon and Cornwall, is a product of chemical alteration of granite possibly due to some late stage uprise of solutions connected with the mineralization of that region. Feldspar is altered to kaolin and dark micas to white mica but quartz is unchanged. The so-called ball clays of Bovey Tracey near Newton Abbot and those of Poole near Bournemouth may represent transported china clay deposited in water; they are more plastic than kaolin.

SLATES   Only a small proportion of the rocks affected by the lateral pressures producing slaty cleavage provide slates for roofing. Such slates often occur in relatively narrow belts. They range in age from pre-Cambrian to Devonian. In England the pre-Cambrian of Charnwood produced durable slates but Dalradian and Moine are common in Scotland along the Highland Border about Aberfoyle, Easedale near Oban, about Ballachulish and in northern Aberdeenshire. Welsh slates range from Cambrian about Snowdon to Ordovician north of Blaenau Ffestiniog and Corris.

Those of the Lake District include the green slates of Borrowdale ashes and the Silurian Burlington blue slates. The famous glistening Delabole Slates of north Cornwall are of Devonian age.

Other rocks used for roofing material are not true slates but rather fissile slabs. They include sandstones mainly of Carboniferous age in the north of England and limestones such as the Collyweston Slates of the Lincolnshire Limestone and the Stonesfield Slates and similar rocks of the North Cotswolds.

BRICKS AND TILES   The mention of slates introduces the artificial variety known as tiles and made from clays and loams at some time or other in most counties, usually along with brick-making, crude pottery, and drain tiles. While almost any

ground-up rock will make bricks of some kind, good clays are usually required for tile making. At the present time some are made in the Cheltenham area, about Colchester and in the Weald but the main centres are in the coalfields particularly in the Midlands. Bricks are made in the same areas and also from the Keuper Marl but the Oxford Clay which has almost enough bituminous matter for its own firing is the leader in its own class of bricks. The strong dark blue engineering bricks are made from Etruria Marls.

REFRACTORY AND SANITARY WARE These are mostly manufactured from grey clays in the Coal Measures usually from the low alkali seatearths or fireclays, though some are of ganister, the very siliceous seatearth of certain coal seams. In Scotland a highly aluminous clay which is a product of weathering of Millstone Grit lavas is in great demand.

In addition to moulded products refractory material is required for furnace linings. Some is got from ganisters but dolomite from the Permian Magnesian Limestone and from dolomitized Carboniferous Limestone supplies many such needs.

FLUXES Large quantities of pure limestone strong enough to stand the burden are required in iron smelting. Most of it is provided by the Carboniferous Limestone though some Lincolnshire Limestone is also used. Another home produced flux for iron making is fluorspar got chiefly from Derbyshire and Durham.

ROAD METALS In the past owing to lack or cost of transport all kinds of stones including cobbles from arable land and flints have been used for road metal. Today while local sandstones and limestones may be used in the initial stages the roads are either built of concrete or metalled with broken stone bound with asphalt and the like. Similar stones are used for railway ballast. Modern transport has led to concentration of quarries and the chief sources today are the hard tough igneous rocks, Carboniferous Limestone and quartzites similar to those of the Nuneaton area.

SANDS AND GRAVELS White sands, of low iron content, are used in glass making, for example, the Shirdley Hill Sands near Liverpool and the Lower Greensand near Leighton Buzzard and some are used for moulding. Formerly these moulding sands were largely got from the Upper Mottled Sandstone around Birmingham, which are red sands with a clay pellicle to the grains, but now-a-days the bonding matter is added to graded sand. The bulk of the sand, however, is used in mortar, plaster or cement. Almost any sandstone formation will provide sand by weathering or pulverizing but most sands are got from the soft Triassic and Cretaceous sandstones, or from glacial or alluvial deposits that also provide much of the gravel as, for example, in the Thames Valley west of London and in the Trent Valley though some gravel is got directly from the Bunter Pebble Beds.

LIME AND CEMENT In most limestone areas there are scores of disused limekilns. Today lime-burning both for agricultural use and for building purposes is concentrated. Some is got from the Silurian limestones and some from the oolites and the

Magnesian Limestone but the main sources are the Carboniferous Limestone and the Chalk. For cement manufacture some clay matter in addition to lime is required. The argillaceous limestones of the Lower Lias, as in the Rugby area, and the Chalk Marl at the base of the Chalk provide almost the right mixture but in many cases shales or clays are added to purer limestones, as in the Chalk north of Dunstable and in the Carboniferous Limestone of Derbyshire.

BUILDING STONES   In the past almost every formation provided building material for local use though in the broad clay areas such as Shropshire and Cheshire recourse had to be made to wattle or to brickwork in a frame of wood—later elaborated into the famous 'black and white work'. Chalk has been used extensively though usually armoured externally by dressed flints and the Totternhoe Stone is still quarried near Dunstable. In most cases, however, even where good stone is available bricks or concrete are prevalent. Of the igneous rocks granite has been most widely used as, for example, at Aberdeen; in the slate areas slabby material is still used for walling; Old Red Sandstone has been used extensively in Scotland, as also the buff sandstones of the Lower Coal Measures in Lancashire and Yorkshire, the red and buff sandstones of the Trias within easy reach of its outcrop, and the grey-buff Pennant Sandstone in South Wales. Magnesian Limestone and the oolites though dominating building in their outcrops have gone farther afield but even in their case the use of stone is declining except as a mere veneer or as an ornament to brick and concrete structures. The Magnesian Limestone is available in pale buff and reddish colours; the latter chiefly as a sandy dolomite in the Mansfield area. Of the oolites the best known are the Inferior and Great Oolites and the Portland Stone. The northern development of the Inferior Oolite crops out from north of Lincoln to Rutland; it is the pale oolite known as Lincolnshire Limestone and formerly much quarried about Ancaster and Grantham. Southwards to Oxfordshire the formation is largely sandstone and ironstone and the red-brown sandstone is in demand for local building. In the Cotswold country the Inferior Oolite is again well developed as a limestone. The Great Oolite also reaches its maximum development as a building stone in the Cotswolds and to beyond Bath; it is usually paler than Inferior Oolite. In addition to numerous quarries there are vast underground workings in the Great Oolite at Box and Corsham.

Portland Stone is a white oolitic freestone and takes its name from the Isle of Portland where it is still quarried; it is extensively used on large buildings in the London area in particular.

ORNAMENTAL STONES   Many rocks and minerals will take a polish and in the past were worked on a considerable scale, for example, the Petworth Marble used as pilasters and the like in many churches and the less known Marston Marble with ammonities from Marston Magna near Yeovil. The Carboniferous Limestone of Derbyshire (plain black or creamy or with crinoids), of Furness (light and dark patches), of Poolvash in the Isle of Man (nearly black) at one time supplied much material and the Devonian limestone of Devon is still in favour. Other stones not

true marbles include the serpentine of the Lizard, while examples of polished granites from Cornwall, Shap, Aberdeen and Peterhead are to be seen in any town or city.

The purple and banded variety of fluor known as Blue John and got near Castleton in Derbyshire, gypsum in the fine granular form of alabaster and in fibrous form (satin spar) chiefly from the Newark area and jet from Whitby are no longer popular.

OIL   Britain is sadly deficient in supplies of home oil. Such as occurs is in two forms, oil shale and free oil. The former is mined in the Lothians from beds in the Oil Shale Group of the Lower Carboniferous which yield about 19 gallons per ton and 20 to 40 lb. of sulphate of ammonia on distillation. Some parts of the Lias and of the Kimmeridge Clay are also oil shales but purification of the oil they yield appears to be too expensive to warrant exploitation. The carbonaceous material in the Oxford Clay which lessens firing costs very considerably is probably part oil.

Free oil has been noted in many of the coalfields where occasionally it has been worth collecting. It is also present in some of the marine bands in the Millstone Grit and in fossils in the Carboniferous Limestone and a little was tapped in an exploratory boring at Hardstoft near Chesterfield. Whatever the source free oil requires a permeable rock as a reservoir and it is requisite or at least desirable that that rock should be in the form of a dome and that it should be covered by impervious strata that has remained relatively undisturbed since the oil was emplaced, otherwise the oil will escape. With a geological history such as that of Britain these conditions are difficult of fulfilment but at last the searches of the geologists of the Anglo–Iranian Oil Co. were successful particularly in the Newark area (with yields of 100,000 tons per year) and to a less extent at Formby.

WATER   Unlike oil, water is abundant in Britain though not always at the right time and place for the rainfall ranges from 20 to 30 inches in eastern England to over 60 inches bordering the west coasts and double that amount locally. Some of that rain runs off via rivers to the sea; some of it directly from the impervious formations such as characterize Wales, the Lake District, the Southern Uplands and the Highlands, and some indirectly from springs. Some of it finds its way underground through pervious soils and may collect there in porous rocks such as sandstones or in heavily jointed rocks such as limestones including chalk. It is obvious that gentle downfolds of the strata, as synclines or basins, will assist in the conservation of the underground water. Usually quite a lot of this water will escape as springs or seepages when the level of the water in the rocks coincides with any escape route, at the appropriate level, to the surface. Such an escape route is provided by faults and joints and by the reservoir stratum itself where that crops out at relatively low levels. The level of the water thus controlled is known as the water table and it is to this level that wells or borings have to be sunk. All rocks but the stiff clays will yield some water to wells but the amount varies from a mere weeping to thousands of gallons. The most prolific water-bearing formations are the Chalk, the New Red Sandstone, the Magnesian Limestone and the Oolites. The other

formations are more suitable for water storage at the surface; such reservoirs require suitable topography with impervious sides and floor, yet capable of sustaining the weight and thrust on and of the dam on its foundations and abutments together with adequate gathering ground and rainfall. Some of the deep valleys of Wales are utilized not only by Welsh towns but by cities in England—reservoirs about Rhayader supply Birmingham and Lake Vyrnwy Liverpool. In the Lake District Thirlmere and Haweswater whose levels have beeen raised by dams supply Manchester. Valleys in the Millstone Grit Pennines have provided about 400 reservoir sites for towns mainly in Lancashire and Yorkshire. In Scotland and in parts of Wales such reservoirs and lakes serve hydro-electric schemes as well as providing water supplies. London gets most of its water from the Thames but there are still thousands of borings helping to unduly depress the water table in the Chalk beneath that great city. In the Midlands many large towns depend largely on underground supplies—Coventry and Nuneaton from the Upper Coal Measures, Wolverhampton from the Trias.

REFERENCES

For a useful selection of information and localities see *Guides to Excursion*, 'A1: Economic Geology' and 'A18: Hydrogeology', both of England and Wales, for the International Geological Congress of 1948. For further details of the subjects the reader is referred to the mineral, coalfield and water memoirs of the Geological Survey.

SHEET 1

SOUTH-EASTERN ENGLAND

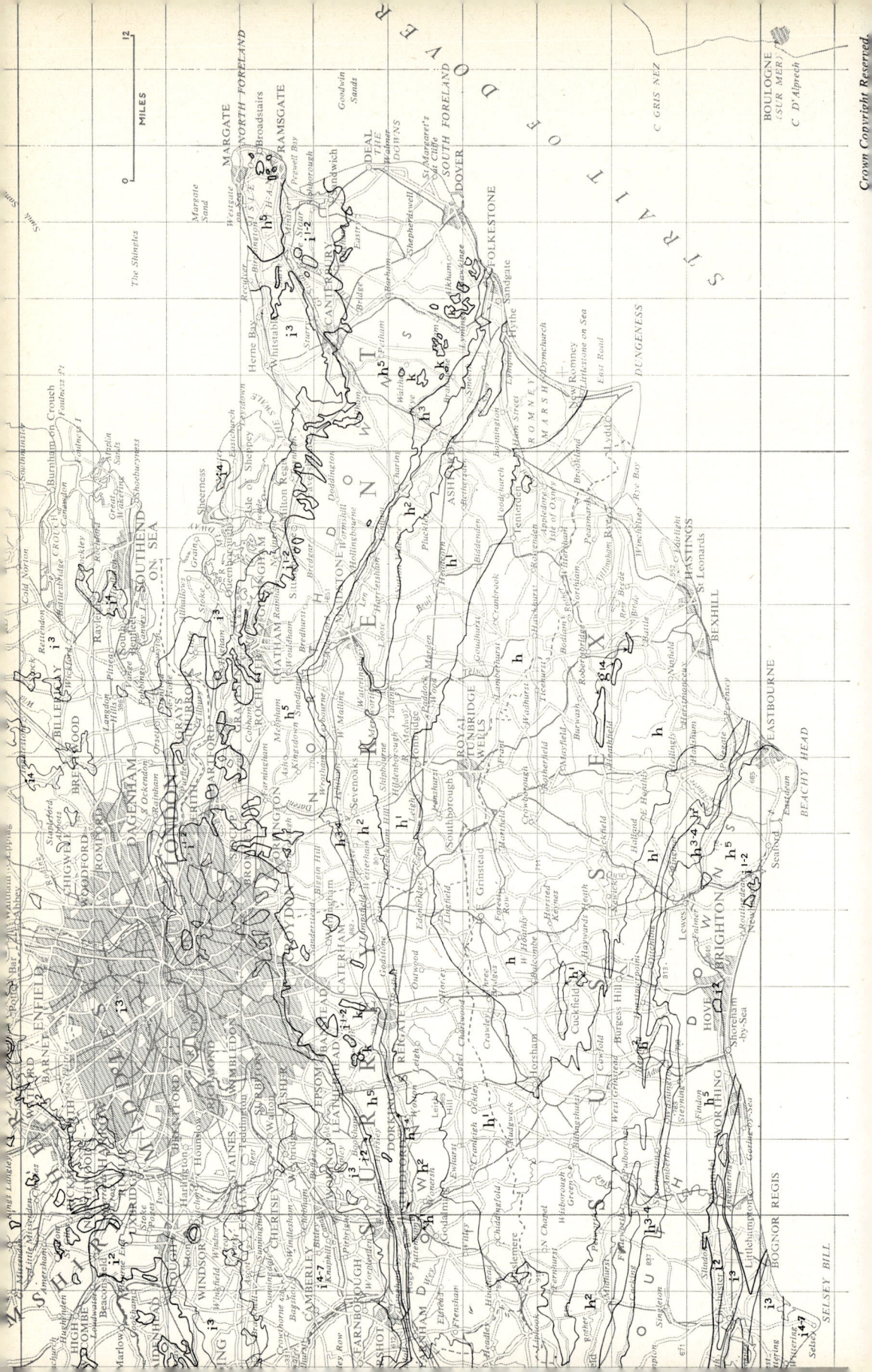

STRAIT OF DOVER

MILES

BOULOGNE
(SUR MER)
C. D'Alprech

C. GRIS NEZ

NORTH FORELAND
Margate
MARGATE
Broadstairs
RAMSGATE
SOUTH FORELAND
Goodwin Sands
DEAL
THE DOWNS
DOVER
FOLKESTONE
CANTERBURY
Whitstable
Herne Bay
Sandwich
DUNGENESS
ROMNEY MARSH
ASHFORD
Hythe
New Romney
Lydd
K E N T
Sheerness
Isle of Sheppey
SOUTHEND ON SEA
CHATHAM
ROCHESTER
GILLINGHAM
Sittingbourne
Maidstone
Tenterden
HASTINGS
St Leonards
BEXHILL
EASTBOURNE
BEACHY HEAD
ROYAL TUNBRIDGE WELLS
S U S S E X
Lewes
BRIGHTON
HOVE
Shoreham-by-Sea
WORTHING
Littlehampton
BOGNOR REGIS
SELSEY BILL
CHICHESTER
S U R R E Y
REIGATE
CATERHAM
CROYDON
DORKING
LEATHERHEAD
EPSOM
ESHER
WIMBLEDON
SURBITON
BRENTFORD
STAINES
WINDSOR
CAMBERLEY
FARNBOROUGH
ALDERSHOT
B E R K S H I R E
LONDON
DAGENHAM
ROMFORD
WOODFORD
CHIGWELL
BRENTWOOD
BILLERICAY
Burnham-on-Crouch
E S S E X
BARNET
ENFIELD
M I D D L E S E X
HORSHAM
CRAWLEY
E Grinstead
Sevenoaks
M A R S H

SOUTH-EASTERN ENGLAND

THIS sheet includes London, the whole of Kent, most of Surrey, Sussex and Middlesex and the southern part of Essex. It includes the Thames below Windsor with various tributaries and the Medway which with their shipping facilities contribute much to the commercial importance of the district today and have been of prime importance for over 2,000 years. Other rivers, of little interest commercially today but of moment in the past, drain east and south; they include the Stour of Canterbury and Richborough, the Rother of Rye, the Cuckmere of near Seaford, the Ouse of Newhaven, the Adur of Shoreham and the Arun of Littlehampton. The dominant topographical features are the North Downs extending from Dover to the south of London and the South Downs ranging westerly from Beachy Head to join the former on the high ground of the Hampshire border. Contained in this horseshoe is the lower ground of the Weald from which rises the central elevated tract east of Horsham and through Tunbridge Wells to Ashdown Forest.

A glance at the map (Sheet 1) will show that there is a close relationship between the topographical features just mentioned, and the geology for the low ground outside the horseshoe is occupied by the soft Tertiary strata of the London and Hampshire Basins whereas the shoe hills are made up of Chalk and Lower Greensand enclosing the low ground of Weald Clay with a resistant core of Hastings Sand. Since all these beds dip away from the central ridge the main structure is obviously anticlinal though there are many subsidiary folds or wrinkles on the main structure which give rise to apparently anomalous distribution of outcrops of certain Cretaceous beds that will be referred to later; attention may here be drawn, however, to wrinkles in the core of the anticline which bring to the surface the three inliers of Purbeck Beds between Battle, Robertsbridge and Heathfield to the north-west of Hastings. These are the uppermost beds of a fairly complete series of Jurassic rocks which in their turn further conceal the Kent Coalfield that lies roughly between Ramsgate, Canterbury and Dover in a syncline pitching south-east beneath the Channel. Rimming this syncline are the still older Carboniferous Limestone, Old Red Sandstone and Silurian strata which have been proved in many borings in East Kent. Silurian and Old Red Sandstone rocks have also been found buried to a depth of 1,000 ft. or so beneath Tertiary and Cretaceous strata in the London area. This old platform, the surface of which appears to have a very gentle slope to the south, has emerged several times with the result that Jurassic and Cretaceous rocks of various ages have been deposited on or banked against it, and it has contributed material towards these deposits. With the concealed old rocks this account has no further concern except in the case of the Coal Measures. These attain a maximum thickness of about 2,800 ft. of which the lower and upper

quarters are shales with coal seams separated by a thick median belt of sandy strata. There are large collieries at Chislet east of Canterbury and at Snowdown, Betteshanger and Tilmanstone west of Deal; the initial pit at Dover was abandoned before much coal was got.

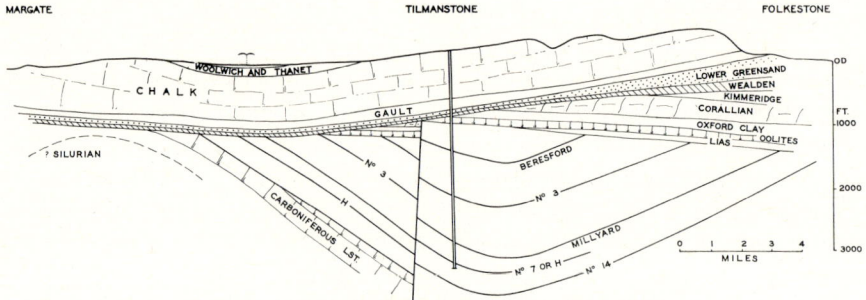

Figure 27. Section across the Kent Coalfield

Note: The coalfield is in a syncline pitching eastwards and is wholly concealed by newer unconformable strata in which Jurassic beds dip southwards and the again unconformable Cretaceous strata dip northwards into a gentle basin.

JURASSIC The Purbeck rock are the oldest strata exposed at surface and may be seen in streams and cuttings about Heathfield and Mountfield as grey clay shales with limestones and sandstones. From the sea or salt lake in which some of these beds were deposited three closely associated beds of gypsum were precipitated. Gypsum is worked near Mountfield for the manufacture of plaster of paris and plaster board.

CRETACEOUS The succeeding Wealden Series are made up of the Weald Clay above and the Hastings Beds below and the latter are further subdivided downwards into Tunbridge Wells Sands, Wadhurst Clay, Ashdown Sand and Fairlight Clays each named after type localities but not always present throughout the district. The Fairlight Clays locally developed to 400 ft. thick about Fairlight east of Hastings are grey and variegated clays and pale or white fine sandstones and silts. The Ashdown Sand, of which the Fairlight Beds may be regarded as a peculiar basal phase, is usually a soft sandstone such as may be seen at Hastings, near Uckfield and in Ashdown Forest. The thickness varies from 160 ft. at Hastings to 500 ft. at Heathfield. Lignite is not uncommon.

The Wadhurst Clay, averaging 150 ft. in thickness, is made up of rapid alternations of bluish-grey clays and thinner siltstones and sandstones with local developments of shelly limestones and clay ironstone; the latter furnished much of the ironstone of Kent and East Sussex. Some of the sandstones which are hard and calcareous are known collectively as Tilgate Stone. There are sections of Wadhurst beds at Quarry Hill, Tonbridge, again near Battle and at Cooden near Bexhill.

The Tunbridge Wells Sand is locally cemented into sandrock as at High Rocks, near Tunbridge Wells, at West Hoathly and in quarries at Pembury near Tonbridge.

Ranging from 180 ft. at Tunbridge Wells to 400 ft. near Cuckfield the Sand includes clay beds of which two have been named from their localities as Grinstead Clay and Cuckfield Clay.

Weald Clay is a shaly brown or blue clay, though occasionally mottled or red in colour, ranging from 400 ft. to over 1,000 ft. in thickness. There are intermittent limestones rich in the shells of the freshwater snail *Paludina* which constitute the Sussex Marbles of Petworth, Laughton, Charlwood and Bethersden and the more earthy beds as near Ockley. There are also fissile and calcareous sandstones often showing sun cracks; the most important of these, Horsham Stone, was much quarried for building and for roofing purposes and may still be seen in a small quarry near Southwater. The Clay is dug for brick-making near Dorking, South-water, Pluckley, Lingfield, Warnham, Berwick and Ockley; at the last-named place it has yielded remains of the dinosaur *Iguanodon* a giant herbivorous lizard-like creature.

Up to this stage the formations were largely of freshwater origin ascribed to the 'Wealden Lake'; further subsidence, however, converted this to an arm of the sea but land still persisted though now only as a promontory through North Kent and London. Into this sea the Lower Greensand was deposited beginning with the Atherfield Clay (0–60 ft.) not unlike that of the Wealden but with marine fossils. The next subdivision, the Hythe Beds (0–350 ft.) are sandstones and give rise to hills such as Coneyhurst or Pitch Hill (about 7 miles S.E. of Guildford) where they are quarried. Succeeding these sandrocks come the Sandgate Beds (30–120 ft.) usually clays and sands but locally with fuller's earth which is worked about two miles east of Redhill. The uppermost formation, the Folkestone Beds (5–250 ft.) are current-bedded sandstones in considerable demand for building sand and, where white, for glass sand; there are numerous quarries particularly near Folkestone, Reigate and Dorking.

These subdivisions are variable in character and thickness and cementing with silica, lime or iron converts soft sands into resistant stone as, for comparison, the hard rocks of Leith Hill south of Dorking and the soft sands east of that town. Certain beds have locally yielded building stone—Kentish Rag of North Kent and Bargate Stone farther west.

Further submergence introduced the stiff dark blue and grey clays of the Gault (100–300 ft.) which extends right across the old land beneath London. Folkestone Cliffs are the type locality and the Gault there is divisible into eleven zones based on ammonites though gastropod, lamellibranch and brachiopod shells are also common. There are brickworks at Dunton Green (near Sevenoaks) and Albury (3½ miles east of Guildford).

There is a gradual upward and lateral transition from Gault to Upper Green-sand; the latter is about 50 ft. thick and of variable constitution. A greenish soft sandstone is mined for hearthstone near Reigate.

Widespread subsidence introduced a clear fairly deep sea in which the Chalk was laid down not only in this south-eastern district but over the greater part of Britain. Chalk usually has over 95 per cent calcium carbonate; it contains many

foraminifera but also large numbers of shells (sea-urchins, lamellibranchs and bra-chiopods) and so cannot be strictly correlated with the deep sea *Globigerina* ooze; most of its material is very fine and may represent a chemically precipitated mud.

Certain bands, harder or tougher than usual, have been used for building and are known as 'rocks'. Two of these are used to subdivide the Chalk into Lower Chalk (170 ft. to the Melbourn Rock 10 ft.) a grey chalk or chalk marl zoned by *Schloenbachia varians* and *Holaster globosus*; Middle Chalk (170 ft. up to the nodular Chalk Rock) a blocky white chalk with few or no flints and zoned by *Rhynchonella cuvieri* and *Terebratula lata*; and the Upper Chalk (550 ft. of soft white Chalk with nodular and tabular flints) zoned by *Holaster planus*, *Micraster cortestudinarium*, *M. coranguinum*, *Marsupites testudinarius* and *Actinocamax quadratus* (see Fig. 19).

The cliffs from Birchington through Margate to Ramsgate, from Deal through Dover to Folkestone and again from Beachy Head at Eastbourne to west of Brighton furnish excellent sections while inland chalk is quarried at numerous places: Lower and Middle at Dorking, Betchworth, Merstham, Medway Valley, Lewes, and Upper Chalk about Horsley (between Leatherhead and Guildford) and west of Gravesend where it furnishes part of the raw material for cement-making.

TERTIARY Between the Chalk and the Tertiary strata there is a great uncon-formity and the uppermost parts of the Chalk are frequently cut out; of the Tertiary the middle formations Oligocene and Miocene are entirely absent from south-east England but the Eocene is well represented and there are remnants of Pliocene.

The Eocene consists of a median dark blue but brown-weathering clay, London Clay, about 400 ft. thick, between mixed strata of sands, gravels and clays.

Thanet Sand, 0–75 ft. of pale yellow or grey fine sand, with marine shells, directly succeeds the Chalk and has a layer of green loam with green-coated unworn flints at its base. It is followed by Woolwich and Reading Beds (40–90 ft.). In East Kent these are marine sands; in West Kent, East Surrey and Essex they are of Woolwich facies comprising estuarine clays, loam sands and conglomerates; farther west and north these pass into Reading Beds of mottled plastic clays and pale silts.

From the London Clay there is transition by way of alternations of clay and sand (Claygate Beds) into the Bagshot Beds at the base of the Upper Eocene; these are vari-coloured sands with some beds of pale pipe clay and of gravel forming high heaths near London. Next come the Bracklesham Beds about 50 ft. of lilac and variegated clays with some sands and pebble beds, followed by Barton Beds, fine even-bedded yellow sand.

Of these Tertiary strata exposures may be seen of Thanet Sand in cliffs at Pegwell Bay and near Reculver and in sandpits at Sturry near Canterbury in East Kent and at the entrance to Chislehurst 'caves' and beneath Woolwich and Reading Beds at Charlton, near Woolwich. The Woolwich Beds are seen also in the cliffs east of Herne Bay. Reading Beds are worked for brick-making at Clapham near Worthing.

Apart from the cliffs of Herne Bay and Sheppey natural exposures of London Clay are infrequent though the underground railways of London are driven in it. Most of the pebbles in the Tertiary Beds are of well-rounded black flint; cemented lumps of these gravels survive as Hertfordshire Pudding Stone and of cemented sands as 'Sarsens'.

PLIOCENE Patches of ferruginous sand on top of the North Downs, particularly between Folkestone and Wye though there are others north of Reigate, and on the South Downs near Beachy Head are referred to the Pliocene. Similar material from pipes in the chalk has yielded Pliocene fossils.

DRIFT More recent deposits, which are not shown on the map, include wide-spread masses of 'Clay with Flints' surmounting many chalk hills and similar material on other formations. While there is no evidence that the district south of the Thames was invaded by ice these stony beds may be the result of the alternate freezing and thawing of the local products of weathering. There are also the alluvial and terrace deposits along streams, which have yielded flint implements used by early man and fossils of coeval animals, old beaches such as Dungeness and marshes such as Romney and of patches of submerged forest such as at Galley Gap near Bexhill which indicates that considerable variations in level have taken place since its formation.

REFERENCES

Geological Survey
   Regional Handbooks: Wealden District, ed 3, 1954; *London and Thames Valley*, ed 2, 1947.
Excursions and Field Meetings
   Geological Excursions round London, Davies, G. M., 1914, London.
   International Geological Congress 1948.
   B Excursions based on London: 1, Hindhead and Midhurst; 3, London to Brighton; 5, Box Hill; 6, Leith Hill; 8, London to Beachy Head; 9, Rye and Dungeness; 10, Charlton, Abbey Wood and Plumstead; 12, Oxsted and Coulsden; 14 Crowhurst, Telham Hill and Battle; 15, N.W. Weald; 28, Wrotham and Folkestone; 34, Brighton; 36, Soil of Kent; 40, Guildford and Hogs Back; 45, Surrey Agricultural Land Drainage; 51, Dunton Green (Gault); 52, Swanscombe (Terrace gravels); 54, London–Fairlight–Rye; 56 Horsley and Netley Heath (Chalk and Pliocene); 63, Southborough, Tunbridge Wells and Eridge (Wealden); 64, Isle of Sheppey (London Clay); 66 Dorking, Betchworth and Headley (Reading Beds Gault and Greensands); 71, Tonbridge, Horsham and Dorking (Wealden); 72, Herne Bay and Canterbury (Chalk to London Clay); 73, Dover (Chalk to Lower Greensand; landslips); 76, Harefield (Chalk, with drift-pipes, and Lower Eocene); 86, Wrotham Heath (Gault and Lower Greensand); 87, Lewes (Chalk zones); 94, Westerham, Sevenoaks and Tonbridge (Gault to Wealden).
Geologists Association, Proceedings or Circulars
   1945, Guildford; East Malling; Merstham and Red Hill; Tunbridge Wells. 1946, Pull-borough and Godstone. 1947, Reigate; Central Weald. 1948, Godalming; Lewes; N.W. Weald; Oxsted. 1949, Romney Marsh; Sevenoaks (Gault); Folkestone (Gault). 1950, Lewes–Newhaven (Chalk). 1951, Fittleworth; Reigate; Mantell's Weald; Sheppey; Elmstead Woods and Blackheath; Oxshott and Claygate; Holmbury and Godstone. 1952, Lenham; Maidstone. 1953, East Kent. 1954, Hindhead; Sheppey; Sevenoaks; Borough Green; Ightham; Tunbridge Wells; Oxshot. 1955, Charlton; Central Weald; Guildford; Battle. 1956, S.W. Surrey.
Geologists Association, Guides
   24, Central Weald. 29, Weald. 30, London Region.

SHEET 2

MID-SOUTHERN ENGLAND

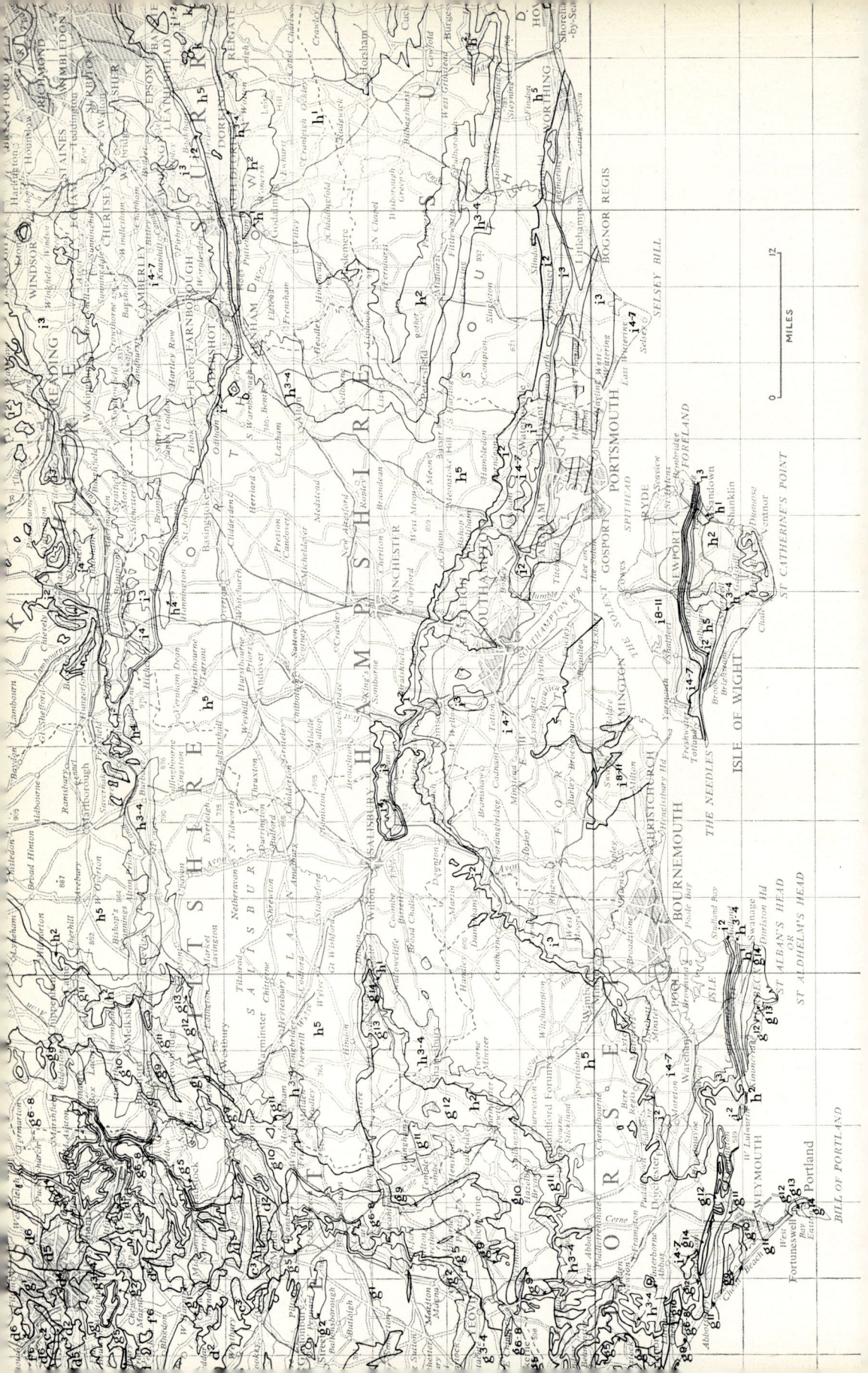

SURREY

SUSSEX

SOUTH DOWNS

HAMPSHIRE

WILTSHIRE

DORSET

READING

WINDSOR

CAMBERLEY

FARNHAM

BASINGSTOKE

WINCHESTER

SOUTHAMPTON

PORTSMOUTH

GOSPORT

SPITHEAD

THE SOLENT

RYDE

ISLE OF WIGHT

THE NEEDLES

ST CATHERINE'S POINT

BOGNOR REGIS

SELSEY BILL

WORTHING

SHOREHAM-by-Sea

NEW FOREST

BOURNEMOUTH

CHRISTCHURCH

POOLE

WAREHAM

SWANAGE

ST ALBAN'S HEAD OR ST ALDHELM'S HEAD

WEYMOUTH

PORTLAND

BILL OF PORTLAND

DORCHESTER

SALISBURY

ANDOVER

SALISBURY PLAIN

STAINES

EPSOM

REIGATE

MILES

MID-SOUTHERN ENGLAND

This district stretches west from Windsor and Bognor to just beyond Portland Bill It includes the whole of Hampshire and the Isle of Wight with portions of West Surrey and Sussex and South Berkshire, much of Wiltshire and Dorset and a little of Somerset. In it lies the great upland of chalk forming Salisbury Plain and the oolite country from Sherborne towards the Cotswolds, the western parts of the London Tertiary basin and of the Wealden anticline and the Hampshire Tertiary Basin. Apart from the Thames and its tributaries the drainage is mainly southwards, and though there are no rivers navigable to ships there are the inlets of the sea serving Portsmouth, Southampton, Poole and Portland.

Chalk occupies about half the surface of the area giving rise to broad rolling uplands of which Salisbury Plain forms the middle tract. On the north side of the Plain the Chalk outcrop is almost severed by tongue-like outcrops of pre-Chalk rocks through Bradford and Devizes brought up by an anticline eroded to give the Vale of Pewsey. East and slightly north of this tongue are the Tertiary Beds about Newbury at the western end of the London Basin. Farther south a similar but less extensive tongue along the Vale of Wardour almost reaches Wilton while near the eastern margin pre-Chalk rocks appear again in the broad end of the Wealden anticline. Just to the south of the line of the Wilton upfold the Tertiary rocks of the Hampshire Basin appear and occupy most of the country down to a line between Wareham and Bognor including the northern half of the Isle of Wight, with Chalk and older rocks re-appearing on the south. In addition to the major folds thus indicated there are others to be alluded to later but these serve to stress the, in general, east–west grain of the country.

The western margin is largely along the outcrop of the oolites though interrupted by older strata at intervals including Coal Measures, Carboniferous Limestone and Old Red Sandstone at the southern end of the Bristol–Somerset Coalfield; these latter are described in another section (Sheet 3).

JURASSIC   The Inferior Oolite of the west is usually entirely of limestone but in this south-western region may be represented in part by sands which replace also part of the Upper Lias. Single beds or small groups of beds often of local occurrence only have often received individual names; description and correlation is difficult without recourse to zoning based on specialized study of fossils particularly of the ammonites. This zoning indicates that Lower and Middle Inferior Oolite are absent in places and that Upper Inferior Oolite directly succeeds Upper Lias.

The Upper Inferior Oolite is about 45 ft. thick near Sherborne where the basal portion is an ironshot oolite; other beds there include the Sherborne Building Stone (10–20 ft.) and the Rubbly Limestone (12–21 ft.).

The Great or Bath Oolite Series is named after a thick massive oolite extensively worked near Bath but includes other rock types. Of these the most important is the Fuller's Earth which directly succeeds the Inferior Oolite. The Fuller's Earth is essentially a clay formation of which only a portion consists of the true earth originally used by fullers for the cleaning of wool by the absorption of fat and oil. The Fuller's Earth clay, grey in the lower part and greenish above and each portion about 100 ft. thick, is parted by a cream-weathering argillaceous limestone that may be in two lenses of which the lower one is known as Fuller's Earth Rock and may reach 35 ft. in thickness. At the bases of both clays there is usually an oyster bed; that of the lower has small shells with fine ribbing on one valve (*Ostrea knorri*); that of the upper is *Ostrea hebridica* and there is another shell bed at the top made-up of the rhynchonellid *Goniorhynchia boueti*. This Boueti Bed indicates that the Upper Fuller's Earth Clay is the equivalent of much of the Great Oolite of the Bath district.

At the top of the Great Oolite Series is the Forest Marble named from Wychwood Forest north of Witney in Oxfordshire; it is a hard false bedded limestone rich in oyster and pecten shells and is usually underlain and succeeded by greenish–brown sandy clays each about 30 ft. thick.

The succeeding Cornbrash so named from the brashy or stony soil to which it gives rise is a rubbly limestone about 30 ft. thick.

Oxford Clay at its base usually has a sandy bed succeeding a few feet of grey clay; these together make up the Kellaways Beds and though thin (10–20 ft.) they persist with the Oxford Clay across England from the Dorset coast to that of Yorkshire. They are named from the village of Kellaway in Wiltshire. Kellaways Beds and basal Oxford Clay are exposed in brickpits east of Chickerell (about 2 miles N.W. of Weymouth pier).

The Oxford Clay proper, 500–600 ft. in thickness, begins with rusty shales but soon passes into blue grey shales such as are well seen in the low cliffs two miles N.N.E. of Weymouth pier; the large *Gryphaea dilatata* is abundant here, along with the stout *Bellemnites oweni*.

Conditions obviously remained much the same throughout Oxford Clay times but with the onset of the Corallian there begins a repeated sequence of clay, grit, limestone—usually oolitic and coralline. These beds, some 200 ft. in thickness, are well exposed in cliffs between Osmington and Ringstead on the north side of Weymouth Bay. The sequences beginning with (a) Oxford Clay are (b) Nothe Grits (12–35 ft.); (c) Trigonia Limestone, massive brown limestone, 6 ft.; (1) Nothe Clay, blue and sandy 40 ft.; (2) Bencliff Grit, yellow sands 10–14 ft.; (3) Osmington Oolite 60 ft.; (i) Sandsfoot Clay, 20–30 ft., grey brown or blue with the large triangular oyster *O. delta*; (ii) Sandsfoot Grit, 0–25 ft. of ferruginous sandstone followed by the Ringstead Waxy Clay; (iii) Ringstead Coral Bed, a foot of green marly grit with shells and corals. It is difficult to recognize these beds inland but the same sort of lithology persists, for example, the Calne Freestone and a reef at Steeple Ashton equate with the Osmington Oolite; the Westbury Ironstone, of red and green oolitic ironstone, is believed to be about the horizon of Ringstead Coral Bed.

Kimmeridge Clay is named from Kimmeridge Bay (south of Wareham). Near there its full thickness has been proved in a boring for oil to be 1,651 ft., i.e. 581 ft. below that visible in the cliffs and about twice the thickness at Ringstead. Thin bands of hard mudstone give rise to dangerous ledges on the coast and there is one band of oil shale, about 3 ft. thick and known as Kimmeridge Coal, which crops out in Kimmeridge Bay and in Ringstead Bay; the sulphur content is too high for successful exploitation for oil.

With the onset of the Portland Beds the clay phase declines. There is a gradual passage from Kimmeridge Clay to the Portlandian and the base of the latter has been chosen at the Massive Bed—5 ft. of hard calcareous sandstone weathering yellow brown with *Exogyra nana* on Hountstout Cliff (west of Chapman's Pool

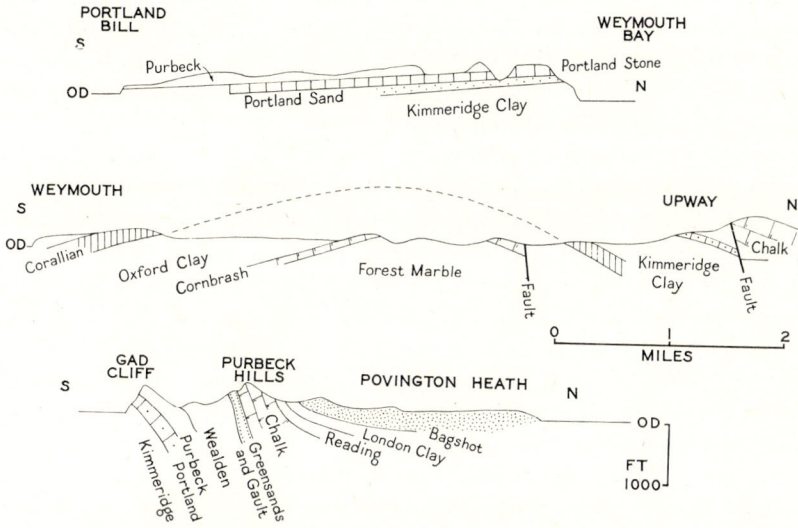

Figure 28. Sections in the Weymouth Area

Note: The even anticline between Weymouth and Upwey, of which Portland Bill forms a gentle southern limb, compared to the steep north limb of a fold at Gad Cliff and Purbeck Hills followed by Tertiary strata with low dips and broad outcrop at Povington Heath. (Based on the One-inch Geological Map)

5 miles west of Swanage) about 50 ft. above the old road round the cliff. The succeeding beds become more sandy upwards and are referred to the Portland Sands (100 ft. thick). These are followed by the Portland Stone—a series of limestones that give rise to the five miles of almost vertical cliffs between St. Alban's and Durlstone headlands near Swanage, to the Isle of Portland (marly beneath a cover of Lower Purbeck) and to Gad's Cliff two and a half miles west of Kimmeridge. The Portland Stone is a variable series of limestones of which the lower 60 or 70 ft. is a chalky limestone with layers of chert nodules (similar to flint) while the rest (30–70 ft.) is made up of partly shelly limestones and of cream oolitic freestones in demand for building stone. The stone is quarried on Portland but was largely

mined in Purbeck (e.g. Tilly Whim Caves); there are quarries also in the Vale of Wardour around Tisbury, Chicksgrove and Chilmark (the last yielding the famous Chilmark Stone) and in the Vale of Pewsey (Pottern, Coulston and Crockwood).

Purbeck strata show a change from the shallow marine of Portlandian to fresh-water and land conditions marked by gypsum layers (indicating cut off lobes of the sea), shell beds (particularly oysters), and 'dirt beds' with stumps of trees. Zoning of the strata is based on ostracods (minute crustaceans of bean like form) but shells are fairly common and the remains of dinosaurs have been found.

The full sequence, 400 ft., may be seen in Durlston Bay, Swanage; the beds thin to 290 ft. at Worbarrow (10 miles west of Swanage) and Lulworth.

A threefold subdivision is made of Purbeck Beds. At the base of the Lower Purbeck are the Cap Beds (9–19 ft.) two tufaceous limestones each with its dirt bed on top and well seen on cliffs east of Lulworth Cove and also on Portland. Then come the Broken Beds (15 ft. of fragmented limestone bands) followed by marls, shales and clays with gypsum up to 135 ft. thick; black cherts carry sponges and *Protocardia purbeckensis* forms 'cockle' beds.

The Middle Purbeck begins with a 1-ft. Dirt Bed, with the bones of mammals, crocodiles, etc., followed by a few feet of shales and then limestones up to 80 ft. thick which include cream building stones mined extensively in Purbeck. The limestones, with both marine and freshwater shells, are parted by the Cinder Bed rich in oysters, but with *Trigonia* and *Hemicidaris purbeckensis* a small sea urchin. Then come the 'Beef and *Corbula* Beds'—shales with bands of shelly limestone up to 34 ft. thick.

The Upper Purbeck, mainly of freshwater origin, begins with the Broken Shell Limestone (10 ft.) followed by clays with *Unio* (5–6 ft.) and these by the Purbeck (or *Paludina*) Marble formerly much used for interior pilasters, etc., of churches.

Purbeck Beds are present in the Vale of Wardour and are quarried between Dinton and Tisbury; there are quarries also near Upwey (6 miles north of Wey-mouth).

CRETACEOUS   Purbeck Beds pass gradually upwards into Wealden strata of sands, grits, mottled clays and shales, with some lignite and thin *Paludina* lime-stones, deposited in lagoons. The beds are 2,350 ft. thick at Swanage; to the west though coarse and conglomeratic they thin to 1,200 ft. in Worbarrow Bay and 750 ft. in Mupe Bay (respectively 11 and 12 miles west of Swanage) and to 350 ft. at Upwey near Weymouth. To the east, in the Isle of Wight, Wealden Beds consist of varicoloured clays followed by dark clays with black papery shales; both are exposed in Compton Bay.

The beds of the western end of the Wealden anticline include the *Paludina* limestone of Petworth (Petworth Marble).

Lower Greensand, the succeeding formation, attains its maximum thickness of 800 ft. at Atherfield (in the Isle of Wight 4 miles N.W. of St. Catherine's Point) from which is named the lowest division the Atherfield Clay—80 ft. of light blue clay with cakes of ironstone followed by the fossiliferous Lower Lobster Bed

(25–30 ft.). Next come the Ferruginous Sands (500 ft. and equivalent to Hythe and Sandgate beds of the Weald) with fossiliferous concretions especially near the base; they form bold cliffs with deep ravines (e.g. Blackgang Chine). The succeeding Sandrock (100–180 ft.) correlated with Folkestone Beds is a white or yellow sand capped by a coarse brown ferruginous grit known as the Carstone. There are good coast sections at intervals between Compton Bay (south of Freshwater) and Sandown.

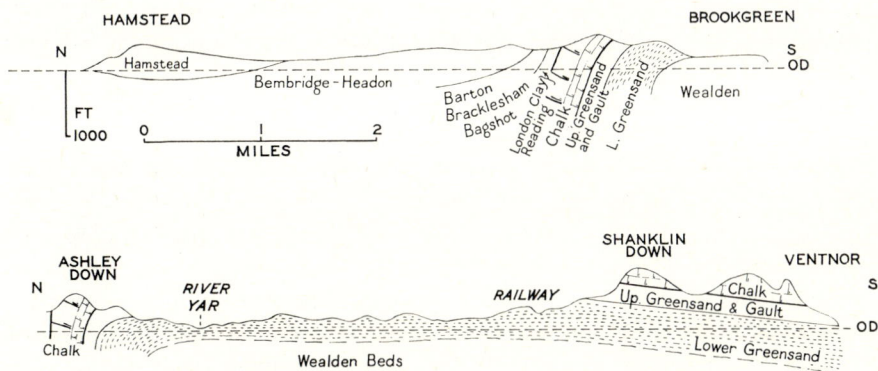

Figure 29. Sections across the Isle of Wight

Note the steep northern limb of the anticline especially in the Chalk. (Based on the One-inch Geological Map)

The above subdivisions cannot be recognized at Swanage and the formation cannot be traced west of Mupe Bay where it is only 66 ft. thick; in the Vale of Wardour there is only about 20 ft. of glauconitic sand. In the western Weald there is about 60 ft. of Atherfield Clay between Petworth and Haslemere and about 200 ft. of Hythe Beds near Midhurst; the Sandgate Beds around Godalming are shelly sandy limestones (Bargate Beds, about 40 ft. thick); Folkestone Beds (about 200 ft.) are dug for sand near Farnham.

Gault and Upper Greensand form one stratigraphical group but the sand facies overlies the clay and becomes more dominant westwards. In the Isle of Wight the Gault, as in most places, is a blue clay; it is there about 100 ft. thick and is followed by 100 ft. of Upper Greensand—seen in the Undercliff from Bonchurch to Blackgang and in the central ridge. The Gault is responsible for the extensive landslips near Ventnor. (See Fig 29).

Around Shaftesbury the Gault is about 90 ft. of brownish clays beneath 150 ft. of Upper Greensand comprising soft sands, sandstone and cherty beds formerly extensively quarried. Somewhat similar strata occur near Warminster. In the western Weald the Gault is about 250 ft. thick near Petersfield.

The Chalk is about 1,600 ft. thick; it is similar in fossil zones and lithology to that in south-east England (see page 61). There is conformable passage upwards from the Greensand into Lower Chalk (200 ft.) by way of a few feet of glauconitic

sand with concretions and chloritic marl in the Isle of Wight and in Wiltshire—at Dead Maid Quarry, Mere and at Maiden Bradley (south of Warminster). The Middle Chalk is up to 200 ft. thick of firm white chalk but Upper Chalk is much thicker and reaches 1,300 ft. in the Isle of Wight, with flints throughout. The narrow outcrops of the Chalk and Gault in the Hogsback west of Guildford are attributable to steep dips accompanied by faulting.

TERTIARY   Tertiary strata occur in two basins; that on the north lies at the western end of the London Basin in the triangle Beaconsfield–Newbury–Aldershot–Guildford; that on the south includes Bognor–Romsey–Wareham and the northern half of the Isle of Wight.

Thanet Sand is absent in these areas and the next formation is entirely of Reading facies (about 100 ft.) consisting largely of mottled clays.

London Clay is 400 ft. thick in Alum Bay and 320 ft. in Whitecliff Bay respectively west and east in the Isle of Wight where complete sections may be seen. Farther west it thins and near Dorchester is overlapped by the succeeding Bagshot Beds.

In the London Basin the Bagshot Beds are mainly fine white, buff or occasionally crimson sands locally with flint pebble beds and seams of pale pipe clay; they form the heaths about Chertsey, Esher and Bagshot and total about 120 ft. thick.

In the southern area the sands are coarser in parts; the total thickness is 200–250 ft. divisible into a lower Pipe Clay group—well developed around Poole in which leaves, etc., are common near Studland and Corfe—and the Bournemouth Freshwater Beds above made up of lenses of white and yellow sands, loams and fireclays such as may be seen in the cliffs west from Bournemouth pier.

The succeeding Bracklesham Beds are about 50 ft. thick west of London, 200 ft. at Bramble Hill, Bramshaw (6 miles S.E. of Salisbury), 320 ft. at Netley near Southampton and 600 ft. in the Isle of Wight. Grey and yellow sands and clays with lignite followed by sand and shingle occur east of Bournemouth pier to Boscombe; next come green and then brownish clays about Hengisbury and the yellowish sands of Highcliff (3 miles east of Christchurch station). In the Isle of Wight, where the beds are almost vertical, the best sections are at Alum Bay (near the Needles) with bright coloured mostly estuarine sands with lignite, and at Whitecliff Bay at the eastern end of the island where they are of marine origin with *Venericardia* and *Nummulites*.

The Barton Beds of fine yellow sands (50 ft.) with a basal pebble bed cap Chobham Ridges (near Bagshot) but are better developed at the type locality of Barton (5½ miles east of Christchurch station) where they are 190 ft. thick, and in Alum and Whitecliff bays (about 350 ft.) as blue and green sandy clays followed by sands.

Oligocene strata are only known in the Hampshire Basin where they occupy the northern half of the Isle of Wight and the southern part of the New Forest, with a small outlier capping Creechbarrow (south of Wareham). The deposits do not differ markedly from those of the Upper Eocene. Four divisions are recognized and named after type localities in the Isle of Wight. They are (1) Headon Beds

(150–200 ft.) mainly coloured clays with thin creamy limestones with the fresh-water 'snail' *Limnaea* exposed at Headon Hill, Whitecliff Bay and in Hordwell (or Hordle) Cliff about four miles S.W. of Lymington; (2) Osborne Beds (80–110 ft.) mainly clays with thin limestones but at St. Helens and Nettlestone at the east end of the Island of sands and grits respectively; (3) Bembridge Beds with 20 ft. of limestone well seen in Whitecliff Bay, followed by shelly clays (70–120 ft.) seen on the coast between Cowes and Yarmouth and between Priory Bay and Whitecliff Bay at the east end of the Island; and (4) Hamstead Beds (255 ft.) coloured clays, sands and shales.

Fossils indicate that the Oligocene is mainly of freshwater origin with occasional marine incursions; gastropod shells predominate though bivalves are common.

REFERENCES

Geological Survey
    Regional Handbooks: Hampshire Basin, ed 2, 1948; *Wealden District*, ed 3, 1954; *London and Thames Valley*, ed 2, 1947.
    District Memoirs: Isle of Wight, 1921; *Purbeck and Weymouth*, 1898; *Weymouth, Swanage, Corfe and Lulworth*, 1947.
Excursions and Field Meetings
    Dorset Coast, Davies, G. M., ed 2, 1956, London.
    International Geological Congress 1948.
    Long Excursions: A3 Bath; A8 Dorset Coast; C3 Bristol; C8 Isle of Wight.
    B Excursions based on London: 4, Reading and Kingsclere; 26, Worthing; 88, Pagham Harbour and Bognor (Tertiary Beds); 93, Trundle Hill and Bracklesham Bay.
Geologists Association, Proceedings or Circulars
    1909, Frome. 1932, Dorset Coast. 1933, Isle of Wight. 1934, Isle of Purbeck. 1941, Bath. 1945, Pangbourne and Sulham. 1946, Reading. 1948, Isle of Wight; Weymouth. 1949, Worthing; Bognor and Bracklesham Bay. 1950, Milford and Barton. 1954, West Sussex; Isle of Wight. 1956, Alum Bay (I.O.W.). 1959, Weymouth. 1961, Wessex Chalk. 1962, Isle of Wight (Cretaceous).
Geologists Association, Guides
    14, Southampton District. 22, Dorset coast. 25, Isle of Wight.

SHEET 3

DEVON–SOMERSET

BRISTOL CHANNEL

MOUTH OF THE

CARDIFF

BARRY

Penarth

Lavernock Pt.

Tusker Rock

Trwswmadoc

Nash Pt.

Lundy Island

WESTON-SUPER-MARE

Clevedon

BRIDGWATER BAY

Watchet

Minehead

Lynton

Ilfracombe

Morte Pt.

Woolacombe

Baggy Pt.

Croyde Bay

BARNSTAPLE OR BIDEFORD BAY

HARTLAND POINT

Hartland

Clovelly

Westward Ho!

Appledore

Bideford

Great Torrington

EXMOOR FOREST

BRENDON HILLS

QUANTOCK HILLS

TAUNTON

BRIDGWATER

Burnham-on-Sea

Brean Down

Steep Holme

Flat Holme

Morwenstow

Sharpnose Points

BUDE BAY

Bude

Stratton

Holsworthy

Okehampton

DARTMOOR FOREST

DEVONSHIRE

SOMERSET

EXETER

LYME BAY

Sidmouth

Budleigh Salterton

Exmouth

Dawlish

Teignmouth

TORQUAY

TOR BAY

Babbacombe BAY

WEYMOUTH

BILL OF PORTLAND

Portland

BARNSTAPLE

Lundy Island

MILES

0   12

Crown Copyright Reserved.

DEVON-SOMERSET

THIS sheet includes Portland Bill, Bristol, Cardiff, Bude and much of Dartmoor; it therefore covers most of Devonshire and Somerset, West Dorset, and a little of Glamorgan and Cornwall. Apart from Bristol and Cardiff, both of which are dependent on extra terrain, there are no large industrial centres; the country is mainly agricultural. There are no large rivers; those of Devon mostly rise round Dartmoor and flow north-west or south-east save the Exe which begins on Exmoor within sight of the Bristol Channel; the eastern rivers are fairly evenly spaced flowing from the Dorchester Heights.

The formations range from Devonian to Tertiary; in Devon they are mainly Devonian in the north succeeded on the south by Carboniferous (Culm); farther east Triassic and Jurassic rocks predominate; the main igneous masses are those of Dartmoor and Bodmin Moor.

The dominant structure of Devon is the major east–west syncline of the Culm with Devonian on its flanks; an east–west grain is also discernible farther east south of the Bristol Coalfield and in the Weymouth area but this is partly masked by the roughly north–south strike of the oolites. Subsidiary structures include folds almost at right angles to the major lines and innumerable corrugations of which striking examples may be seen in the Culm of Hartland Point.

DEVONIAN The Devonian formation of north Devonshire differs considerably from that of the south (Sheet 4); the latter in its Middle Devonian is characterized by thick limestones and in its Upper Devonian by lava flows; these types are but feebly developed in the north and the detailed sequence is somewhat uncertain.

In North Devon the Lower Devonian is mainly of reddish and grey sandstones with shales parted by a middle group (Lynton Beds) of shales with calcareous beds. The lowest group (Foreland Grit) extends from Foreland Point to Minehead; the Lynton Beds locally yield *Pteraspis*, spirifers and corals; the succeeding Hangman Grits range from Lower to Middle Devonian since they contain scales of *Coccosteus*.

A mixed group of beds of which the relationships to one another are in doubt are collectively known as the Ilfracombe Beds. They consist of shales and grits with limestones that are often siliceous. A limestone at the western foot of Little Hangman (on the east side of Combe Martin Bay) contains *Stringocephalus*; presumably lower beds yield *Cucullaea unilateris* and beds believed to be higher and exposed at Davids Hole and West Hoggington beach have many poor shells in addition to felted masses of fucoids. Presumably still higher beds, the grey Morte Slates, extend from Morte Point, four miles W.S.W. of Ilfracombe into Somerset;

amongst many fossils of doubtful age occurs the characteristic Devonian shell *Spirifer verneuili.*

The Pickwell Down Beds—sandstones of various colours interbedded with grey shales—crop out from Morte Bay along Pickwell Down, north of Barnstaple, to Wiveliscombe (14 miles S.S.E. of Minehead) and carry fish remains including *Bothriolepis* and *Holoptychius.* At the base is a volcanic ash—25 ft. thick at Bittadon but at Mill Rock 500 yd. south of Woolacombe just a few inches; it extends east-south-east to Bratton Fleming.

The succeeding greenish sandstones (Baggy and Marwood Beds) extend from Baggy Point at the south end of Morte Bay past Marwood and Sloley (3 miles N.N.W. and north of Barnstaple) to near North Molton; to the south of them lie the Pilton Beds—grey shales with thin sandstones and limestones that grade upwards into Culm Measures. *Spirifer verneuili* occurs in both Marwood and Pilton beds.

Across the Bristol Channel the Devonian is represented by the Old Red Sandstone of continental and freshwater origin and this facies is also present around the Bristol–Somerset Coalfield.

CARBONIFEROUS In Devonshire the whole of the Carboniferous is represented by the Culm Measures—a thick series of dark shales with thin limestones, cherts and sandstones and occasional poor sooty coals locally known as culm; limestones are common in the lower part; sandstones become more abundant upwards. Fossils (including goniatites and plants) indicate that Carboniferous Limestone, Millstone Grit and Coal Measures are represented at least in part.

In the Bristol area the sequence is more normal and for the Carboniferous Limestone the section along the right bank of the Avon Gorge at Bristol is regarded as standard. It begins on the north-west near Sea Walls and crosses Durdam Down to Windsor Terrace and has a thrust fault near Observatory Hill which repeats Seminula Beds.

The limestone yields fossils some of which are characteristic of but seldom prolific in certain groups of beds which are then said to belong to a particular zone. Zoning in the limestone is chiefly by corals and brachiopods; the zones range upwards from K to D.

AVON SECTION

K or Cleistopora Beds (500 ft.) shales with thin limestones including Palate Bed with fish scales and the Bryozoa Bed a massive crinoidal limestone with bryozoa.

Z or Zaphrentis (336 ft.) massive black crinoidal limestones. Small *Zaphrentis* common; some large *Caninia*; lower beds crowded with *Spirifer*, etc.

C or Caninia or Syringothyris divided into C_1 below (200 ft.) and C_2 above (80 ft.). C_1 begins with shale and pale partly dolomitized limestone known as Laminosa Dolomite followed by massive white oolite with *Caninia*. C_2 is of thin dolomitized limestones in shales (Caninia Dolomite); fossils scarce.

S or Seminula. Lower part (S_1, 80 ft.). Shale with limestones, particularly the compact fine-grained 'chinastone'; *Seminula* and *Lithostrotion* common.

Upper part (S$_2$, 800 ft.). Massive limestones much quarried; lower part with bands of coarse oolite (pisolite); middle part with a 60-ft. oolite; upper part (125 ft.) of concretionary beds with algal layers. *Lithostrotion martini* in large masses; *Productus hemisphericus* and *Seminula* abundant.

D or Dibunophyllum (500 ft.). Limestones (with some shale and red grit) include reddish oolite and 'pseudobreccia' (light indeterminate patches in a dark 'matrix'). Corals abundant. Lower part (D$_1$) *Dibunophyllum* and *Palaeosmilia* (*Cyathophyllum*) *murchisoni* and *Productus giganteus*; upper part (D$_2$) same forms with narrow *Lithostrotion* and *Lonsdaleia*.

Near Observatory Hill S$_2$ Beds are thrust over D Beds by a fault estimated to have a throw of 1,100 ft.

Carboniferous Limestone is worked in many large quarries for road metal and as a source of lime. Attention may be drawn to those at Vobster (where there is over-thrusting) in Vallis Vale and Burrington Combe and the fine sections in Cheddar Gorge.

In the past certain thick sandstones were styled Millstone Grit; these are now referred to the Carboniferous Limestone Series. The goniatite *Gastrioceras cancellatum* in faulted shales at Vobster indicate that some of the upper part of the true Millstone Grit Series is present but to what thickness is unknown.

Coal Measures—The coal bearing strata of the Bristol–Somerset Coalfield are divided into an Upper and a Lower series by a thick group of grey sandstones (over 2,000 ft.) known as Pennant. The Coal Measures appear partly at surface but considerable areas are concealed by Triassic and later rocks. There are four main structural areas with smaller isolated basins at Nailsea, Clapton and Avonmouth. Of the four main areas that of Radstock is the southernmost; essentially a north–south syncline, it impinges on the Mendips and is there overthrust by Carboniferous Limestone. To the north it is separated from the Pensford Basin by the great compressional zone of the Farmborough Fault. At the north side of the Pensford Basin the east–west Kingswood Anticline, a dual fold with much thrusting, brings up the Lower Coal Series. North of it lies the Coalpit Heath–Parkfield Basin.

In spite of steep and variable dips and much overthrusting the comparatively thin coals of this region have been worked extensively.

PERMO-TRIASSIC ROCKS These lie mainly east of a line through Exeter and Minehead. They are of good red colour and comprise breccias, conglomerates, sandstones and marls. The marls are most abundant in the uppermost part of the strata (Keuper Marl) while conglomerates and breccias predominate in the lower part; some, which may weather purplish red, being separated off as Permian while the rest are regarded as Trias though there is little difference and the old name of New Red Sandstone for the whole would be more appropriate in this district.

A considerable unconformity between the New Red and the Carboniferous marks the interval when the latter rocks were folded, intruded by granite, upraised and denuded. This erosion provided much of the material for the New Red for the

breccias of Devon include many fragments of Devonian limestones and material from Dartmoor Granite. Some of these breccias represent scree material washed out into the lowlands and recall the brockrams of Cumberland. Such breccias may occur at any local base as, for example, the so-called Dolomitic Congolomerate at the base of the Keuper Marl where that formation overlaps lower members of the New Red and oversteps on to or near the Carboniferous Limestone in the Bristol and South Wales areas.

About Exeter contemporary spilitic lavas occur at or near the base of the Permian. Sandstones, breccias, conglomerate and marls of the latter are well exposed in the cliffs from Torquay to beyond Exmouth. A few miles east of the latter town there appears above the red marls of the Permian a conglomerate 80–100 ft. thick made up of well rounded quartzite pebbles followed by 300–400 ft. of coarse softish pink sandstones with occasional pebbles. These beds greatly resemble and represent the Bunter of the Midlands. The Pebble Beds are particularly well seen near Budleigh Salterton and are named after that locality. The quartzite pebbles are believed to have come from across what is now the English Channel but some stones are from Devon. The pebbles become smaller as the beds are traced northwards; they include grit and Carboniferous Limestone near Williton.

The base of the Keuper is taken at a hard breccia visible low in the cliffs at Otterton Point east of Budleigh in red sandstones which continue towards Sidmouth where the deep red Keuper Marl, with some sandy bands, appears. The marls contain gypsum in Dunscombe Cliffs. At Branscombe Mouth, five miles east of Sidmouth, Cretaceous rocks descend to beach level but the uppermost Keuper—the red and green Tea-green Marls—followed by Rhaetic with black shales below white limestones come in just east of the mouth of the Axe.

The Keuper, mainly Marl with a thickness up to 1,400 ft. covers considerable areas northwards to beyond Bristol; it contains salt at Purton near Bridgwater and at Yate near Bristol yields gypsum and celestine (strontium sulphate).

The Tea-green Marls and the succeeding Rhaetic are also well displayed further north at Blue Anchor Point west of Watchet. Here about 110 ft. of the Marls are followed by 45 ft. of black shales with, about 20 ft. above the base, the *Ceratodus* Bone Bed with fish teeth, which elsewhere may rest on Tea-green Marls. A few feet of greenish mud followed by some inches of porcellanous Cotham Marble with landscapes of dendritic markings complete the Rhaetic. There are similar beds exposed at Penarth near Cardiff and the beds though thin extend right across England; they are important as marking a widespread marine transgression on to the continental Trias country and marine conditions persisted almost throughout Jurassic times giving rise to the mainly clay Lias then the Oolitic limestones followed by the further thick clays of Oxford and Kimmeridge. There are many lithological subdivisions, often of but local interest; zoning, chiefly by ammonites, is more effective than lithology but demands specialized knowledge.

JURASSIC   The Lias consists principally of grey clay shales but there are also limestones and sandstones. In the Lower Lias south of the Bristol Channel a white

limestone (White Lias) appears at the base and is much quarried in mid-Somerset where it reaches 20 ft. in thickness. Elsewhere limestones (Blue Lias) are developed at higher levels but still low in Lower Lias sequence which covers 400–600 ft. There are excellent coast sections east from Watchet but those of Lyme Regis are better. There the Blue Lias (limestones and shales 105 ft.) has a Fish Bed and a Saurian Bed near the top. Next come 70 ft. of black papery shales with fibrous calcite ('beef') then 150 ft. of black marls or clays with thin limestone; these make up most of Black Ven Cliffs which are capped by pale grey clays (with belemnites) that reach 75 ft. in thickness on Stonebarrow and below Golden Cap where they are followed by 105 ft. of grey clays with green ammonites.

The Middle Lias in the Lyme Regis area begins with 35 ft. of calcareous sandstone in three tiers near the foot of Golden Cap followed by 155 ft. of blue grey clay with a Starfish Band of greenish sandstone at the top. Then come about 120 ft. of sands and clays with a hard sandy limestone midway and one at the top (a thin representative of the Marlstone elsewhere). In the Radstock area Middle Lias is absent but it reappears farther north.

The Upper Lias is about 200 ft. thick; the lower third is clay, the rest a yellow concretionary sandstone known as Bridport Sands. Northwards in many cases almost the whole of the Upper Lias is of sands—Yeovil, Cotswold or Midford Sands—with in the Yeovil area a thick lens of shelly limestone (Ham Hill Stone).

Upwards from this level limestone predominates beginning with Inferior Oolite so named because it lies below, i.e. inferior to Great Oolite. The zones representing the lower and middle Inferior Oolite are thin or absent and where the Upper Inferior Oolite is also thin the three subdivisions may only amount to 10 ft. of limestones as, for example, in the cliffs between Bridport and Burton Bradstock. The upper Oolite is 45 ft. thick near Sherborne where about 20 ft. in the lower part is the Sherborne Building Stone. The corresponding Doulting Stone, an oolite used in the west front of Wells Cathedral and about 50 ft thick, rests with conglomeratic base on Upper Lias; farther north at Vallis Vale near Frome flat Upper Inferior Oolite rests on highly inclined Carboniferous Limestone.

Zoning and correlation depends on fossils—chiefly ammonites.

The Great Oolite Series is comprised of a clay group, known as the Fuller's Earth, followed by limestones of which the most widespread is the shelly Forest Marble at the top. The great development of limestone of the Bath area with its famous oolitic freestone known as the Great or Bath Oolite disappears southwards and in the coastal region Forest Marble succeeds the Fuller's Earth. How much of the latter may be equated with the former has not yet been fully determined.

The Fuller's Earth Clay totalling over 200 ft. of clay may be split, as between Bath and Sherborne, by a creamy rubbly argillaceous limestone up to 35 ft. thick, known as the Fuller's Earth Rock. The true fuller's earth, early used for the cleansing of wool and now in the refining of oils and fats, is confined to a bed a few feet thick in the Upper Fuller's Earth Clay south-west of Bath. The Forest Marble (named from Wychwood Forest north of Witney, Oxfordshire) consists of flaggy

limestone, rich in broken oyster shells, sandwiched between greenish clays with shelly bands; each portion is about 30 ft. thick.

The best section in the coastal tract is furnished by Wotton Cliff (between West Bay, Bridport and Eypesmouth) where Forest Marble forms the upper third of the cliff; the large quarries in the 'marble' about Bothenhampton have been long abandoned.

The Cornbrash though only 30 ft. thick extends across England as a limestone rubbly to compact which gives a brashy soil (limestone fragments in clay or loam). There are sections at East Chickerell (west of Weymouth) and at Yetminster (5 miles S.E. of Yeovil) but the most complete is by the shore of the Fleet at Abbotsbury Swannery (west of Weymouth).

Oxford Clay, 500–600 ft. with the sandy Kellaways Beds at the base, is well exposed near Weymouth but away from the coast is seldom seen except in brickpits.

CRETACEOUS   The great overstep of these beds causes them to rest successively westwards on lower strata—Upper Jurassic near Weymouth to Permian south of Exeter.

Gault, the lowest member, is a dark blue clay up to 30 ft. thick. The Greensand, which represents Upper Greensand and part of the Gault of south-east England, comprises sands, hard grits and cherts, 200 ft. thick at Beer, 156 ft. at Peak Hill, Sidmouth and 90 ft. in Haldon Hills south of Exeter; it forms a resistant capping to many of the hills visible from the railway.

The main mass of Chalk ends north of Weymouth but there are substantial outliers farther west as, for example, on the coast at Beer Head and thence almost to Sidmouth, and inland between Crewkerne and Chard. In the west about Wilmington (3 miles east of Honiton) Lower Chalk passes into calcareous grit which weathers into sand. The Middle Chalk remains fairly normal; at Beer it includes the Beer Freestone (in the *Inoceramus labiatus* zone and made up of shell fragments) which is mined. The Upper Chalk—nodular with prominent black flints—is well exposed on Beer Head, and at Whitecliff between Beer and Seaton.

REFERENCES

Geological Survey
   Regional Handbooks: South-west England, ed 2, 1948; *Hampshire Basin*, ed 2, 1948; *Bristol and Gloucester*, ed 2, 1948.
   Metalliferous Mining Region of South-west England, 2 vols., 1956.
Excursions and Field Meetings
   Dorset Coast, Davies, G. M., ed 2, 1948, London.
   Bristol District, Excursion Handbook for, Reynolds, ed 2, 1921, Bristol.
   International Geological Congress 1948.
   Long Excursions: A4 Minerals; A5 General; C3 Bristol.
Geologists Association, Proceedings or Circulars
   1911, Ilminster–Chard. 1914, Watchett. 1922, Combe Martin. 1926, Dartmoor. 1929, Bristol. 1936, Lyme Regis. 1954, Lynton. 1955, North Devon; South Devon. 1957, Bristol District (Jurassic). 1962, North Devon (Devonian).

CORNWALL AND WEST DEVON

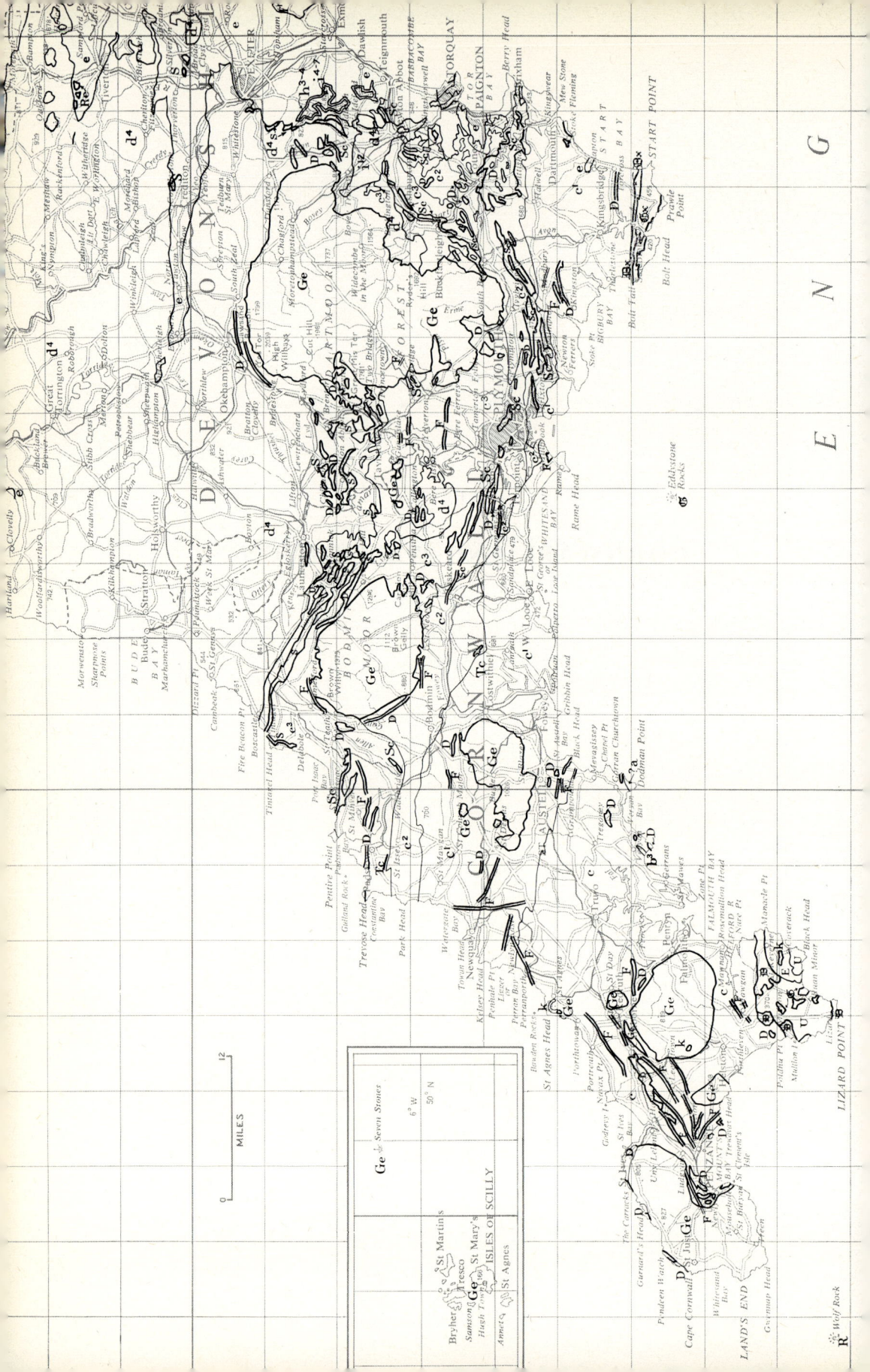

DEVONSHIRE

ENGLISH CHANNEL

D   E   V   O   N

C   O   R   N   W   A   L   L

DARTMOOR FOREST

BODMIN MOOR

PLYMOUTH

PAIGNTON

TORQUAY

TORBAY

BABBACOMBE BAY

START BAY

START POINT

Start Point

Prawle Point

Bolt Head

Bolt Tail

Berry Head

Dartmouth

Kingsbridge

Stoke Fleming

Salcombe

Exeter

Exmouth

Dawlish

Teignmouth

Newton Abbot

Bovey Tracey

Moretonhampstead

Chagford

Okehampton

Hatherleigh

Holsworthy

Stratton

Bude

BUDE BAY

Morwenstow

Stratmore Points

Hartland

Clovelly

Great Torrington

Woolfardisworthy

Bideford

Barnstaple

Bickleigh

Brixham

Ugborough

Ivybridge

Modbury

Newton Ferrers

Wembury

Plympton

Plymstock

Yealmpton

Rame Head

WHITSAND BAY

Mount Edgcumbe

Looe

West Looe

Polperro

Fowey

St Austell

Mevagissey

Chapel Pt

Gorran Haven

Dodman Point

Gribbin Head

Black Head

St Blazey

Par

Lostwithiel

Liskeard

Callington

Saltash

Torpoint

Launceston

Camelford

Tintagel Head

Boscastle

Delabole

Port Isaac

Padstow

Wadebridge

Bodmin

Brown Willy

Rough Tor

Trevose Head

Park Head

Constantine Bay

Watergate Bay

Newquay

Perranporth

St Agnes Head

Portreath

Godrevy Pt

St Ives

St Ives Bay

Hayle

Gwithian

Camborne

Redruth

Truro

St Day

Falmouth

FALMOUTH BAY

Pendennis Pt

Zone Pt

St Mawes

St Anthony Head

Rosemullion Head

HELFORD R

Nare Pt

Manacle Pt

Black Head

Coverack

Lizard Point

LIZARD POINT

Cadgwith

Mullion

Poldhu Pt

Mullion Cove

PENZANCE

MOUNT'S BAY

St Michael's Mount

Marazion

Mousehole

Lamorna

Porthcurno

LAND'S END

Cape Cornwall

Sennen

Gurnard Head

Pendeen Watch

St Just

St Buryan

Newlyn

Wolf Rock

Eddystone Rocks

ISLES OF SCILLY

St Mary's

St Martin's

St Agnes

Tresco

Bryher

Samson

Hugh Town

Annet

Bishop Rock

Seven Stones

MILES

0   12

50° N

6° W

CORNWALL AND WEST DEVON

THIS district embraces the whole of Cornwall and that quarter of Devon lying west of Torquay and Exeter and south of a line about seven miles north of Bude. The geology is diverse and the scenery of the coast is magnificent, but that of much of the land is rendered somewhat monotonous by the effect of the so-called 400-ft. platform that has bevelled the outcrops of vastly differing rocks to about that height save that some areas stand up almost as islands above the platform. There has been some tilting of this platform southwards and it may be noted that rivers on the north are short and enter the sea by gorges or falls whereas those on the south emerge in fiord-like inlets of the sea which obviously are drowned valleys as, for example, those in the Falmouth area.

The rocks range in age from the old ones of the Lizard to Tertiary, of which there is a large outlier preserved in the Bovey Tracey Basin near Newton Abbot (see Fig. 30), but the greatest spreads belong to the Devonian, mainly in the southern portion, and to the Carboniferous in the north. Carboniferous rocks lie in a great east–west syncline. Dominating the whole, however, are the granite masses of Dartmoor, Bodmin Moor, Hensbarrow (St. Austell), Carn Mellis, and Land's End; it is to these granites that Cornwall and south-west Devon owe the great mineralized zone which made the district famous formerly for tin and copper and still for china clay. Mining is but a shadow of its former state but the working of china clay and of the Bovey clays still flourishes. The bulk of the people, however, live by agriculture for which the mild climate provides early crops and by the tourist trade.

OLD ROCKS   The Lizard area is famous for its serpentine (a green, grey or reddish rock composed largely of the mineral serpentine—an alteration product of olivine—and allied gabbro (a dark rock of lime feldspar and olivine) with which are associated foliated granite, schists of various kinds (foliated rocks) characterized by various minerals mica, hornblende, etc. made by the metamorphism (alteration) of pre-existing rocks often shales and sandstones; the alteration may be effected by the heat of intrusions or more often that arising from earth movements.

The main, almost circular, mass of serpentine lies on the west but there is a smaller almost contiguous mass to the east between Coverack and Black Head; separating the two and extending north of the smaller outcrop of serpentine is the main mass of gabbro. The serpentine and gabbro are almost encircled by schists—mainly dark green striped grey hornblende schists but with mica schists at Old Lizard Head—into which the then molten serpentine and gabbro were introduced. The foliated granites lie mainly within the serpentine outcrop. Most of these rocks show the effect of earth squeeze and nearly all have been invaded by dykes and veins of dolerite and other rocks.

In addition to the places mentioned exposures are to be seen in the cliffs between Mullion Cove and Porthallow but attention is drawn to sections of foliated granite at Man o'War Rocks and with serpentine in the cliffs above granite, on Kennack beach; of mica schists at Polbream Cove and fault junction with hornblende schists at Church Cove, Polpeor Cove and at The Balk fault between schist and serpentine. Serpentine: Kynance Cove; Compass Cove at St. Keverne with dykes of gabbro; Coverack Cove, with dykes of gabbro and dolerite; quarries on Goonhilly Downs; Lizard Boundary Fault: Polurrian Beach and Porthallow.

Schists also form the tip of the Devon promontory with Start Point, Prawle Point and Bolt Head.

South from Perranporth and Mevagissey is a series of slaty and quartzitic rocks of doubtful ages but mostly indicated on the map as Devonian though the finely striped rocks of Dodman Point are shown as ?Cambrian; quartzites near Veryan, however, contain fossils probably of Ordovician age.

DEVONIAN North of the Perranporth–Mevagissey line the rocks are truly Devonian; of these an outcrop ten miles wide extending from Newquay to Dartmouth is referred to Lower Devonian. The purple and green Dartmouth Slates at the base are succeeded by the grey Meadfoot slaty beds of Torquay that pass westwards into the grits of Staddon Heights (Plymouth), the downs north of the St. Austell Granite and the cliffs about Newquay. Fossils include such shells as *Spirifer* and the remains of fish (*Pteraspis* and *Cephalaspis*).

The Middle Devonian rocks in the east, about Torquay, Brixham, Totnes and Plymouth, are characterized by two limestones, rich in corals, amidst grey shales; farther west there are merely thin lenses of limestones in shales. The lower limestone is dark and thin bedded; the upper one is more massive, is white, pink or mottled, and furnishes a fine marble.

The Upper Devonian is made up of grey-green and black slaty rocks associated with thick soda-rich lavas and tuffs and minor sandstones and limy beds. The well-known lustrous Delabole Slates occur in the lower part of this series west of the Bodmin Granite. The characteristic fossil here is the 'Delabole Butterfly'— *Spirifer verneuili*. In the west the coast from just south of Boscastle to beyond Padstow furnishes good exposures of rocks and structures; in the east the best is in Saltern Cove near Torquay.

CARBONIFEROUS The Carboniferous rocks of Cornwall and Devon are unlike those of the rest of Britain and although fossils indicate that they range in age from Carboniferous Limestone to Millstone Grit and Coal Measures no such lithological divisions are possible. The rocks are mainly dark shales; sandstones become more abundant upwards whereas limestones in thin bands are commoner downwards. There are also beds of chert in some cases associated with spilitic lavas and tuffs. The only coal is the soft sooty material known as culm to which these measures owe their name.

The best exposures are on the coast north from Boscastle; many show the rocks to be highly contorted; they are usually too crushed to provide good fossils.

Fossils from small inland exposures (e.g. near Launceston) range from trilobites, crinoids, corals and shells (including *Phillipsia* and *Posidonia becheri*) but more important are goniatites and plants. The former include *Goniatites sphaerico-striatus*, *Reticuloceras* and *Gastrioceras*; and the latter *Neuropteris schlehani*, *Alethopteris lonchitica, Mariopteris muricata*.

PERMIAN   Permian rocks are confined to the eastern part of the area (Torquay–Exeter) apart from a long east–west tongue through Crediton north of Dartmoor. They consist of red clays and sandstones followed by breccias and conglomerates with abundant pebbles of Devonian limestone. Exposures are good in the cliffs north of Torquay. Contemporary lavas of spilitic type occur at and near the base of the Permian in the Exeter area.

CRETACEOUS   These rocks are represented by outliers on the Haldon Hills between Exeter and Torquay; they consist of cherty sandstones and sand with nodules and layers of chert and are considered to be equivalent to part of the Gault and Upper Greensand.

TERTIARY   Tertiary strata are represented in gravels, probably of Bagshot age, capping the Haldon Hills but of much more importance are the Oligocene sands, ball clays and lignites of the Bovey Basin near Newton Abbot (Fig. 30). The sands become coarser on the margins of the basin and indicate derivation from Dartmoor from which, too, the ball clays probably represent washed down china clay.

At St. Erth sands and clays occur in the bottom of a wide valley that is presumed to have existed before the 400-ft. platform bevelled the country. This deposit has yielded many shells of Mediterranean aspect and has been referred to Upper and to Lower Pliocene and to Miocene.

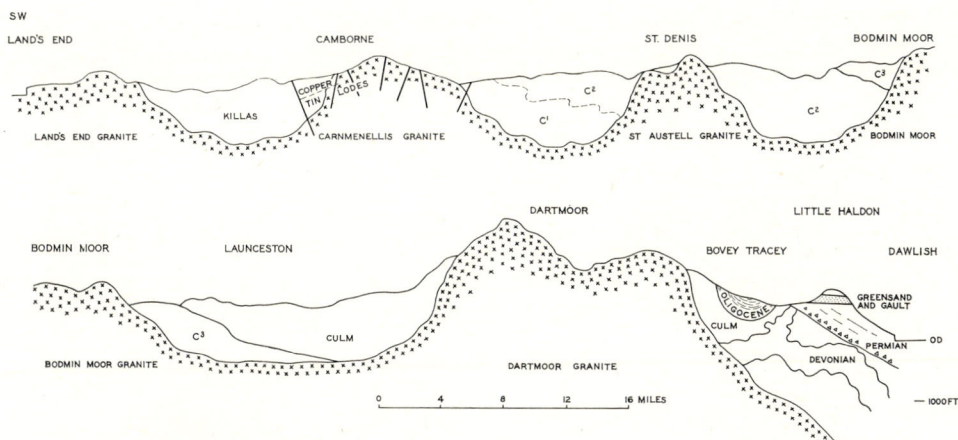

Figure 30. Diagrammatic sections across Cornwall and Devon

Note that the granite was introduced after the folding affecting the Devonian and Culm strata.

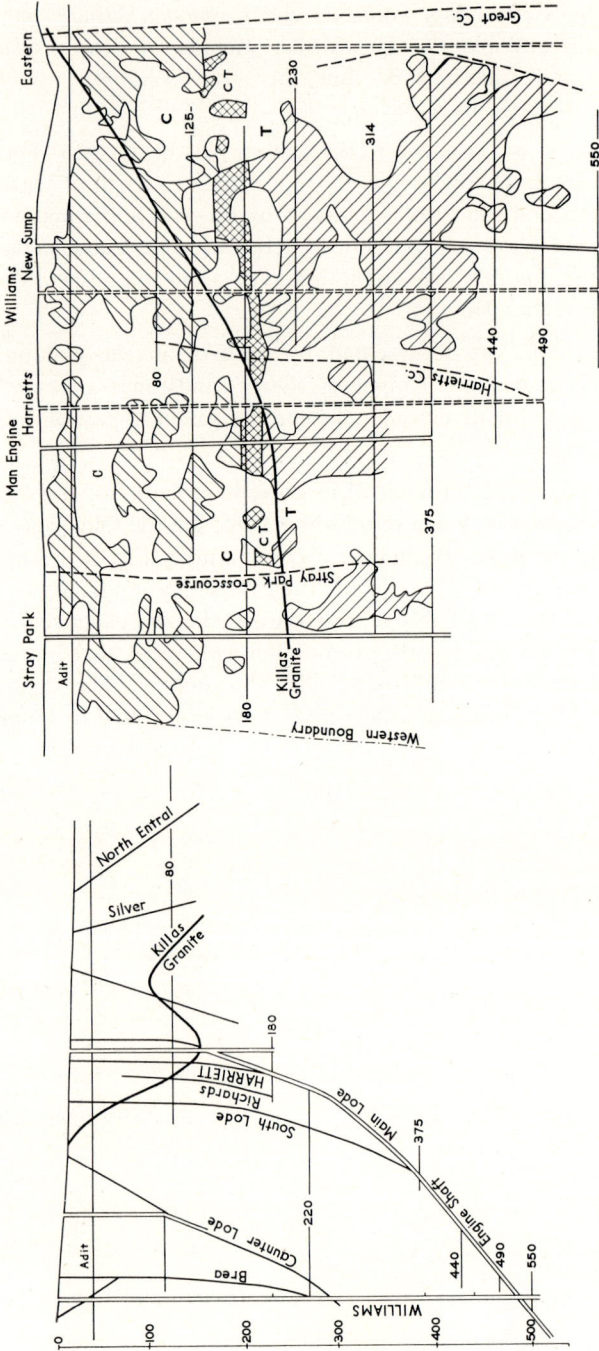

Figure 31. Dolcoath Mine: the most prolific and deepest in Cornwall
Section on right along Main Lode showing relation of Copper (C), Copper-tin (CT) and
Tin zones to granite surface. Transverse section on left to show altitude of lodes. Mine
measurements are in fathoms along the curved lodes; true depth given on left. (Based on
Plate IV and Fig. 3 G.S.M. *Copper Ores—Devon and Cornwall*)

GRANITES Most of the granites are coarsely crystalline and have large crystals of white feldspar but there are also more even-grained types (such as most of Land's End and Bodmin Moor) and the later pegmatites (coarse-grained in which the crystals are freely developed) and the fine-grained aplites and elvans usually occurring as dykes. These granitic rocks are intrusive into strata up to and including the Culm Measures (which range up to Coal Measures in age) and since fragments are included in the Permian rocks the age of the granites is post-Carboniferous and pre-Lower Permian—a time of much earth folding. Some of the granites are emplaced in gentle upfolds or domes.

The usual minerals are quartz, feldspar and the black (biotite) and white (muscovite) micas, but tourmaline is common in some pegmatites and topaz and apatite have been noted in others (Cligga Head and St. Michael's Mount).

Apart from hardening, the effect of granite intrusion on the slates is not marked except in the case of Dartmoor where the Meldon quarries, two miles S.W. of Okehampton, show that many new minerals appear in Culm Measures as these approach the granite; in one quarry a Culm limestone is highly crystalline.

At some, usually late, stage of intrusion solutions of various kinds were introduced into the granitic and neighbouring 'country' rocks usually along fissures and from them and by their reactions various mineral deposits were formed. One such alteration, largely by carbon dioxide at a very late stage affects the feldspar converting it into soft white kaolin or china clay. All the granite masses show some kaolinization but that of Hensbarrow is particularly affected much to the benefit of the clay trade of St. Austell, though the resulting pyramids of dazzling white quartz waste may be considered an eyesore.

With fluorine as an active agent the feldspars were altered to quartz and white mica and the rock is known as greisen. Such rocks often contain fluor and topaz as well as ores such as cassiterite and wolfram, as, for example, at Cligga Head.

The influence of boron is denoted when the rock is tourmalinized. Mica may be replaced giving a tourmaline granite, as, for example, that of Luxulian four miles N.E. of St. Austell, but if feldspar also is affected it becomes a quartz-schorl (tourmaline) rock as, for instance, at Roche Rock at Roche (5 miles N.N.W. of St. Austell).

The bulk of the granite, however, remains a good solid rock suitable for building, road metal, ornament, etc. but in the absence of great local demand quarrying is dependent on cheap transport particularly by water. For this reason the Land's End mass is more extensively quarried near Penzance than the others on account of access near Mousehole to the sea.

MINERAL DEPOSITS Connected with the alteration of granite by natural chemical agents is the deposition of mineral substances in the fissures traversed. The fissures may be ramifying cracks or larger fissures following a definite direction such as faults. After filling, the former are known as stockworks and the latter, which are much more important, as veins or lodes. It is obvious that fissures are less likely to remain open and so provide channels for solutions in soft rocks; most sizable

veins are therefore in hard rocks such as granite or the slaty rocks hardened by granite intrusion—the killas of the miner. Most of the veins range E.N.E. though there are others roughly at right angles which displace or shift the former. The first set usually carry tinstone and copper ores with associated ores such as arsenic or tungsten, whereas the later set carry lead, zinc and iron ores though these may occur near surface in tin lodes. The distribution of mines in Cornwall and west Devon indicates that the richest fall into a belt of country about ten miles wide ranging E.N.E. through the northern halves of the Land's End and Carn Menellis granite outcrops, including most of Hensbarrow, skirting the south end of that of Bodmin to the southern half of the Dartmoor mass. The belt is not uniformly rich, however, and the concentration of mineral wealth about the two western and between the two eastern granite masses with less concentration around Hensbarrow and poor intervening ground suggests not only close association with granite but definite centres of emanation of mineralizing agents. Mining has revealed that the condensation, freezing or crystallization of the minerals followed a definite pattern, tin being deposited deep or near to a centre with copper at higher levels or farther away and so on. Mining has also revealed that the granite areas gradually increase in size with depth so that it is likely that the separate outcrops merely represent 'islands' standing up in a 'sea' of killas. It has also revealed that in at least one case, Castle an Dinas mine eight miles east of Newquay, there was either a mineralization stage early in the granite intrusion phase or that the granitic intrusion was in two stages for there a vein worked in killas for tungsten is invaded and locally obliterated by granite.

REFERENCES

Geological Survey
    Regional Handbook: South-west England, ed 2, 1948.
    Metalliferous Mining Region of South-west England, 2 vols. 1956.
Excursions and Field Meetings
    International Geological Congress 1948.
    Long Excursions, Devon and Cornwall: A4 Minerals; A5 General Geology.
Geologists Association, Proceedings
    1923, Brent Tor. 1928, Torquay. 1930, Helston. 1938, Cornwall. 1952, Tintagel. 1960, Mid and West Cornwall. 1962, Devonian of Tor Bay.
Geologists Association, Guides
    33, Dartmoor.

SHEET 5

LONDON—SUFFOLK

SUFFOLK

ESSEX

HERTFORDSHIRE

BEDFORDSHIRE

HUNTINGDON SHIRE

CAMBRIDGESHIRE

MIDDLESEX

ORFORD NESS

THE NAZE

IPSWICH

COLCHESTER

CLACTON-ON-SEA

Walton on the Naze

Felixstowe

Harwich

BURY ST EDMUNDS

NEWMARKET

CAMBRIDGE

LETCHWORTH

LUTON

ST ALBANS

CHELMSFORD

BILLERICAY

BRENTWOOD

ROMFORD

DAGENHAM

SOUTHEND ON SEA

LONDON

ENFIELD

BARNET

BRENTFORD

WIMBLEDON

HOUNSLOW

WINDSOR

SHEERNESS

MARGATE

Margate Sand

Westgate

The Shingles

MILES

0   12

LONDON–SUFFOLK

SHEET 5 ranges from near Southwold, Thetford and St. Ives to Thrapston, thence to the western suburbs of London and to the Thames estuary. It includes Essex, most of Suffolk, the southern half of Cambridge, most of Hertford and parts of Huntingdon, Bedford and Middlesex. It is an area of simple geology and of low relief for though traversed by a broad outcrop of Chalk from the St. Albans district to that of Thetford much of this formation is covered by Drift deposits while those below and succeeding the Chalk are mainly of soft rocks ranging from Oxford Clay in the west to London Clay in the south-east and Crag deposits in the east. Notwithstanding this the district is far from flat. The main drainage is easterly and south-easterly and as these streams have wide estuaries they provide access for light shipping and barge traffic for some distance inland but the only port of consequence apart from London is Harwich. Other drainage is to the Wash mainly by the Ouse; with this is associated the great stretch of fen country north of Cambridge through which rise 'islands' of various rock formations. The area is essentially one of agriculture.

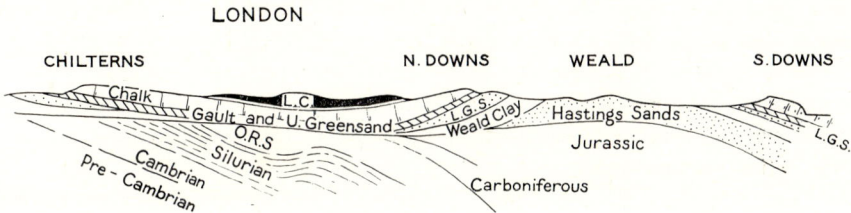

Figure 32. Diagrammatic section from Hitchin area to Beachy Head showing the London Basin and the Wealden Anticline

JURASSIC In addition to the Palaeozoic rocks of the London–North Kent platform similar rocks have been penetrated in deep borings at Harwich and at Ware but the oldest at surface are the thin representatives of the oolites; since these only just enter the district they are described with those of Sheet 6 to the west.

Oxford Clay succeeding the oolites is almost entirely of stiff dark bluish-grey clay or shaly clay though there are occasional nodules of limestone and of pyrite. There are large brickpits in it south of Bedford.

Fossils are fairly common especially the large oyster-like *Gryphae dilatata* and belemnites but the zone fossils are ammonites. These indicate a gradual overstep eastwards by the succeeding formation, the Corallian.

In the Corallian of this region usually only the basal 5 to 15 ft. is of limestone (and even that may be parted by shale) with an abundance of small oysters (*Exogyra nana*). This variously known as St. Ives Rock, Elsworth Road or Oakley Beds; it is succeeded by the very dark Ampthill Clay (from Ampthill 8 miles south of Bedford) which near its middle may have a thin limestone. At Upware (10 miles N.E. of Cambridge), however, the Corallian is represented by a reef of shelly oolite some 50 ft. thick with an outcrop a mile wide and three miles in length.

North of the latitude of Cambridge the Corallian is succeeded by the dark bluish-grey somewhat shaly Kimmeridge Clay (125 ft.). Oyster shells are common both flat (*Ostrea delta*) and curved radially ribbed (*Exogyra virgula*) but ammonites are again chosen as zone fossils. Elsewhere in this region, apart from a small inlier near Ampthill, Kimmeridge Clay is followed directly by Lower Greensand and this in places cuts down into the Oxford Clay.

CRETACEOUS Wealden strata are absent and the Cretaceous begins with the Lower Greensand, 0–200 ft.; even this does not extend beneath London. The formation is first present in force north of London around Leighton Buzzard where it greatly resembles the Folkestone Beds being a golden or white sand. Thence it continues north-east as a continuous outcrop with small outliers at Ely and elsewhere of brown and yellow sands with, at Woburn, a bed of fuller's earth near the middle. In places, as at Upware and at Potton, the Greensand contains many fossils derived from the Jurassic formations as well as phosphatic nodules (coprolites) and pebbles of much older rocks.

The Gault outcrop unlike that of the Lower Greensand is continuous across a great stretch of country. A dark grey clay it varies in thickness from 230 ft. near Dunstable to 90 ft. at Soham; it was formerly extensively used in small yards for brickmaking but these are now superseded by the large pits by Three Counties Station near Arlesey. Farther north it continues to thin and becomes calcareous and eventually a limestone.

In Cambridgeshire the upper part of the Gault was washed up leaving behind a deposit of sand, phosphatic nodules and rolled fossils, known as Cambridge Greensand, which passes upwards into basal Chalk. Though only a foot or so in thickness the deposit was worked at intervals all along the fifty-mile stretch from Harlington (East Bedfordshire) to Soham. The true Upper Greensand cannot be traced with certainty beyond Dunstable.

The Chalk marks the onset of a widespread submergence though the lower 70 to 80 ft. is clayey and is distinguished as Chalk Marl; this falls into the *Schloenbachia varians* Zone. It is followed by about 20 ft. of the more solid Totternhoe Stone and that by the irregularly jointed Grey Chalk (70–80 ft.) of the *Holaster subglobosus* Zone with a few feet of Plenus Marls between that and the Melbourn Rock at the bottom of the Middle Chalk.

The Melbourn Rock, a hard yellowish chalk is about 10 ft. thick; the rest of the Middle Chalk is white with a considerable development of flint just beneath the Chalk Rock at its top. (These flints were mined on a considerable scale at Brandon

10 miles N.W. of Thetford.) Two zones have been established; the lower of *Rhynchonella cuvieri* and the upper with *Terebratulina lata.*

The Chalk Rock (15 ft.) is a hard creamy chalk or a nodular yellow chalk, alternating with white chalk, with, in places, green-coated nodules. The rest of the Upper Chalk is soft and white and has scattered flints throughout; most of it has been denuded from Bedfordshire and Cambridgeshire but about 230 ft. may be present near St. Albans.

EOCENE The Eocene beds are markedly unconformable to the Chalk and this transgression is accompanied by north-westerly overstep of Reading Beds across the Thanet Sand; borings indicate that Thanet Sand does not extend farther than a line through Weybridge, Ealing, Hendon beyond which Reading Beds rest directly on Chalk with a similar bed of green-coated flints at the base to that at the bottom of the Thanet Sand.

Thanet Sand (0 to 75 ft.) is usually a fine-grained, pale grey or yellow sand clean enough in North Kent to furnish excellent moulding sand though in East Anglia the sands are more colourful and argillaceous; in the Ipswich area, where they are exposed in chalk pits, they are only about 14 ft. thick but are proved thicker eastwards in borings.

Woolwich and Reading Beds occur in three facies. In East Kent they are marine sands up to 100 ft. thick often crowded with small fossil shell *Corbula.* In West Kent, East Surrey and Essex they are estuarine deposits (Woolwich Beds) comprized of yellow, green and white sands and mottled clays with some pebbly beds locally cemented into conglomerate. In addition to shells pieces of lignite are not uncommon and in one locality, in Shorne Wood adjoining the Dover road north of Cobham, lignite occurs as a seam which during the 1948 coal shortage was mined. Farther west and north-west the Woolwich Beds merge into the fluviatile Reading facies with white, red and mottled plastic clays and white silts with some sands; a maximum thickness of 90 ft. is attained at Southall on the west side of London decreasing to 20 ft. around Ipswich.

London Clay is a blue clay weathering brown containing muddy limestones as nodules (septaria) or as lenticular bands; at the base is a thin layer of rounded black flints amidst which sharks teeth are fairly common; locally the clay carries shells, fossil wood and plant leaves, fruits and stems; crystals of selenite (gypsum, hydrated calcium sulphate) formed by the interaction of pyrite (iron sulphide) and the limy shells of fossils are of frequent occurrence.

From a maximum of about 430 ft. on the west side of London the thickness decreases eastwards largely as a result of the removal of the upper portion by pre-Pliocene denudation.

Exposures are not common but it may be seen in the cliffs of Sheppey, in pits near Ipswich and beneath Crag at Felixtowe and Bawdsey.

To the south-west of London between Staines and Aldershot the London Clay is succeeded by a great spread of sands, gravels and clays constituting the Upper Eocene and giving rise to heath lands. In the area under review remnants only of

the lower part (Bagshot Beds) of these strata survive between Chelmsford, Southend and north-east London and about Minster on the coast of the Isle of Sheppey.

PLIOCENE   The interval between the deposition of the Bagshot Beds and the Pliocene is considerable and during that time Oligocene strata were laid down elsewhere; then the earth's crust was subject to considerable movement, of which the upheaval of the Weald was but a distant ripple, followed by denudation before the eastern part of Britain was again submerged beneath the sea in Pliocene times. The deposits there laid down are collectively known as 'crag' from the East Anglian name for shelly sand. Around Ipswich these beds rest on London Clay; farther north they spread well back on to the Chalk. The several members of the crag vary considerably in their distribution with the result that any one of them may rest directly on London Clay or Chalk but at this local base to the Pliocene there is usually a Nodule Bed a foot or so in thickness made up of phosphatic nodules, bones and teeth derived from the London Clay, flints and other stones. This deposit was actively worked for phosphates in the triangle Ipswich–Orford–Harwich.

Coralline Crag, the lowest and so named from the notion that its abundant polyzoan remains were those of corals, is made up of white sand and shells locally cemented into building stone and is the only one now referred to the Pliocene. Most of this crag occurs between Aldeburgh and Orford. Its shells indicate a warm climate and some of the species still live in the Mediterranean.

PLEISTOCENE   The succeeding Red Crag, named from the colour of the current bedded sands, is also rich in shells; it may rest on an eroded surface of or be banked against Coralline Crag or rest on London Clay or, as in the Stour Valley, the Chalk. Three subdivisions are recognized and these carry an increasing proportion of northern shells; they occur chiefly in the Walton-on-the-Naze–Sudbury–Ipswich–Aldeburgh area.

Norwich Crag extends over a breadth of about twenty miles from the Suffolk coast to Sheringham on the Norfolk coast. It is made up of yellow or red sands and gravels and laminated clays with local shelly beds, and attains a total thickness of 150 ft. at Southwold. The shells include the common cockle, mussel, whelk and periwinkle of today and its basal bed is famous in that it contains rostrocarinate flint implements as well as bones of mastodon, elephant, hyaena and leopard.

The Chillesford Beds are about 20 ft. in thickness and consist of fine micaceous sands succeeded by micaceous clays; the abundance of mica is attributed to derivation from mica schists, such as those of the Ardennes, and the beds are believed to have been laid down in an estuary—part of the delta of the ancient Rhine.

Weybourne Crag and Cromer Forest Bed are confined to the area farther north (Sheet 9, and see page 126).

DRIFT DEPOSITS   The outcrops of the 'solid' formations just described are largely obscured by superficial 'drift' deposits, mainly glacial in origin but including the more recent alluvial deposits, peat and blown sand etc. There are large drift-free areas in the Hertford–Huntingdon–Cambridge tract ranging from Oxford Clay to

Gault and, apart from its own clay-with-flints, a broad band of bare Chalk from the Chilterns through Baldock, Newmarket and Brandon and another broad belt chiefly of London Clay in the Colchester–Harwich–Thames Estuary–North London tract. Most of the 'drift' is of boulder clay but there are widespread gravels and sands from near Southwold through Ipswich to the Stour, again round Colchester and Chelmsford and in the valleys with Hadleigh, Sudbury, Halstead and Braintree and north of London with extensive loams between the lower reaches of Stour and Colne.

From just north of Cambridge between Yaxley and Brandon there is the broad spread of the Fens through which emerge islands of 'solid' rocks, such as at Ely, and there are considerable patches of coastal alluvial material—as, for example, between Aldeburgh and Harwich, behind The Naze, bordering the Crouch, Blackwater and Colne estuaries—and the valley gravels, brickearths and alluvium along the rivers.

Most of the boulder clay is referable to the Chalky Boulder Clay and to the period of main glaciation. Both matrix and stones are of chalk and flint but the admixture of Lower Cretaceous and Jurassic material becomes more marked in a westerly direction. Far travelled stones include erratics from Scandinavia probably partly picked up from earlier glacial deposits of the East Anglian coast. Brickpits give the most worthwhile sections and those in the neighbourhood of Ipswich are particularly good.

The Chalky Boulder Clay is known to rest on or to succeed products of an earlier glaciation; of these the most important are the Westleton Beds of sand and gravel of the coastal tract about Southwold and so named from Westleton about midway between Saxmundham and Southwold, with which are correlated the sandy deposits east of Ipswich.

Of the later glacial deposits probably the most important are those succeeding 24 ft. of the Chalky Boulder Clay in a brickpit at Hoxne about five miles E.S.E. of Diss. These include 40 ft. of lacustrine beds with a median peat marking the change from a temperate earlier lake to a very cold one which drowned the peat. Then comes some 12 ft. of gravels and brickearths not only with bones of mammoth and reindeer but also with worked flints of Acheulian pattern and these deposits are overlain by 6 ft. of an Upper Chalky Boulder Clay.

The Fens consist of a flat expanse of peat, silt and clay of varying consistency. The peats denote freshwater but the clays and silts range from fresh through brackish to salt. In some the shell *Scrobicularia* is abundant and this organism can only flourish below mid-tide. The peats range in age from early Neolithic to recent times. Drainage and cultivation has led to considerable wastage of surface peat; in one case amounting to 11 ft. in 70 years.

REFERENCES

Geological Survey
    Regional Handbooks: London and Thames Valley, ed 2, 1947; *East Anglia*, ed 3, 1954.
Excursions and Field Meetings
    Geological Excursions round London, Davies, G. M., 1914, London.

International Geological Congress 1948.
Long Excursions: A17 East Anglia; A1 Economic.
B Excursions based on London: 20, North Mimms; 39, St Albans & Hitchin Valley; 89 Barrington, Cambridge (Drift with fossils, Chalk and Cambridge Greensand).
Geologists Association, Proceedings or Circulars
1922, Felixstowe and Ipswich. 1932 and 38, Ipswich area. 1948, East Suffolk. 1951, Hainault Forest; East Suffolk. 1952, Nazeing and Broxbourn; Barrington; Stour Estuary. 1954, Wrabness. 1955, Chelmsford; Thaxsted. 1956, North Weald. 1958, Cambridge; East Anglia.

SHEET 6

SOUTH MIDLANDS

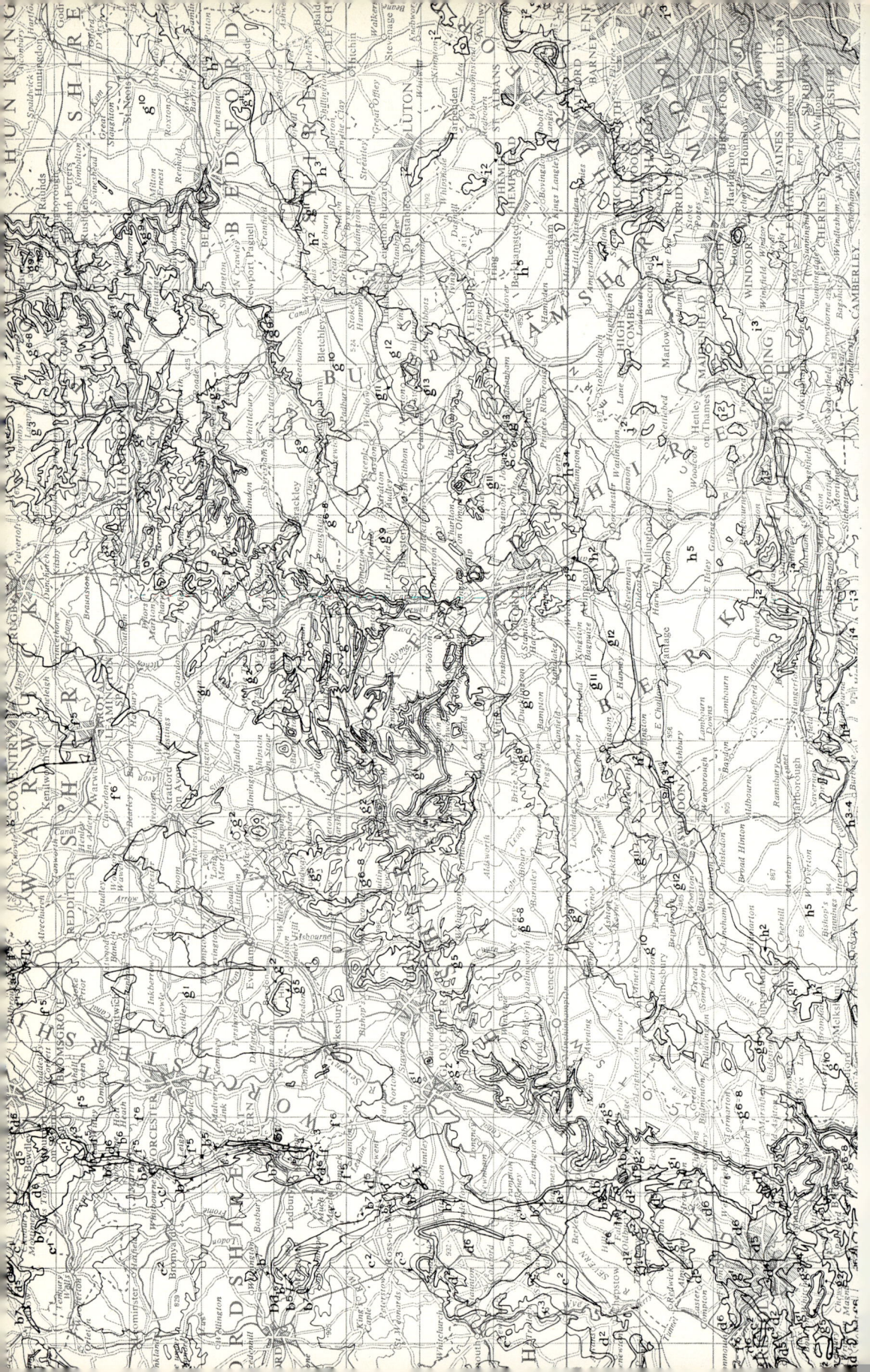

SOUTH MIDLANDS

THE country of this sheet stretches from the western outskirts of London to Bristol, and from Kettering through Coventry to Kidderminster. It includes rocks from the most ancient, near Malvern, to the Tertiary beds of the London basin but Jurassic strata predominate and crop out in a wide north-east—south-west belt flanked south-east by Cretaceous and north-west by Trias and older rocks. In addition to this marked north-east—south-west grain there is an obvious north–south alignment of strata in the Malvern–Forest of Dean–Bristol region and a similar but not quite as obvious pattern about the South Staffordshire and War-wickshire coalfields and in the Jurassic country to the south of them, where tongues of Lias extend both north and south of their general line of outcrop. While it is true that the old rocks make considerably high ground it is the oolites which domin-ate the topography and give rise to the Cotswolds; where these fade somewhat to the north-east owing to limestone giving place to clay the Marlstone of the Middle Lias becomes more prominent especially about Banbury where the Edge Hill Plateau rises to 700 ft. O.D. In the south-east the Chalk of the Chilterns and the Berkshire Downs forms a broad ridge breached by the Thames which, however, rises in the Cotswolds. Some drainage goes east and north-east to the Wash but the bulk goes by the Severn and its tributaries to the Bristol Channel.

The following counties are concerned: Worcestershire; most of Oxford, Glouces-ter, Buckingham and Berkshire; much of Warwick and Northants; West Bedford, North Wiltshire, East Hereford, East Shropshire and small parts of Hertford and Middlesex. The industrial centres are mainly marginal, e.g. London, Bedford, Kettering, Northampton, Rugby, Coventry, Birmingham, Worcester, Gloucester, Bristol with engineering, iron ore and smelting, boots and shoes, bricks and collieries though Banbury near the centre produces much iron ore.

PRE-CAMBRIAN   The oldest rocks in the district crop out as a narrow core in the north–south range of hills known as the Malverns. For the most part they consist of gneisses—irregularly foliated crystalline rocks resulting from great earth squeeze (metamorphism) on what are presumed to have been mainly granites and diorites; of these some less altered remnants remain on North Hill and Worcestershire Beacon near Great Malvern. To the south a brecciated quartzite amidst foliated rocks on Raggedstone Hill suggests that some sedimentary rocks have contributed to the melange. All types have been intruded by veins of pegmatite (coarsely crystalline quartz-feldspar rock) as, for instance, at Gullet Quarry near Hollybush Hill where also there is an intrusive dolerite. Examples of the latter may be seen, too, at the Dingle and Tank quarries between West and Great Malvern.

In the southern half of the range for a mile south of Herefordshire Beacon the gneisses are succeeded by volcanic rocks (Warren House Group) of rhyolitic and spilitic lavas and tuffs. Pebbles of similar rocks occur in the Cambrian Malvern Quartzite.

CAMBRIAN   These rocks occur at the southern end of the Malverns. They comprise a pebbly quartzite (Malvern Quartzite) succeeded by a greenish flaggy sandstone—the Hollybush Sandstone which carries a small horny brachiopod (*Micrometra phillipsi*). The two probably represent Lower and Middle Cambrian. The Upper Cambrian comprises Black shales (named from the Whiteleaved Oak Inn), followed by 1,000 ft. of light blue or greenish shales, known as the Bronsil Shales with abundant *Dictyonema* and some trilobites. Outliers of the shales occur on the old rocks but the main outcrop lies on the west side of the range. They are invaded by numerous sills of dioritic rocks.

SILURIAN   There are no Ordovician sediments in the Malverns and the Silurian beginning with Upper Llandovery rests unconformably on Cambrian and Pre-Cambrian which, from the pebbly nature of the basement bed, presumably formed a shore line. The sandstones pass up through purple shales with *Stricklandinia* (Woolhope or Tarannon Shales) into the blue flaggy Woolhope Limestone. This is followed by a soft grey shale (Wenlock Shale) above which rises an escarpment made by about 100 ft. of the richly fossiliferous Wenlock Limestone. This is followed by the thick Ludlow Shales with a limestone though this is not so well developed as at Ludlow; *Conchidium knighti* is not present but other shells are numerous.

Somewhat similar beds are present at May Hill about eight miles west of Gloucester, where the pine trees on top of the hill of Llandovery (May Hill) Sandstone form a conspicuous landmark, and in the Woolhope area six miles S.E. of Hereford. The Woolhope area is a dissected dome of Silurian strata rising as an inlier from the surrounding Old Red Sandstone. It has a high central core of Llandovery Sandstone rimmed in turn by Woolhope Limestone and the wooded ridges made by Wenlock and Aymestry limestones with intervening low ground in the Wenlock and Ludlow shales.

Silurian beds from the Wenlock upwards are also present in the Abberly Hills to the north of the Malverns of which they are structurally a part though now separated by Trias. There they are overturned to the west and surmounted on Woodberry Hill by an outlier of the Haffield Breccia.

The highest bed of the Ludlow of the region is the Ludlow Bone Bed rich in fish remains. This thin bed forms a convenient base to the Old Red Sandstone though the succeeding yellowish Downton Castle Sandstone, about 40 ft. thick, is often classed with the Silurian.

OLD RED SANDSTONE   The top part of the Downton Castle Sandstone is in places sufficiently fissile to have provided roofing slabs (Tilestones). Next comes about 120 ft. of olive shales (Temeside Shales) with small lamellibranchs, *Lingula cornea* and fish beds. *Lingula cornea* occurs again some 700 ft. higher in red and

102

purple marls (Red Downtonian) which also yield fish remains linking this group of strata with Old Red Sandstone rather than with Silurian. The succeeding 2,000 ft. of measures are red marls interleaved with sandstones. Then comes the Brownstones of more massive sandstone followed unconformably by the Quartz Conglomerate group (500 ft.), including the Farlow Sandstone, of the Upper Old Red Sandstone.

CARBONIFEROUS Carboniferous Limestone is confined to the south-western part of the area bordering the Forest of Dean and Bristol coalfields; in both regions the passage from Old Red Sandstone appears to be conformable. In the Forest of Dean the basal 200 ft. is of shales with limestone (Lower Limestone Shales) referred to the Cleistopora or K Zone; next comes 200 to 400 ft. of so-called Lower Dolomite presumably deposited as such and referred to Zaphrentis or Z and the lower part of the Caninia or C_1 zones. The Crease Limestone (30–100 ft.) which has carried most of the haematite deposits and the Whitehead Limestone (50–150 ft.) are relatively pure limestones except for patchy subsequent dolomitization; these range from C_2 to S_1. The succeeding Drybrook Sandstone with, in the south, an interleaved Drybrook Limestone is referred to the Upper Seminula or S_2 Zone and reaches 700 ft. in thickness; at one time it was classed as Millstone Grit.

The Coal Measures of the Forest of Dean, up to 2,000 ft. thick, rest unconformably on Carboniferous Limestone and transgress in the south-east on to Old Red Sandstone. Much of the Coal Measures consists of grey sandstone known as Pennant and referred to the Upper Coal Measures which in the Midlands are mainly red in colour.

The principal coal, the Coleford High Delf, lies low in the sequence; both it and numerous higher coals have been exhausted or spoiled at shallow depth by surface workings.

The basin is not only asymmetric in that the eastern margin approaches the vertical whereas rocks on the west dip at 10–20° but also has a subsidiary north-south anticline.

North-east of the Forest of Dean there is a small coalfield near Newent but the coal is sulphurous and not worked; the measures rest directly on Old Red Sandstone and pass eastwards under the Trias.

West of Kidderminster there is another coalfield which is part of the Midland group of fields and is known as the Wyre Forest Coalfield; it, too, rests directly on Old Red Sandstone. The main coal-bearing strata (1,000 ft. thick) are known as the Kinlet or Sweet Coal group to distinguish them from an upper series of sulphurous coals.

Farther east the southern tip of the South Staffordshire Coalfield is included in the map; it there contains no coals of value and near Rubery where there is an inlier of pre-Cambrian, Cambrian and Silurian rocks (see page 145) the Upper Coal Measures overstep Productive Measures on to the older rocks.

Still farther east there is the southern portion of the Warwickshire Coalfield; in it coals are worked beneath the Trias at Binley east of Coventry on the eastern

limb of the field but over most of the ground the Productive Measures are deeply buried beneath the bright red marls and sandstones with breccias and conglomerates of the Upper Coal Measures which extend as far south as Kenilworth.

TRIAS Resting unconformably on Coal Measures and older rocks is a series of red strata, the Trias, consisting of red sandstones in the lower part of restricted outcrop followed by a much wider spread of clays and shales—Keuper Marl. The Keuper Marl furnishes bricks in the Birmingham area and at Leamington and salt (as brine) at Droitwich; such gypsum as it carries in this region is not workable. While red is the prevalent colour alternations of red and green marls occur near the summit—the Tea-green Marls; these are well exposed at Westbury and Aust in the Severn estuary between a local base of Dolomitic Conglomerate and a cover of Rhaetic. The Keuper Marl ranges from 100 ft. in the south-west to 600–1,000 ft. to the east and north-east. In places, at a high level, some greenish sandstone (Arden Sandstone, from the old Forest of Arden west of Warwick) is developed.

The Rhaetic begins with black shales in which there is usually a bone bed (with *Ceratodus*) at or near the base in the southern part of the region.

At Aust the black shales are 15 ft. thick and are followed by 11 ft. of yellowish clay and that by the thin limestones at the bottom of the Lias.

JURASSIC The Lower Lias usually has beds of limestone (often rich in oyster shells) in the lower part (Blue Lias) used in cement manufacture, e.g. at Rugby and at Southam, but the bulk of the measures are clay shales with thin beds of clayey porcellanous limestone. The formation ranges from 50 ft. thick near Bristol to 200 ft. at Chipping Sodbury, 500 ft. about Gloucester and 960 ft. at Mickleton in the Vale of Evesham. The upper portion is worked at Battledown Brickworks, Cheltenham.

In addition to the main mass there is a small outlier of Rhaetic and Lower Lias at Copt Heath near Knowle and 14 miles north of Stratford on Avon.

Middle Lias in mid-Gloucestershire is of sands and clays with but a thin shelly ferruginous limestone to represent the Marlstone Rock Bed which does, however, give rise to a step-like feature in topography as in the lower part of Leckhampton Hill, Cheltenham. Farther to the north-east clays predominate beneath a thick Marlstone Rock Bed which caps Edge Hill and furnishes the ironstone of the Banbury area; this is a green, brown-weathering rock with about 20–30 per cent of metallic iron. From 25 ft. of rusty sandstone on Edge Hill the bed becomes a 10 or 12-ft. ironstone around Banbury but in Northamptonshire is valueless and only 6 ft. thick.

The Upper Lias near Stroud shows a remarkable change in strata for thereabouts the sandy facies—the Cotswold and Midford Sands—that dominates this division of the Lias to the south gives place to clays which are about 270 ft. thick on Bredon Hill. The sandy phase does not return and the Upper Lias Clay is only about 80 ft. thick about Moreton, Stow and Burford, 30 to 40 ft. at Chipping

Norton and 5 to 12 ft. at Fawler though it thickens to 70 ft. near Banbury and to 200 ft. in Northamptonshire.

In the Cotswold country a considerable development of oolitic limestones follows the Lias and there are no thick widespread clay belts until the Oxford Clay is reached. The limestones, however, are less persistent than the general use of their names—Inferior Oolite and Great Oolite—for stratal subdivisions would suggest. In fact both appear to be subject to lateral and vertical changes and this is probably due to lithological types occurring as overlapping lenses rather than as definite beds though partly due to inter-formational folding and erosion. For example, the lower and middle parts of the Inferior Oolite reach their maximum thickness of 300 ft. about Cheltenham; of this the greater and lower part is of freestones whereas the upper part includes so-called grits (really fragmental or pisolitic limestones, though some beds are arenaceous) and occasional clay bands as well as freestones. After suffering some lateral changes all these disappear to the north and south until near Stow in the Wold and near Sodbury Upper Inferior Oolite transgresses on the Lias—even Lower Lias near Bath. The Upper Inferior Oolite, usually about 50 ft. thick, has a fairly constant 'grit' with *Trigonia* at the base followed between Stroud and Cleeve Hill by another 'grit' with the sea urchin *Clypeus* which, however, to the south passes into normal limestones and freestones and to the north is overlapped by the 20-ft. Chipping Norton Limestone—in places flaggy at others an oolitic freestone—referred to the bottom part of the Great Oolite. To the north-east the lower part of the Inferior Oolite is represented by the North-ampton Ironstone; this is succeeded by sands and flaggy limestone which eventually, about Kettering, include the Lincolnshire Limestone which thickens north-east.

Separating the Inferior Oolite from the Great or Bath Oolite in the south-west is a clay formation known as the Fuller's Earth though it is only near Bath that it includes a 6-ft. bed of commercial fuller's earth; in that area the clay formation is about 100 ft. thick but it thins northwards. The basal 30 ft. or so of the Great Oolite is often sufficiently fissile for roofing and is known as Stonesfield Slate from a village near Witney where it was mined. Next come the oolitic freestones, up to 120 ft. thick, of Bath, Minchinhampton and Taynton, followed by lenses of splintery limestone, marls and clays up to the shelly Forest Marble (10–15 ft. thick, of Wychwood Forest, North Oxfordshire). There is a general though irregular thinning of the Great Oolite formation throughout Oxfordshire and into Northamptonshire accompanied by changes in strata. For example, the Chipping Norton Limestone, a white or cream fine-grained oolite with black specks of lignite and 15 to 20 ft. thick, passes laterally into massive brown sandstone with flaggy limestones (Hook Norton Beds 10–15 ft.) followed by 10 to 15 ft. of Swerford Sands. In Northamptonshire and Lincolnshire the Great Oolite formation consists of the Upper Estuarine silts (10–35 ft.), Great Oolite Limestone 15 to 30 ft., followed by 5 to 30 ft. of Blisworth Clay.

Both Inferior and Great Oolite limestones have been extensively quarried and sections are common—in the former mainly along the escarpment and valley sides

while those in the latter are often on the plateau. More continuous sections are furnished by the railway cuttings.

The Cornbrash may be regarded as the natural top of the Oolites for it is mainly of rubble limestones separating the Great Oolite from the Oxford Clay; indeed some authors would include lower Cornbrash with the Great Oolite formation. Both upper and lower Cornbrash are subject to considerable variations in thickness and lithology attributable in part to unconformity; the total thickness seldom exceeds 50 ft. and is often much less; usually the lower part is the better developed but one or other is present at outcrop between Fairford, Witney, Bicester and Buckingham separating the Great Oolite plateau and dip slope from the low-lying Oxford Clay.

At the base of the Oxford Clay are the Kellaways Beds (named from Kellaways 2 miles N.E. of Chippenham) usually 30–40 ft. thick with clay in the lower half and sandstone above giving a small rise in the topography. The Oxford Clay comprises 400–500 ft. of grey and blue clays with occasional earthy limestone bands or nodules. There are now no good exposures about Oxford but large brickpits begin west of Aylesbury and continue through Calvert, Bletchley and Bedford.

The Corallian, usually about 100 ft. thick, indicates a return to oolite conditions though limestones are interspersed with sands and clays. South-west of Oxford these limestones are well developed but they disappear abruptly five miles east of Oxford close to the great limestone quarries at Wheatley and, apart from small reef-like patches are replaced by Ampthill Clay giving as a result a broad clay belt extending from the Kellaways Beds to the top of the Kimmeridge Clay.

The Kimmeridge Clay, apart from a thin intercalation of sand near Shotover, consists of about 300 ft. of leaden grey clays. Near Chippenham in the west the outcrop is overstepped by Gault and on the east near Leighton Buzzard by the Lower Greensand. At intervals between these places small tracts of Portland and Purbeck strata survive particularly between Thame and Aylesbury but the strata bear little resemblance to the rocks of the type localities on the south coast. The former are rubbly limestones separated by clays and sands; in the latter the limestones are thin-bedded in shales; each formation is about 30 ft. thick.

CRETACEOUS   In this region the earliest continuous Cretaceous formation is the Gault; there are intermittent deposits of Lower Greensand but earlier strata such as are well represented in the Weald and in Yorkshire are absent apart from remnants near Oxford and Brill of red and white silts and clays of Wealden age too small to show on the map.

The Lower Greensand of the Faringdon area is peculiar in that it consists largely of about 50 ft. of gravels (rich in fossil sponges) that appear to have accumulated in hollows. In the main mass of Lower Greensand which emerges from beneath the Gault and oversteps the upper Jurassic on to the Oxford Clay near Leighton Buzzard there are numerous large pits where yellow and white sands are dug.

The Gault and Upper Greensand cannot always be differentiated. Out of a total of 250 to 300 ft. the lower half is usually a stiff grey clay whereas the upper half is

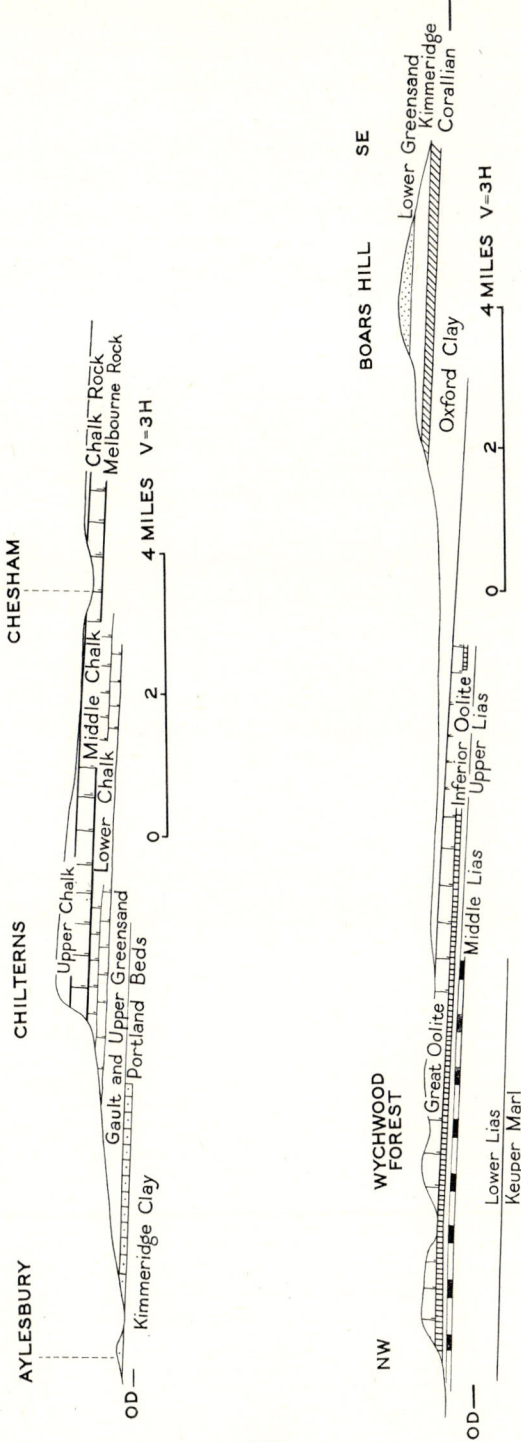

Figure 33. Sections in the Chiltern and Oxford areas
(Based on One-inch Geological Sheets 236 and 238)

107

mainly light silty marl or the soft siliceous rock rich in sponge spicules known as malmstone or firestone (used for kiln-lining) though locally the top few feet are of sand.

The 100 ft. or so of marly beds at the base of the Chalk afford a passage into the Upper Greensand–Gault from which they are not always easy to distinguish on account of their grey colour and sticky nature. The remainder of the Lower Chalk (100–150 ft.) is ordinary white chalk apart from about 2 ft. of Belemnite Marl at the top and is without flints. There are excellent sections of these beds just north of Dunstable.

The Middle Chalk 150–200 ft. begins with the hard creamy nodular Melbourn Rock about 10 ft. thick; this is usually fossiliferous and resting as it does on soft marl can usually be located by the step it makes in the escarpment. Beginning with the Chalk Rock (hard creamy 1-ft. beds interbedded with nodular chalk) at the bottom the Upper Chalk ranges from 200 to 300 ft. of white chalk with flints. Apart from the escarpment and valleys much of its outcrop is obscured by clay-with-flints a deposit partly remaine partly of glacial origin.

EOCENE   There are no Thanet Sands in the district and the basal formation is the mottled plastic clay and fine grey-buff sand known as Reading Beds (60–90 ft.). The lumps of conglomerate known as Hertfordshire Pudding Stone and of the hard sandstone (Sarsens) found occasionally at surface were probably derived from silicified Reading Beds. The succeeding formation is the dark but yellow-brown-weathering London Clay about 400 ft. thick in the London area but thinner to the west where it is succeeded by the sands, with gravel and pipe clays, of the Bagshot Beds.

REFERENCES

Geological Survey
  Regional Handbooks: Central England, ed 2, 1947; *London and Thames Valley*, ed 2, 1947; *Bristol and Gloucester* ed 2, 1948; *Welsh Borderland*, ed 2, 1948.
  Mesozoic Ironstones: Northampton Sands Ironstone, 1951; Liassic Ironstones, 1952.
Excursions and Field Meetings
  Bristol District, Excursion Handbook for, Reynolds ed 2, 1921, Bristol.
  Cheltenham, Handbook of Geology, Richardson, L., 1904, Cheltenham.
  International Geological Congress 1948.
  Long Excursions: A6 Oxford; C3 Bristol and Gloucester; C1 England & Wales; A1, Economic; A11 Geomorphology.
  B Excursions based on London: 2, Chilterns; 16, Banbury; 27, Aylesbury and Princes Risborough; 29, Bletchley; 37, Northampton; 53, Leighton Buzzard (Lower Greensand and Gault).
Geologists Association, Proceedings or Circulars
  1906, Evesham and N. Cotswolds. 1908, Mid-south Cotswolds. 1921, Banbury; Northamtonshire. 1925, Cirencester. 1926 and 1931, Oxford area. 1932, Vale of White Horse. 1934, Gloucester. 1936, Witney. 1937, Swindon. 1946, Leighton Buzzard; Northampton; Hook Norton. 1949, North Chilterns. 1950, Farringdon; Cotswolds. 1951, Reading and South Chilterns; Harefield; Henley and Beaconsfield; Aylesbury and North Chilterns. 1952, Oxford; Chilterns. 1953, Oxford area. 1955, Cotswolds; Oxford area. 1956, Gloucester–Malverns. 1956 and 60, Oxford Clay.
Geologists Association, Guides 3, Oxford.

SHEET 7

SOUTH WALES (EAST)

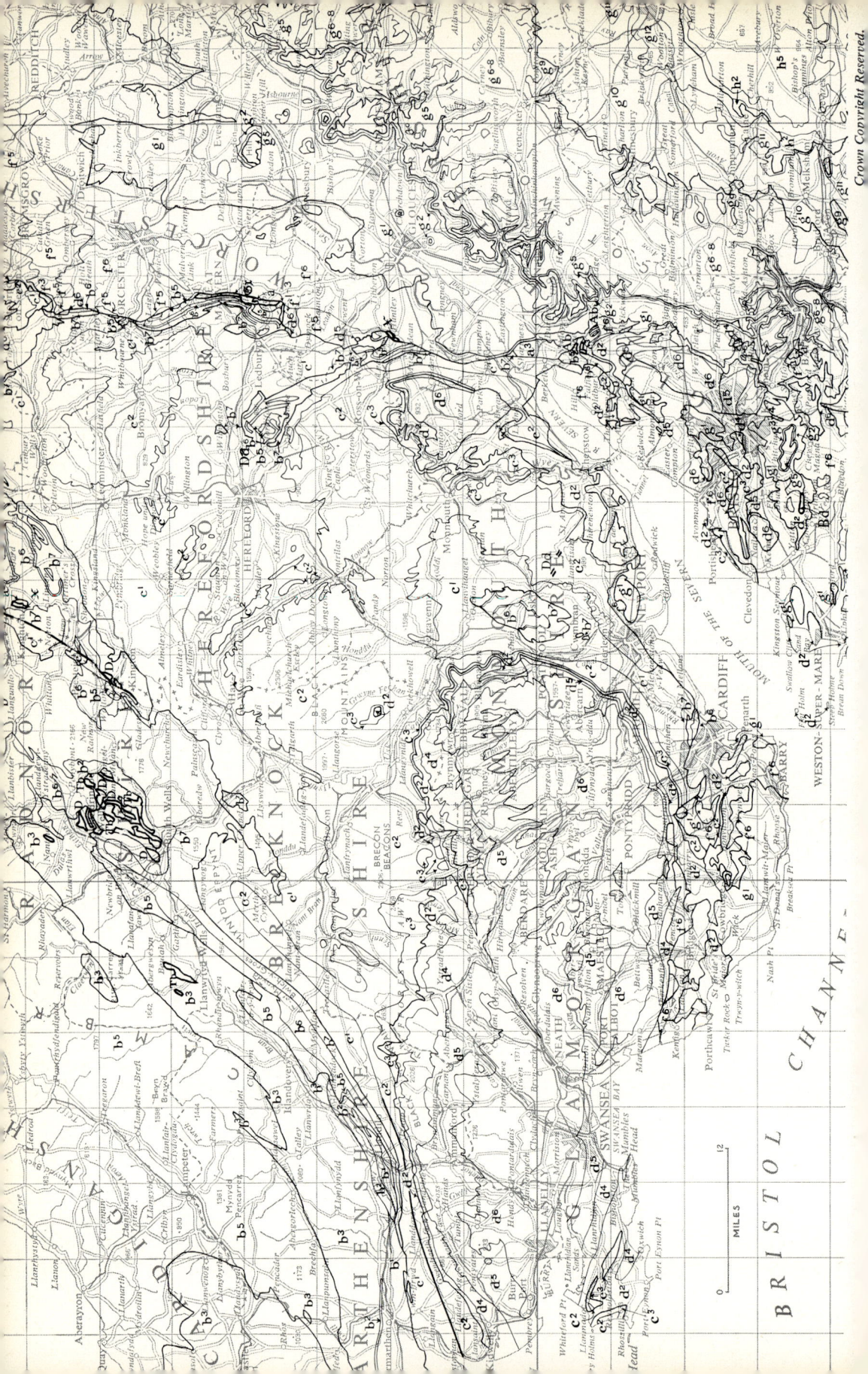

SOUTH WALES (WEST)

(Overleaf)

C A R D I G A N   B A Y

RADNORSHIRE

BRECKNOCKSHIRE

CARDIGANSHIRE

CARMARTHENSHIRE

GLAMORGAN

PEMBROKESHIRE

SWANSEA BAY

CARMARTHEN BAY

ST BRIDES BAY

BLACK MOUNTAINS

BRECON BEACONS

Aberystwyth

Aberayron

New Quay

Cardigan

Swansea

Mumbles Head

Worms Head

Strumble Head

Dinas Head

St David's Head

St Ann's Head

St Govan's Head

Linney Head

Worms Head

MILES

0   12

SOUTH WALES

IN ORDER that the account of the South Wales Coalfield and of the St. David's area be as complete as possible and without undue repetition the geology of two overlapping sheets is described together. The sheets are St. David's extending northwards to beyond Aberystwyth and eastwards to New Radnor; the other, Swansea and Cardiff, includes Worcester and Gloucester though an account of this eastern tract will be found elsewhere (pages 101–108). The district, therefore, includes much of sparsely populated Mid Wales as well as the coalfield areas of South Wales and Forest of Dean with their iron and steel, tinplate, smelting and engineering plants as well as the ancilliary quarrying. The South Wales Coalfield is thickly populated in the valleys only for the interfluves are almost in their pristine state. Altitudes range from Plynlimmon, 2,469 ft., and the Brecon Beacons, 2,907 ft., to a fairly general level of 1,500—2,000 ft. over much of the country though declining southwards. Many streams flow directly into the Irish Sea or the Bristol Channel; others take a more circuitous route as, for example, the Severn and the Wye which rise on Plynlimmon but do not approach each other again until they reach the Severn Estuary.

Rocks from pre-Cambrian to Jurassic are included with the old rocks mainly to the west and north-west, then a broad tract of Old Red Sandstone followed to the east by Trias and Jurassic strata and to the south by the coalfields. This disposition gives some indication of the broad structure which may be supplemented by a glance at the geological map. There it will be seen that the ancient rocks occur in belts near St. David's bordered by Ordovician strata with an outcrop looping irregularly from Cardigan Bay towards Carmarthen and then swinging up towards Shropshire; further, that there are islands of Ordovician in the broad tract of Silurian of Mid Wales. These indicate folds along arcs of general north-east trend with a main syncline occupied by the Silurian of Mid Wales and a major anticline to the east with complementary syncline farther east bringing in the Ludlow and Old Red Sandstone. On the other hand the shape of the South Wales Coalfield betrays a basin elongated east-west separated by older rocks on north-south folds from the Forest of Dean Coalfield which also obviously follows a north-south trend parallel to the Malvern axis. Still farther east the Jurassic rocks obviously dip east and south-east since higher and higher members come on in those directions.

PRE-CAMBRIAN These, the oldest rocks are confined to the St. David's area where they occur in the cores of several anticlines, one through St. David's, another through Hayscastle, a third through Roch and a fourth more detached brought up by a fault through Johnston and Benton. The rocks consist of tuffs over 4,000 ft. thick (varying from fine-grained hard splintery halleflinta to conglomerates, green

to red in colour, known as the Pebidian Series), invaded by masses of granitic rocks (the Dimetian Series).

The rocks were considerably broken, folded and eroded before Cambrian strata were deposited over them.

CAMBRIAN   This formation begins with about 900 ft. of purple and green felds-pathic sandstones—the Caerfai Series. This has a conglomerate at the base with pebbles of the local pre-Cambrian and, more important, about the middle has a bed of red shales which has provided *Olenellus* the trilobite diagnostic of Lower Cambrian. (Fig. 6). These rocks may be seen in the cliffs at Caerfai, at Castell on Ramsey Sound and in Caerbwdy Bay.

The succeeding Solva Series of 550 ft. of green and grey sandstones with a median belt of flags and mudstones has yielded *Paradoxides* and other trilobites of Middle Cambrian age. They may be seen in Solva Harbour and Caerbwdy Bay. These are followed by the dark grey flags and mudstones, totalling 750 ft., of the Menevian Series which also carry *Paradoxides*, and are well exposed at Porthyrhaw between Solva and Caerbwdy.

Lingula Flags, of which the 2,000 ft. known here represent only the lower part of the North Wales sequence, are the uppermost beds of the Cambrian. They are thin hard flags in grey shales yielding *Lingulella davisi*, and the small trilobite *Agnostus* as well as the zone fossil of the Upper Cambrian—*Olenus catactes*. They may be seen at Porthyrhaw, in Whitesand Bay and on Ramsey Island.

ORDOVICIAN   This thick belt of strata has a wider distribution than the foregoing. It not only contains shells and trilobites but also forked graptolites, by means of which it is zoned. In the Arenig or basal series there is a sequence of grits, sandstones, mudstones often intermixed, and dark brown shales. On Ramsey Island such trilobites as *Ogygia* and *Calymene* are common in the lower beds. (Fig. 7).

The upper part, Tetragraptus Shales, carries abundant *Didymograptus extensus* and *D. hirundo* in ascending sequence as well as *Tetragraptus* and trilobites.

The rocks include contemporary rhyolitic and andesitic lavas and tuffs in some districts as, for example, between Carmarthen and St. Clears, in the Cleddau Valley, in the Prescelly Hills, about Abercastle and last but not least, for they there total 3,000 ft., in Skomer Island.

Middle Ordovician strata fall into two series of which the lower or Llanvirn (from the type locality near St. David's) does not differ markedly from the beds below for it usually consists of black shales with tuning fork graptolites—*Didymograptus bifidus* in the lower thicker part and *D. murchisoni* above. The series is not much more than 400 ft. thick between Builth and Llandeilo but thickens to 2,000 ft. about St. Clears where it includes much volcanic ash. An ash bed and the overlying 100 ft. of shales crowded with *D. murchisoni* is well exposed in Abereiddy Bay. In some localities, as at Fishguard, Llanrian and Ramsey Island, the ashes are accompanied by thick lavas.

The succeeding Llandeilo Series in the type area about Llandeilo begins with grit

and passes up into calcareous flags and limestones totalling 2,500 ft. and rich in brachiopods and trilobites. Westwards they become ashy and then predominantly shaly and graptolitic. This shale facies persists into the succeeding Caradoc Series of the upper Ordovician, or Bala beds, from beyond Builth to Pembroke; in places it includes lenses of limestone. The typical graptolite *Nemograptus gracilis* is accompanied by *Diplograptus*. The volcanic rocks of Llanwrtyd occur in this series.

The Ordovician sequence is completed by the Ashgill Series (of which the type locality is in the Lake District). In the south calcareous shelly mudstones with limestone bands and nodules prevail, as between Llandeilo and Haverfordwest. Trilobites are common. Northwards the beds pass into olive mudstones and then to shales interspersed with flags, as in Central Wales, where they are graptolitic. The thickness ranges to about 4,000 ft.

SILURIAN This system of rocks also shows variations from the marginal outcrops with shelly facies to a graptolitic facies in Mid Wales.

At the base is the Llandovery Series which in the type area and over much of southern Wales consists of basal sandstones followed by greenish and shelly mudstones with some limy bands probably totalling over 3,000 ft. thick. Whereas brachiopods and trilobites predominate there are some graptolites. In the Rhayader district there is a considerable development of grits and conglomerate but farther west greenish shales and mudstones with flags predominate, though there are some sandstones as at Aberystwyth; in the upper part the shales become paler and of purplish tint as about Tarannon. Various species of *Monograptus* appear for the first time. The lead mining field east of Aberystwyth occurs in this belt of strata.

No beds higher than Llandovery occur in the great stretch of Silurian country of Central Wales but on the eastern borders Wenlock strata appear. They are mainly dark shales and flags with graptolites, such as *Cyrtograptus*, and exceed 1,600 ft. in thickness near Builth but thin southwards due to overstep by Old Red Sandstone. Eastwards the beds become limy and shelly with locally considerable development of limestone. The lowest or Woolhope Limestone is present near Old Radnor where it rests with conglomeratic base on Longmyndian pre-Cambrian rocks; at Presteign it follows Llandovery grits. Shells and trilobites are common. In South Wales this shelly facies is represented about Milford Haven.

There is a considerable spread of Ludlow strata in Radnor but to the south-west the outcrop narrows due to overstep, though small patches of sandy limy facies are present in Pembroke. In the Builth area 750 ft. of dark graptolitic shales with flags are followed by 600 ft. of green shales with limy and sandy bands. Eastwards and southwards all these rocks become more sandy and to the east the Aymestry Limestone appears in the middle of the series; shells and trilobites are common. At the top of the series is the Ludlow Bone Bed—a thin band with fish remains developed at Ludlow and present in the Usk inlier—which forms a convenient boundary between Silurian and Old Red Sandstone strata.

OLD RED SANDSTONE This formation, which is the continental equivalent of the

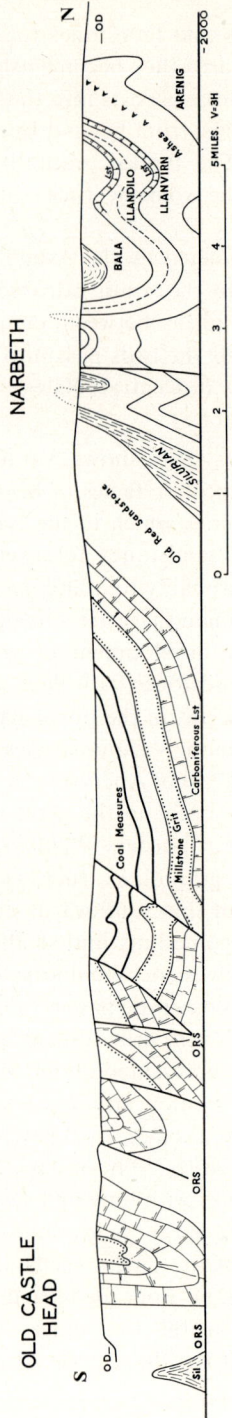

Figure 34. Generalized section near Tenby to show structure and sequence

116

marine Devonian (page 16), occupies a triangular tract between Bridgnorth, Bristol and Milford Haven. It is made up of sandstones and marls, mainly red in colour but occasionally grey and green, with which are associated conglomerates at various horizons and occasional limestones or nodular concretions of lime in sandstone known as cornstones. A few shells occur in the lower part and *Spirifer verneuili* has been got in Breconshire but elsewhere the scanty fossils are the remains of fishes and plants. *Psammosteus*, *Cephalaspis* and *Pteraspis* occur in the Lower and *Holoptychius* in Upper Old Red Sandstone (Fig. 10), the division between the two portions being drawn at the base of a conglomerate made up almost entirely of quartz pebbles. Plants are found in the grey Senni Beds between the reservoirs on the Brecon road and in the upper Skrinkle Beds south-east of Pembroke.

The total thickness of the formation may reach 20,000 ft. but there are considerable variations in thicknesses of the subdivisions and of the sequences. Moreover, there is a widespread unconformity at the base of the Quartz Conglomerate which is usually less than 1,000 ft. from the summit. As a rule red marls predominate in the lowest 2,000–3,000 ft.; sandstones then begin to be noticeable and increase in thickness upwards, at the expense of marl. The Quartz Conglomerate, which often caps escarpments, may be succeeded directly by the Carboniferous, as over much of South Wales, or yellowish sandstones may intervene as in the Forest of Dean. Lower conglomerates are restricted to South Pembroke, where they are 1,200 ft. thick, and to the Llanishen area near Cardiff; this suggests a southern source for the pebbles.

CARBONIFEROUS   In places there appears to be conformable passage from the Old Red Sandstone to the Carboniferous though the latter overlaps on to older strata. Subdivisions based on the range of shells or corals (zones) indicate lateral variations and marked thinning in successive members of the Carboniferous Limestone accompanied by Millstone Grit overstep in proceeding from west to east. Thus all the zones are present in Gower whereas on the eastern crop of the coalfield only a thin bottom zone occurs (see Fig. 35). Still farther east, however, the zonal subdivisions reappear in the Forest of Dean. In both areas the lowest zone, K and up to 600 ft. thick, is of shales with subordinate limestones carrying the zone coral *Cleistopora* and brachiopod shells. The Zaphrentis Zone (Z) which follows is 500 ft. of crinoidal limestones on the borders of Carmarthen Bay but eastwards like the zones above becomes dolomitic. The Caninia Zone (C) of crinoidal limestones in the west parted by dolomite and oolite totalling 1,500 ft. becomes almost wholly dolomite on the east. Next comes the Seminula Zone (S) mostly of massive coarse oolite; here the zone fossil, *Seminula*, is accompanied by other characteristic brachiopods such as *Cyrtina* and *Productus corrugata-hemisphericus*. From 1,000 ft. in Gower it thins to 400 ft. on the north crop of the coalfield. The top zone with *Dibunophyllum* is characterized by pseudobreccias; these are entirely of limestone and the fragmental appearance is due to slight differences in composition consequent on recrystallization which affects the colour. In the upper part shale again predominates. Fossils other than *Dibunophyllum* are

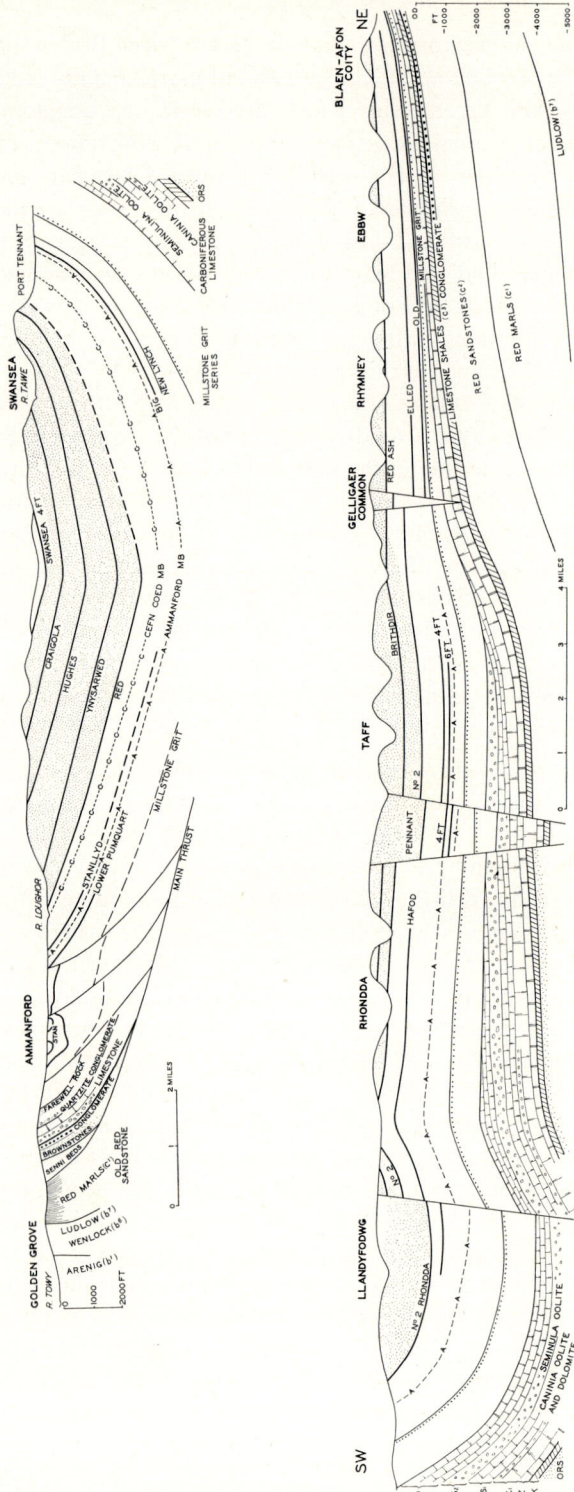

Figure 35. Sections across the South Wales Coalfield

(Upper after Trotter, Q.J.G.S. CIII, 1947 and CIV, 1949; lower based on Pringle and George, *South Wales* Geol. Surv. Handbook for Lower Carboniferous and on Robertson, *Abergavenny* G.S.M. for eastern half)

Lonsdaleia, Lithostrotion and large-shelled *Productus*. From 800 ft. in Gower it diminishes to 300 ft. at Kidwelly. Haematite deposits replace limestone between Llanharry and Taffs Well.

In the Forest of Dean the Limestone Shales of K Zone are about 200 ft. thick; they are followed by 300–400 ft. of Main Dolomite which was deposited as dolomite whereas in the succeeding Crease (70–100 ft.) and Whitehead (40-200 ft.) limestones dolomitization is subsequent and partial. The haematite of the Forest usually replaces Crease Limestone. Lithology does not agree so well with zoning as in South Wales; the Main Dolomite is $Z–C_1$; the Whitehead $C_2–S_1$. Unlike South Wales there is no Millstone Grit. The Drybrook Sandstone of S_2 age and up to 650 ft. thick is followed unconformably by Coal Measures.

The Millstone Grit of South Wales usually has a Basal Grit, often very siliceous and conglomeratic, separated by dark shales with sandstones from the topmost member the Farewell Rock (so named because the chances of finding coal beneath it are remote). Goniatites indicate that all the zones of Lancashire and Yorkshire are present; the total thickness ranges from 200 ft. in the east to 1,500 ft. in Gower.

Coal Measures succeed Millstone Grit conformably. They are divisible into Lower and Upper Coal Series separated by the Pennant Sandstone. The Lower Coal Series, predominantly of dark shales with clay ironstones near the base, carries the principal coal seams; it reaches 3,000 ft. about Swansea but thins considerably north and east. The Pennant Sandstone is of massive, blue-grey, rusty weathering sandstone parted at intervals by thick shale belts which include workable coal seams. Again the maximum thickness is about Swansea (4,000 ft.) but only 600 ft. at Pontypool (see Fig. 35). The Upper Coal Series of sandy shales is preserved only in the deeper synclines such as Caerphilly; coals are of value only in the lower part. Plants and 'mussels' are common fossils but marine shells are restricted to four thin evenly disposed bands in the Lower Coal Series. The non-marine lamellibranchs or mussels indicate that the Communis, Modiolaris, Semilis-Pulchra zones lie in the Lower Coal Series. The coals range from bituminous on the east through steam coals to anthracites in the west of the main field, the principal changes being about the Vale of Neath. In Pembroke excessive folding and faulting renders large tracts of Coal Measures valueless.

In the Forest of Dean the measures are similar but thinner. The best seam lies at the bottom of the Pennant. Coal Measures here, therefore, lie high in the normal sequence; they are unconformable to the Limestone Series and transgress on to the Old Red Sandstone.

TRIAS AND JURASSIC Shortly after the Coal Measures had been deposited the area was folded, mainly along east-west axes, uplifted and then subjected to denudation which is estimated to have removed 10,000 ft. of strata in places. Conditions at first were arid giving the red Trias; later truly marine conditions prevailed in the Jurassic period. Both show that the waters encroached northwards for basal conglomerates step upwards in the sequences in that direction in the Keuper, Rhaetic and Lias. In the Cardiff area there is a fairly normal sequence of

MILES

0   12

LINCOLNSHIRE

NORFOLK

SUFFOLK

CAMBRIDGESHIRE

HUNTINGDONSHIRE

NORWICH

GREAT YARMOUTH

YARMOUTH ROADS

LOWESTOFT

KING'S LYNN

PETERBOROUGH

BOSTON

THE WASH

Burnham Flats

BRANCASTER ROADS

LYNN DEEPS

BOSTON DEEPS

Long Sand

Skegness

Sutton on Sea

Cromer

Sheringham

Hunstanton

Wells next the Sea

Spalding

March

Ely

Thetford

Diss

Bungay

Beccles

Southwold

Walberswick

Dunwich

Wrentham

Kessingland

Corton

East Dereham

Swaffham

Watton

Wisbech

Ramsey

Whittlesey

Chatteris

Godmanchester

Huntingdon

Woodhall Spa

Sleaford

Bourne

Downham

Brandon

Mildenhall

Newmarket

Soham

Harleston

Loddon

Halesworth

Framlingham

Saxmundham

Aldeburgh

Long Stratton

NORFOLK

THE sheet includes Thetford and Ely on the south, Louth on the north and Sleaford and Peterborough on the west; it therefore embraces almost the whole of Norfolk, the northern parts of Cambridgeshire and Huntingdonshire and much of Lincoln-shire. Strata range from middle Jurassic on the west to Pliocene on the east. These rocks are much obscured by glacial and recent deposits; of the latter the most important are those of the Fens extending from Thetford to Yaxley on the south and from the coast to near Sleaford on the north. West of the Chalk outcrop drainage is mainly through the Fens into the Wash by the Ouse, Nene, Welland and Witham; east of the Chalk it is mainly into the North Sea itself but is involved in the Broads of East Norfolk and in the marshes bordering the Lincolnshire coast. Even apart from these Fens, Broads and marshes the district is of low altitude yet is by no means of dull topography; it is a question of scale of relief. Agriculture is the dominant industry assisted by fishing from Yarmouth and Lowestoft, engineering at Norwich and brick-making about Peterborough.

JURASSIC The Oolites crop out on the western margin; an account of them will be found in that of the neighbouring sheet along with the inliers of Cornbrash amidst Oxford Clay near Peterborough and between Bourne and Donnington. In south-western Britain the thick clay formations that follow the Oolites are parted by a limestone group, known as the Corallian, and are succeeded by Portland and Purbeck strata which also include limestones. No such calcareous rocks occur in the area under review.

The Oxford Clay, 300–400 ft. thick, with the sandy Kellaways Beds at the base occupies a great stretch of country as far east as Godmanchester and Holbeach but the outcrop narrows northwards along the Clay Vale of Lincoln; it is a dark grey to inky blue clay with occasional bands and nodules of muddy limestone. Fossils are common and range from ammonites and belemnites to the abundant oyster *Gryphaea dilatata*. Of greater interest, however, are the remains of giant marine reptiles, the plesiosaurs, together with occasional land forms, the dinosaurs, doubtless washed into the sea by rivers; it is unlikely that many such skeletons will be recovered in future as the working of the clays is now fully mechanized.

There are large brickpits around Peterborough and the name fletton for the dry-pressed brick is taken from the village of Fletton there. Brick-making is cheapened by the fact that the clay carries a fair quantity of carbonaceous matter which reduces the amount of coal required for firing.

Ampthill Clay here replaces the Corallian Limestones; it consists of black or very dark clay about 200 ft. thick.

The Kimmeridge Clay which follows is a dark grey clay formation about 300 ft. thick in South Lincolnshire but it thins northwards and disappears at the Humber for several miles. Exposures are mainly in the lower half of the formation where the clay carries many bands of clayey limestone (cementstones). *Ostrea delta* is a common fossil; the ammonite *Rasenia* takes its name from Market Rasen west of Louth.

With these thick and gently dipping clay formations occurring together it is not surprising that the combined outcrops should occupy low ground or that these should be masked by fenland or boulder clay.

CRETACEOUS   In the absence of Portlandian and Purbeck strata Lower Cretaceous beds succeed Kimmeridge Clay unconformably. They appear at surface on the eastern side of the Fens between Downham Market and Hunstanton and again at the foot of the Chalk Wolds across the Wash in Lincolnshire.

In Norfolk the Sandringham Sands (100 ft.) at the base are pale, sharp, silvery sands occasionally cemented into stony bands; they are worked for glass making near King's Lynn.

Next comes Snettisham Clay of clays and loams some 30 ft. thick in the north but a thin ferruginous sandstone in the south. Snettisham Clay has been dug for brick-making at Snettisham, at Dersingham and at Heacham between Hunstanton and Sandringham. Fossils indicate that this and the underlying Sandringham Sands are referable to the Wealden Beds of southern England though loosely included in the Lower Greensand in East Anglia.

The Carstone comprises about 40 ft. of ferruginous sandstone ('carstone'; used for building) and brown sands. At Hunstanton it is a pebbly sandstone and its quadrangular jointing is conspicuous on the foreshore. Phosphatic nodules at its base yield fossils characteristic of the Lower Greensand of southern England; it is directly succeeded by the Red Rock (Red Chalk) at Hunstanton which is the equivalent of the Gault.

In Lincolnshire Lower Cretaceous strata between the Kimmeridge Clay and the Red Chalk present a different facies from Norfolk in an outcrop six miles wide at the south but narrowing northwards. At the bottom is the Spilsby Sandstone—mostly a glauconitic sand but in places cemented into sandstone—with at its base numerous phosphatic nodules and phosphatized fossils bored by the lamellibranch *Martesia*. It is 76 ft. thick near Spilsby but thins northwards; in the latitude of Louth it is 40 ft. and thence decreases rapidly.

The Spilsby Sandstone is succeeded by the Claxby Beds (24 ft.). These are mainly dark or purplish clays but are replaced by oolitic ironstone (Claxby Ironstone) 14 ft. thick at its maximum between Claxby and Nettleton where it is mined; it, too, thins and disappears northwards.

The succeeding grey Tealby Clays have a median limestone, that may reach 13 ft. thick in a total of 90 ft. and are followed by grey to black clays associated with oolitic iron ore and sandstones (known as 'Roach') collectively styled Fulletby Beds (50 ft.) which with the Tealby Clay and Claxby beds constitute the Tealby Series.

Next comes a variable group of rocks consisting in the south of dark clay and marl (Sutterby Marl, 11 ft.) passing upwards into the sandy marls, sands and grits of the Carstone. The grits, at the top, transgress northwards the lower members of the formation and eventually rest on Kimmeridge Clay.

Both in Norfolk and in Lincolnshire the Carstone is succeeded by the Hunstanton Red Rock or Red Chalk whose fossils indicate equivalence with the Gault of southern England though the zones are considerably condensed in thickness. The Red Rock is only 4 ft. thick; the lowest part is gritty, has abundance of quartz pebbles and is deep red in colour; the rest is a red limestone partly nodular.

The Red Chalk of Lincolnshire is 24 ft. thick in the south but diminishes northwards. It is a pink to brick red impure limestone with quartz grains and passes gradually down into the Carstone.

The succeeding white chalk is more nearly comparable with that elsewhere. The Lower Chalk is made up of the Chalk Marl below, belonging to the Varians Zone, and the grey Chalk above, of Subglobosus Zone. The former south of Stoke Ferry consists of 75 ft. of alternating hard and soft beds but northwards thins to 18 ft. of hard greyish chalk at Hunstanton where there is a bed of green-coated nodules associated with a Sponge Bed at the base which rests sharply on Red Rock. In the same localities the Totternhoe Stone, a buff massive chalk, ranges from 5 to 2 ft. in place of 20 ft. farther south. The succeeding Grey Chalk is thin bedded and about 35 ft. thick. The Plenus Marl is about 3 ft. thick.

The Middle Chalk is not more than 100 ft. thick in Norfolk and its basal hard yellow Melbourn Rock is less than 10 ft. thick. On the other hand more of the Upper Chalk, which succeeds the Chalk Rock, is preserved in Norfolk than elsewhere in Britain, the uppermost portion being found at Trimingham on the coast about four miles S.E. of Cromer. Most of the Upper Chalk is white with flint in large and small nodules and rows of flat pieces. Near Norwich there are large hollow cylindrical flints, a foot or two in diameter and 4 ft. in height known as paramoudras.

The Chalk in Lincolnshire gives rise to the Wolds which rise to nearly 500 ft. above sea level near Louth. The Lower Chalk is about 80 ft. thick fairly equally divided by 3 or 4 ft. of Totternhoe Stone into Grey Chalk below, with *Inoceramus* Beds near and a Sponge Bed at the base, and pink and grey chalk up to the Plenus Marl (1 to 3 ft. thick).

There is no Melbourn Rock as such above the Plenus Marl though 10 or 12 ft. of grey shelly chalk with *Inoceramus labiatus* may represent it. Then comes about 120 ft. of Chalk in thick beds, with flint nodules, representing the Middle Chalk and characterized by the small flat fine-ribbed brachiopod *Terebratulina lata*.

In the absence of Chalk Rock no sharp division is possible but about 100 ft. of hard White Chalk, with thick tabular masses of grey flint, well exposed in pits about Louth are referable to the zone of *Holaster planus* of the Upper Chalk. Bands with sea urchins and oysters are frequent.

Throughout the region chalk has been quarried for lime burning; some of the rocks have been used in buildings but these are usually faced with flints; until recently gunflints were made at Brandon about five miles N.W. of Thetford.

There is a great interval between the deposition of the Chalk and the next formation in Norfolk, the shelly 'Crag', which occupies much of the eastern half of the country and extends south to the Stour; in fact the earlier portions of the Crag (Coralline and Red Crag) are confined to Suffolk and Essex and of these only the Coralline is now referred to the Pliocene while the rest are included in the Pleistocene.

PLEISTOCENE   The Norwich Crag extends for forty miles north from Aldeburgh in Suffolk for a breadth of twenty miles inland and is comprised of reddish brown sands, gravels and laminated clays in places highly fossiliferous. Where the base rests on Chalk, as is usually the case, the latter is bored by marine worms and the mollusc *Pholas*. A stone bed at the base, about a foot thick, consists of brown-coated flints with bones, not phosphatized, of mastodon, elephant, leopard etc. The famous rostro-carinate flint implements were found in this bed.

Norwich Crag is about 150 ft. thick in the coastal area. A typical section may be seen at Burghkiln, Aylsham (10 miles south of Cromer). Shells are locally abundant and include forms common today such as cockle, mussel, whelk and periwinkle associated with *Astarte borealis* etc. The succeeding Chillesford Beds of fine micaceous sands and clays do not exceed 20 ft. in thickness.

The Weybourne Crag is made up of clay, sand and pebbles; its shells are similar to those of the Norwich Crag in addition to the vast swarms of the small bivalve *Macoma balthica*. This Crag occurs in the cliffs between Weybourne and Mundesley (6 miles E.S.E. of Cromer).

The Cromer Forest Beds usually have at their base a bed of large flints with primitive implements but locally there is 2 to 5 ft. of green carbonaceous clay with peaty layers. The Forest Bed proper, up to 20 ft. thick, is made up of sands, gravels and laminated clays with tree stumps not in the position of growth and so presumably washed into their present sites. Shells include *Macoma balthica* but more important are the remains of elephants, rhinoceros, sabre-toothed tiger, hippopotamus etc. Next comes 5 to 7 ft. of peaty sands and clay with freshwater shells.

The position of the so-called *Leda myalis* Bed of marine chalky sand and loam is in doubt; it is thought by some to succeed the Forest Beds; others believe it to follow the Arctic Bed (see below). It may be added that this half-inch bivalve is now known as *Yoldia myalis*.

The *Leda myalis* Bed is exposed in the cliffs near Sheringham, and Cromer Forest Beds are to be seen at intervals on the coast between Weybourne (about 6 miles west of Cromer) and Kessingland (about 4 miles south of Lowestoft).

DRIFT DEPOSITS   There is usually a sharp line of demarcation between the stratified and igneous formations classed as solid rocks and the poorly consolidated superficial drift deposits ranging from boulder clay and alluviums to blown sand but in East Anglia no such sharp line exists between some of the drift and Crag deposits. The latter indicate a considerable chilling of the climate while the drifts

show alternations between intense cold and milder episodes of the Glacial Period before amelioration to the present-day conditions.

The Geological Survey formerly regarded the Arctic Freshwater Bed—a few feet of impersistent laminated peaty loams—as the earliest Pleistocene (see *ante*); it contains Arctic Willow and Arctic Birch with such freshwater shells as *Succinea putris* and *Valvata piscinalis*. It occurs on the North Norfolk coast but is rarely exposed. Of much wider occurrence are the heterogeneous boulder clays brought by the ice and the sands, gravels, laminated clays and silts formed either directly by the melting of the ice and the release of incorporated material in ponded water or by the washing up and sorting by melt water of previously deposited boulder clay materials.

In East Anglia four glaciations are recognized as follows:

North Sea Drift—Consisting of two tough grey sandy boulder clays, with erratics from Scotland and Scandinavia along with Jurassic and Eocene material, separated by greyish silty sands (Mundesley Sands and 45 ft. thick at Mundesley) and followed by the Laminated Clays—grey, occasionally chalky, up to 20 ft. thick.

Great Eastern Drift—This rests on eroded and contorted North Sea Drift and consists chiefly of the Chalky Boulder Clay succeeded by sands and gravels. Shallow valleys in these are partly occupied by the interglacial Bacton Valley Gravel.

Little Eastern Drift—The deposits of this third glacial episode are restricted in occurrence. Near Cromer they consist of Sandy Brickearth occupying hollows near the top of the cliffs and the Cromer Ridge Gravels or Moraine with much angular grey flint.

Hunstanton Boulder Clay—The erratics of this red-brown boulder clay, which is confined to lower ground, include many Cheviot rocks but no chalk.

The deposits of the above glaciations are exposed in the Norfolk cliffs between Hunstanton and Happisburgh with particularly good sections west of the chalk at Trimingham.

Much of the Chalk country east of a line through Thetford, Swaffham and Docking is concealed by boulder clay which may reach 150 ft. in thickness whereas on the Crag deposits in East Norfolk there is less boulder clay but much sand and gravel and brickearth. East and west of the Chalk Wolds of Lincolnshire there is much boulder clay referable chiefly to North Sea Drift and Chalky Boulder Clay.

RECENT DEPOSITS The widespread flats of the Fens, made up of silts, clays and peats, are bordered in many places by considerable expanses of gravels as, for example, south of Horncastle, west of Donington and around Peterborough, and again, though narrower, near King's Lynn and Downham Market. These Fen deposits are obviously filling in what was originally a great extension of the Wash. The clays and silts show by their diatom and foraminiferal content that there is a transition from nearly marine to almost freshwater conditions. The so-called *Scrobicula* Clay is of interest in that *Scrobicula*, the shells of which are locally

abundant, flourishes only below mid-tide level. The Shell Marl on the other hand is made up of fresh water shells and the remains of the plant *Chara* and accumulated in the clear freshwater of meres some of which survived into historic times. Peat formation dates back to Neolithic times though interrupted more than once by incursions of the sea. Wastage of the surface peat through drainage and cultivation measured nearly 11 ft. in Denton Fen in Huntingdonshire between 1860 and 1932. Over much of the Fen area peat is not more than 3 ft. thick today. Buried forests have been found beneath the peat in several places particularly near the Isle of Ely.

There is a continuation northwards of the fenlands along the Lincolnshire coast to a breadth of about four or five miles usually behind dunes of blown sand.

On the opposite side of the Wash there are dunes along the North Norfolk coast. These follow spits of shingle, caused by westerly currents, that extend from Weybourne to Hunstanton. Behind these spits there is a mile or so of salt marsh of marine alluvium. Farther east the low cliffs are subject to considerable erosion but on the eastern coast the drift of shingle assisted by blown sand has blocked and deflected the rivers and given rise to the marshes and Broads.

REFERENCES

Geological Survey
  Regional Handbooks: East Anglia, ed 3, 1954; *East Yorkshire and Lincolnshire*, 1948.
Excursions and Field Meetings
  International Geological Congress 1948.
  Long Excursion: A17, East Anglia.
Geologists Association, Proceedings or Circulars
  1923, Cromer and Norwich. 1935, Hunstanton (Scolt Head). 1950, Lowestoft. 1952, Norfolk. 1958, East Anglia. 1959, Norfolk.

SHEET 10

LEICESTER—PETERBOROUGH

LEICESTER–PETERBOROUGH

THE sheet includes the Wash and Cambridge on the east and Matlock and Warwick on the west. Since all of these places are included in the overlapping Sheets (6, 9, 11, 13) this account will deal mainly with the central portion occupied by Jurassic strata. To the west rising through the Keuper Marl are the ancient rocks of Charnwood Forest and Nuneaton (page 140 and page 141), the Carboniferous Limestone of Matlock with the associated igneous rocks (page 165), the Leicester–Derby and Warwickshire Coalfields (page 145) and part of that of York–Notts–Derby (pages 165–8). These support a large population dependent on the mining and quarrying of coal, brick and refractory clays and of road metal. Leicester and Nottingham on the fringes of the coalfields are, on the other hand, like Coventry and Derby, engaged chiefly on engineering and textiles. Peterborough with its huge brickpits in the Oxford Clay marks the eastern limit of industrial development while the median tract is mainly concerned with the Jurassic iron ores in so far as relates to direct geological products though essentially still a farming country. The clay country up to the Norfolk border based on the Oxford, Ampthill (Corallian) and Kimmeridge clays is largely masked by the Fens. Cretaceous strata form the eastern fringe.

Drainage is mainly to the North Sea either by the Trent following the north-western tract of Keuper Marl and Lias or by the Welland, Nene and Ouse to the Wash, the two systems being parted by the mid Jurassic outcrops. A small amount of the rainfall, however, escapes via the Avon to the Bristol Channel.

Most of the country is of low elevation—much of the clay land below 250 ft.; from this the mid Jurassic outcrop rises as a dissected plateau to a little over 500 ft.

TRIAS   Around Leicester the Trias is largely represented by its uppermost member the Keuper Marl as, for example, in Charnwood Forest where this formation envelopes the pre-Cambrian. To the north, however, the overstep is less marked and about Nottingham both Bunter and Keuper sandstones are well developed between the Marl and the Magnesian (Permian) Limstone that there succeeds the Coal Measures though absent farther south. About Newark and in the Chellaston–Tutbury area south of Derby gypsum is present in workable quantity in the Keuper Marl; the latter furnishes brick clays in several localities.

JURASSIC   The lowest group of strata, the Lias, follows the usual tripartite division the thickest member being the Lower Lias (about 500 ft.) made up of grey clays and thin argillaceous limestones such as are worked for cement about Southam and Rugby. The Middle Lias (70-150 ft.) is of pale clays in the lower part but the

131

most important member is the Marlstone Rock bed at the summit. This, from its harder nature, usually caps an escarpment. From a ferruginous sandy limestone it passes in the upper part into an ironstone of workable quality and thickness that is best developed in the area between Grantham and Melton Mowbray though there are workable patches to the north, as at Leadenham, and to the south about Tilton (east of Leicester); it usually carries about 25 per cent iron and is commonly 7 or 8 ft. thick. The darker, Upper Lias clays, up to about 200 ft. thick call for little comment.

That portion of the middle Jurassic represented by the oolitic limestones of the Inferior and Great Oolites of the Cotswolds constitute the most important portion of the sequence owing to the development of iron ore at the base. In passing north-eastwards from the Cotswold country the oolitic limestones of the Inferior Oolite disappear and those of the Great Oolite are of sadly diminished thickness. In the southern part of the Leicester–Peterborough region the Inferior Oolite is represented by calcareous and fissile sandstones, collectively known as the Northampton Sands and up to 60 ft. in thickness, followed by the clays and fine sands of the Estuarine Series. In the Northampton area the ironstone reaches workable thickness and quality and continues so northwards to beyond Grantham. A usual thickness is 8–12 ft. with an iron content of 30–35 per cent and a silica tolerance of about 15 per cent. About the latitude of Market Harborough the Lincolnshire Limestone makes its appearance in the Estuarine Series and increases in thickness northwards to about 120 ft. providing the well known building stones of Ancaster, Grantham and Ketton as well as lime, ironstone flux and cement (Ketton). The basal portion about Stamford is fissile and furnishes the Collyweston Slates. The Upper Lincolnshire Limestone is markedly unconformable to the Lower Limestone and in places transgresses on to and even cuts down into the ironstone. Apart from some loss of ironstone the close juxtaposition of limestone and ore renders mechanical shovelling difficult.

The Upper Estuarine Series, with clays of various colours from black to green and lavender and some development of limestone, aggregating 15 to 45 ft., form the lowest part of the Great Oolite Series. They are succeeded by up to 25 ft. of limestone varying from oolitic to massive and compact referred to as the Great Oolite and that by the inky blue or black Great Oolite Clay which may represent the Forest Marble of North Oxfordshire.

All these beds may be seen in the large ironstone quarries about Wellingborough and Corby.

The Cornbrash is a thin oolite that readily breaks down into a reddish stony loam.

The Oxford Clay with a few feet of brownish Kellaways sand at the base is a dark to light grey clay shale or mudstone, up to 400 ft. thick. Its importance for brick-making depends on the facts that its moisture content is fairly constant at all seasons, that it can be broken down into 'rice' grains which can be dry-moulded by pressure and it contains enough carbonaceous material to greatly minimise fuel for firing.

The Corallian limestones of the south-west are here represented by the nearly

black Ampthill Clay that varies from about 80 ft. thick in north-west Norfolk to about 200 ft. north of the Wash. The succeeding Kimmeridge Clay may reach nearly 500 ft. in thickness. Formerly it was in considerable demand at small brickyards; one is still at work at Stickney (about 6 miles north of Boston). There is some development of poor quality oil shale near the middle of the Kimmeridge Clay.

There are no Portlandian or Purbeck strata in the area and in west Norfolk the Lower Cretaceous Sandringham Sands repose on an eroded surface of Kimmeridge Clay. These light silvery sands, about 100 ft. thick, are followed by various beds up to the Chalk (see pages 124–5).

REFERENCES

Geological Survey
  Regional Handbooks: Central England, ed 2, 1947; *East Yorkshire and Lincolnshire*, 1948.
  Mesozoic Ironstones: Northampton Sand Ironstone, 1951; Liassic Ironstone, 1952.
  Charnwood Forest, Geology of the Ancient Rocks of, Watts, W. W., 1947, Leicester.
Excursions and Field Meetings
  International Geological Congress 1948.
  Long Excursions: C4 East Midlands. A1 Economic. C1 England and Wales.
Geologists Association, Proceedings or Circulars
  1928 and 1937, Charnwood. 1937, Kettering. 1939, Grantham; Stamford. 1946, Kettering. 1950, Charnwood; North Staffs. 1954, Rugby. 1955, Kettering. 1961, Charnwood; Nuneaton.

SHEET 11

NORTH MIDLANDS

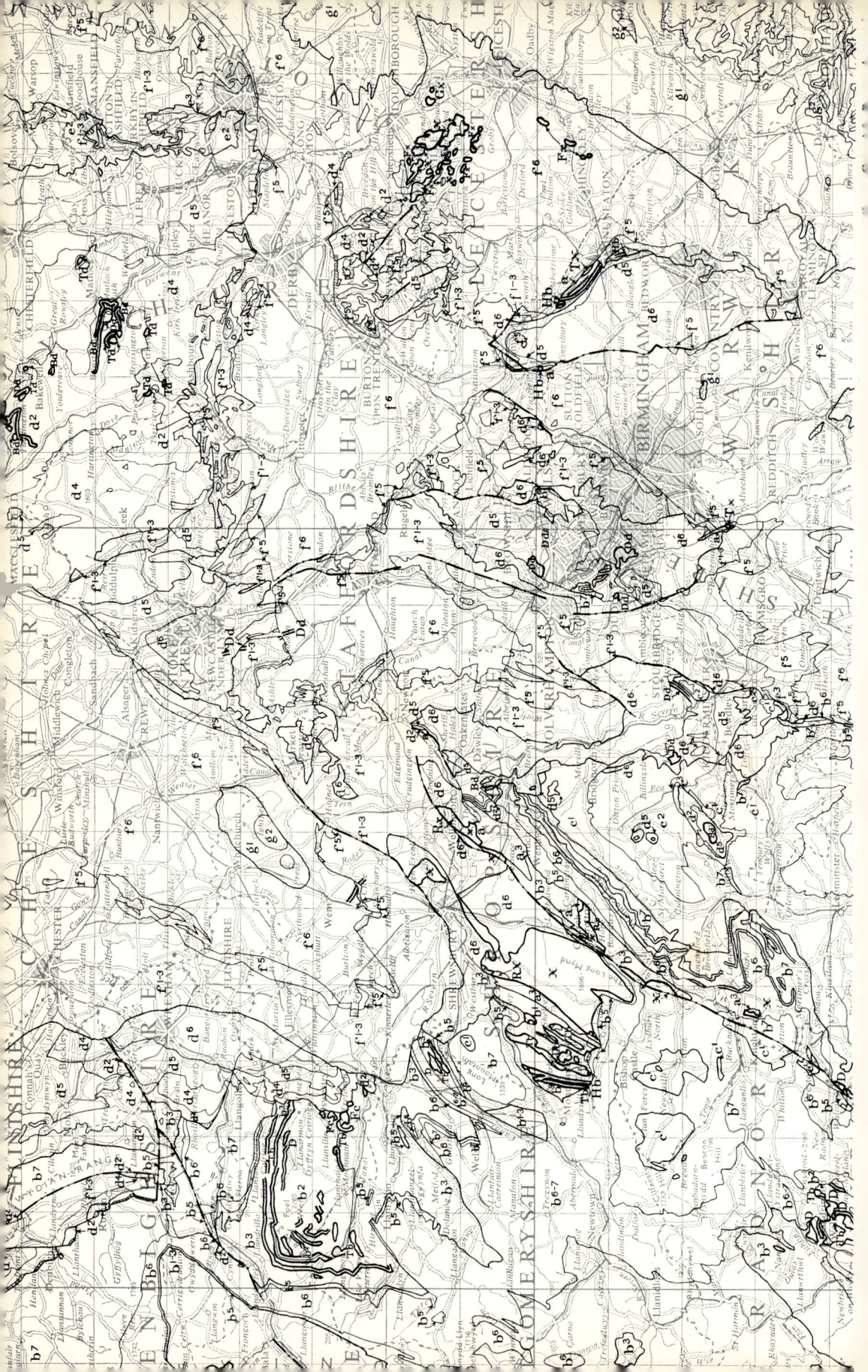

NORTH MIDLANDS

THIS district ranges from a line through Rugby, Kidderminster and Clun Forest on the south to one through Rhyl and Wilmslow on the north while on the east Rugby, Nottingham and Mansfield are marginal. The district therefore embraces the high thinly populated country immediately west of the North Wales Coalfield and that bordering the south-west Midlands beyond Shrewsbury, the highly industrialized Midlands based on Birmingham, the Black Country and the Potteries, the limestone country of Derbyshire and the southern end of the great York–Notts–Derby Coalfield. Its rocks include every formation from pre-Cambrian to Lias though its prosperity is largely determined by coal. The main watershed of England crosses the area obliquely for on the south and south-west drainage is by the Severn, much of that on the east goes to the North Sea via the Trent while that of the north-west feeds the Dee and Mersey.

The counties involved are Staffordshire, Shropshire, Flintshire, with much of Derbyshire, Cheshire and Denbighshire, parts of Merionethshire and Montgomeryshire and North Warwickshire and the western part of Leicestershire. An account of the eastern tract is given with that of the York–Notts–Derby Coalfield (pages 165–8) and of the western overlap with North Wales (pages 155–61) but sufficient is included here to round off the story. The general structure of these tracts is shown in Fig. 37.

PRE-CARBONIFEROUS ROCKS These rocks crop out in force only in the western part of the area where they are continuous from north-east Wales to Shropshire but they evidently make the foundation on which Carboniferous and newer strata are laid for they reappear at surface in South Staffordshire, in Warwickshire and in Charnwood Forest, Leicestershire. Since these rocks of various ages are intimately associated description will be by locality rather than age, beginning in Shropshire.

In Shropshire there are several types of pre-Cambrian rock at various localities but their age relationships are seldom clear. Near the village of Rushton in the Wrekin area quartz-mica schists presumably overlain by Cambrian quartzite bear some resemblance to Anglesey rocks but may be younger. The next group, the Uriconian rocks, adjoin the Rushton Schists but have a much wider distribution both east and west of the Longmynd. They are mainly rhyolites, often streaky banded, but occasionally spherulitic (with pea-like bodies showing radial structure) associated with tuffs and intruded by pale felsites and granophyres and dark dolerites. The rocks are well exposed in the Wrekin with dolerites about Forest Glen and granophyre on the Ercall; to the south-east they are overlain by Cambrian Quartzite. There are other exposures in the hills about two miles N.W. of the Wrekin—at Wrockwardine spherulitic rhyolites and at Charlton Hill conglomerates.

To the south-west Uriconian rocks occur on the Lawley, on Caer Caradoc and on Ragleth and other hills. Somewhat similar types, but invaded by olivine dolerite, occur as a lens between Cambrian and Ordovician strata on Pontesford and Earl hills north of Habberly.

The most important group are the sedimentary Longmyndian rocks which form the core of that upland. Flags and dark shales dip westward in Cardingmill Valley and Lightspout Hollow near Church Stretton and are followed on the crest by grits and conglomerates with pebbles resembling Uriconian.

Cambrian rocks occur both east and west of the Longmynd (see Fig. 36). The white basal quartzite of the Wrekin, 150 ft. thick, rests on and includes pebbles of the Uriconian; it is succeeded by greenish sandstones and about 6 ft. of sandy limestones, which have yielded *Olenellus* a trilobite indicative of Lower Cambrian. The Middle Cambrian with *Paradoxides* is of shales and grits with conglomeratic layers; these are well seen in the Comley area north of Church Stretton.

The succeeding dark shale group, rich in Upper Cambrian trilobites is exposed in Shineton Brook and Cherme's Dingle (south of the Wrekin).

The Ordovician is fully developed in the Shelve-Chirbury area west of the Longmynd, where it commences with the quartzite of the Stiperstones ridge followed by flags that are brought to the surface again west of Shelve Pool by a low anticline. These Arenig flags which form the main mining ground of lead, zinc and barytes, are followed by shales, with occasional sandstones and several volcanic phases, that carry trilobites and graptolites indicative of the rest of the Ordovician (Llanvirn, Llandeilo and Caradoc) subdivisions. These rocks are invaded by dolerites as for example, at Corndon and Squilver hills. In the Breidden Hills similar Caradoc strata, with intrusions of dolerite and diorite are exposed.

East of the Longmynd between Cressage and Craven Arms the Ordovician begins at a higher level than to the west with the Hoar Edge Grit; this lies at the base of the Caradoc, and is followed by shales and flags. No Ordovician strata are known in England east of this area.

The Silurian of Shropshire is of interest in that it lies on the border between the two main types of Silurian strata; to the east shallow-water conditions prevailed with shelly rocks; to the west deeper water was present, shales predominate and the characteristic fossils are graptolites of *Monograptus* type.

In Shropshire the Silurian begins with the unconformable Upper Llandovery Sandstone indicating that land was in existence during Lower Llandovery times. Next come purple and green mudstones representing the Tarannon Shales of Wales. Both are present from the Wrekin to south of the Longmynd, and round by Chirbury and the Breiddens. The shell *Pentamerus oblongus*, which when broken across shows up as a broad arrow, is the characteristic fossil.

The succeeding Wenlock Series has no basal Woolhope Limestone hereabouts but the Shales capped by Wenlock Limestone are well displayed about Wenlock Edge where corals and shells are numerous.

About 800 ft. of Lower Ludlow Shales are followed by the massive blue Aymestry Limestone which, near Craven Arms and again at Shelderton Rock between

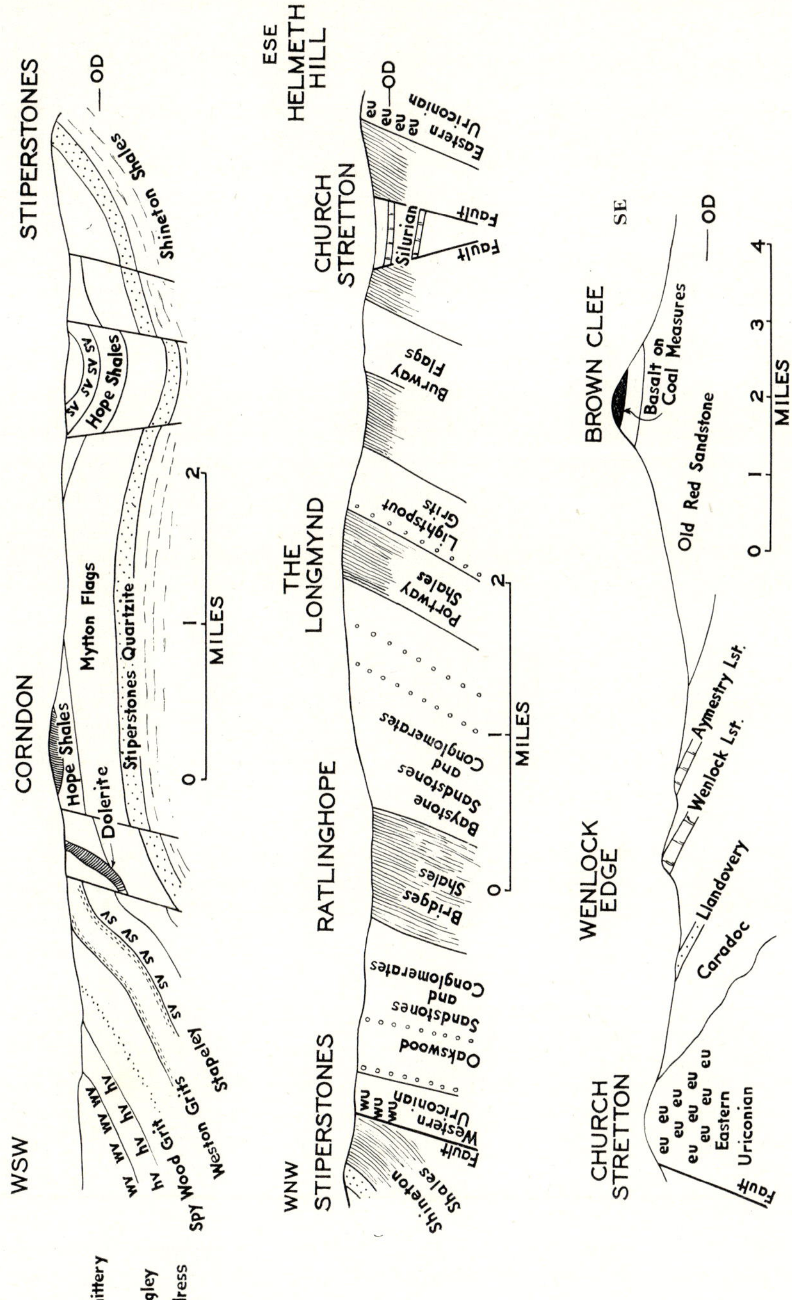

Figure 36. Sections to illustrate structure and sequence in the Church Stretton area (Based on Figs. 10, 21 and 25 of *The Welsh Borderland* Geol. Surv. Handbook)

Onibury and Leintwardine, carries the characteristic shell *Conchidium* (*Pentamerus*) *knighti*.

The Upper Ludlow Shales are flaggy in part but are rich in shells. At the top is the Ludlow Bone Bed with fish remains which is a convenient horizon to adopt as the base of the Old Red Sandstone.

On the above basis the 40-ft. yellow Downton Castle Sandstone and the 110 ft. of greenish Temeside Shales followed by 1,000 ft. of red and purple shales with thin sandstones of the Red Downtonian constitute the lower half of the Lower Old Red Sandstone (C_1). Fish remains occur here ('*psammosteus*', etc.) and in 1,000 ft. of higher similar beds classed as Dittonian with (*Pteraspis*) which are capped by the more massive sandstones (Brownstones) and grouped on the map as C_2. The Upper Red Sandstone, with *Holoptychius*, is represented by the unconformable 500-ft. yellow Farlow Sandstone surrounding Clee Hill (Fig. 36).

North-east Wales (see also page 158)—There is a considerable outcrop of Ordovician rocks in the Berwyns (between Lake Vyrnwy and Oswestry) where Llandeilo and Caradoc strata rise as a dome amidst Silurian rocks. Dark, cleaved mudstones are interspersed with bands of volcanic ash and some limestones.

In the succeeding Silurian rocks the Llandovery is mainly of blue silty mudstones and pale grey and purple shales followed by the mudstones and shales of the Wenlock and Ludlow; the subdivisions are only to be distinguished by graptolites.

South Staffordshire—Volcanic ashes of Uriconian type form a small inlier at Barnt Green where they are faulted against Lickey (Cambrian) Quartzite. The outcrop of the latter extends to Rubery where Upper Llandovery Sandstone, with large well rounded grains, fills hollows in it. Wenlock mudstones occur near the Birmingham Fault. Farther north several Silurian inliers emerge in the Coalfield. In the large Walsall mass Llandovery Sandstone occurs at Great Barr where it is followed by the 30-ft. Barr Limestone (equivalent to the Woolhope Limestone elsewhere) and that by Wenlock Shales. The latter occur, too, in the other inliers followed by Wenlock Limestone made up of 30–40 ft. of Lower Limestone, 90–120 ft. of Nodular Beds and 12 to 33 ft. of Upper Limestone. The limestone was worked extensively at surface and underground and pits are still accessible at Wrens Nest—a very famous fossil locality especially for the Dudley Locust *Calymene blumenbachi*. This fossil appears in the Dudley coat of arms. Lower Ludlow Shales followed by a limestone crop out round Sedgley and with Upper Ludlow calcareous flags in some of the other inliers.

These occurrences mark the most easterly outcrop of Silurian rocks.

Warwickshire—In Warwickshire Uriconian rocks crop out between Nuneaton and Hartshill (Fig. 40). They comprise fine banded and coarse tuffs intruded by dolerite (Blue Hole) and markfieldite (near Windmill). The succeeding Hartshill Quartzite (900 ft.), which at its base includes lumps of Uriconian rocks, is extensively quarried. Near its summit it has a thin band of *Hyolithus* Limestone at Woodlands Quarry, Hartshill, where the succeeding red Purley Shales have yielded *Callavia* a Lower Cambrian trilobite. Dark shales of the next group,

Oldbury Shales, furnish *Paradoxides* and *Olenus* and the greenish grey Merevale Shales *Dictyonema* and *Schumardia* thus proving a full Cambrian sequence in the shales which are collectively known as Stockingford Shales and are about 3,000 ft. thick. On the west side of the Coalfield Oldbury Shales emerge at Dost Hill near Wilnecote. Both shales and quartzite are invaded by numerous sills of diorite.

Charnwood—Stockingford Shales are known from borings through the Trias between the Warwickshire and Leicester coalfields and from a colliery heading (at Desford) but are absent in Charnwood Forest. There a great but unknown thickness of pre-Cambrian rocks is largely of volcanic material—lavas and tuffs and agglomerates or as ashes laid down in water. These are intruded by a type of syenite known as markfieldite, quarried at Markfield, Groby and Bradgate, and some pecular rocks carrying large crystals loosely called porphyroids which crop out at High Tor, Peldar Tor and High Sharpley all in the north-west part of the Forest. The markfieldite is similar to that of Nuneaton where the age is precisely settled as pre-Cambrian.

The stratified sequence is given below. The rocks are arranged as a dome elongated north-west—south-east though complicated by faulting, deeply eroded and often obscured by red Triassic material which fills in hollows of an ancient landscape.

CHARNIAN SEQUENCE

C Brand Series	3. Swithland and Groby Slates: purple slates
	2. Trachose Grit and Quartzites: dark feldspathic grit and quartzite
	1. Hanging Rocks Conglomerate
B Maplewell Series	4. Woodhouse and Bradgate Beds: ashes with halleflintas (hard fine-grained splintery rocks)
	3. Slate Agglomerate
	2. Beacon Hill Hornstones: green halleflintas with coarse ashes
	1. Felsitic Agglomerates
A Blackbrook Series	Silicified ashes and tuffs

A large outcrop of reddish and grey granite (Mount Sorrel Granite) emerges from the Trias off the north-eastern edge of the Forest; its true age is unknown but it is included with the Charnian for convenience.

CARBONIFEROUS The rocks of this system arrange themselves into Carboniferous Limestone, Millstone Grit and Coal Measures. In one form or another they almost encircle the district from north-east Wales via the Midland coalfields and the Derbyshire massif to the Lancashire Coalfield. It is pretty certain that these form part of one great depositional tract though they show considerable variations in detail. Most of the interior area is now occupied by Trias. Before the Trias was deposited the region was subject to folding, faulting and uplift followed by erosion which removed much material from the upfolds; so it is, therefore, a matter

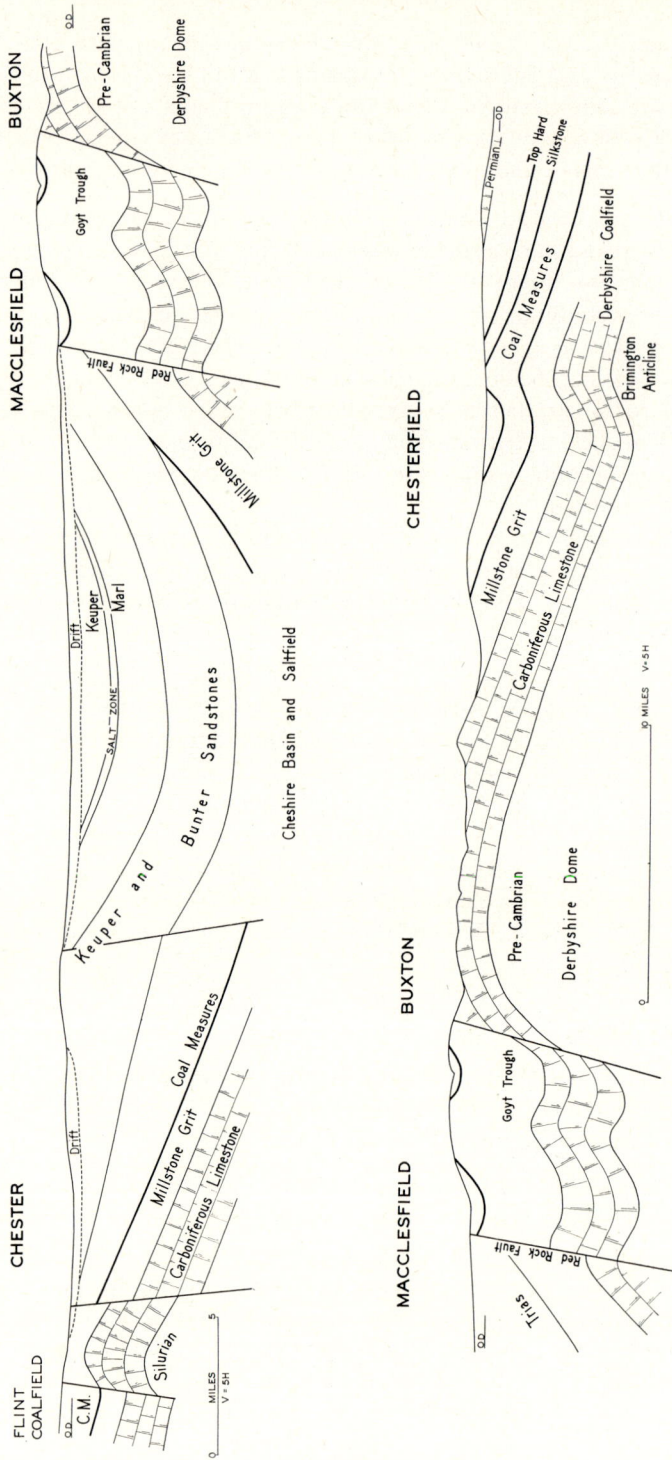

Figure 37. Generalized section from North Wales to Chesterfield

142

of speculation how much of and where Carboniferous rocks remain beneath Trias and the thickness of that red cover will determine whether it is economic to work such coals as may be preserved. In Cheshire the Trias is particularly thick (see Fig. 37) and though it appears likely that Coal Measures from North Wales, Lancashire and Staffordshire will continue beneath most of the Cheshire area the thickness of Trias there added to that of the barren Upper Coal Measures will probably place much coal out of reach. This loss, however, is compensated by the thick beds of salt in the Keuper Marl which extend over much of the area between Knutsford and Wem.

Millstone Grit and Carboniferous Limestone are of far less economic value than Coal Measures but their distribution and variations are of considerable interest. The main outcrops of both lie on the flanks in North Wales and Derbyshire. Both are known from mining and other information to thin and to finally disappear southwards so that Coal Measures eventually rest on older rocks—Cambrian in Warwickshire, for example, and Silurian in South Staffordshire. Patches of both appear at surface north of Ashby-de-la-Zouch and of Carboniferous Limestone between Kidderminster and Shrewsbury. They have also been found in a boring near Lichfield which is fairly close to their local southern limit where oddly enough they succeed Upper Old Red Sandstone at its fartherest north extension yet known in the Midlands.

In North Wales the bulk of the Carboniferous Limestone belongs to the uppermost zone, D, characterized by *Dibunophyllum*; at the base there is a conglomerate resting on Silurian strata; massive pure limestones predominate but these give place to dolomites about Oswestry and Llanymynech.

In Derbyshire the limestone occupies the crest of a dome and the base is not exposed (Fig. 37). Most of the visible strata is pale massive limestone referable to D zone; associated igneous rocks known as toadstones include basaltic lavas intrusive dolerites and agglomerates.

The outcrops north of Ashby, in addition to D may include zones as low as C; the limestones there are often dolomitized.

In the western tract the remnant at Titterstone Clee includes zones K and Z which succeed Farlow Sandstone conformably; these are followed by 1,000 ft. of sandstone resembling Old Red Sandstone and that by Coal Measures, yet a few miles to the north, in Coalbrookdale, limestone of D age rests on Cambrian.

Millstone Grit is equally variable. That on the east belongs to the main Pennine sequence of Lancashire and Yorkshire characterized by thick though often lenticular grits separated by shale belts in which certain bands carry goniatites used in zoning the formation; these are designated by the initial letter of the respective genera (see page 32). In North Wales the same zones are present but the strata in the north are mainly shales (Holywell Shales, 400–600 ft. thick) followed by 300 ft. of fine-grained (Gwespyr) sandstone whereas in the south sandstones and grits predominate; these are known as the Cefn-y-fedw Sandstone and range from 600 ft. thick about Ruabon to less than 300 ft. near Oswestry. Farther south in Shrewsbury coalfields Limestone, Millstone Grit and lower Coal Measures are absent.

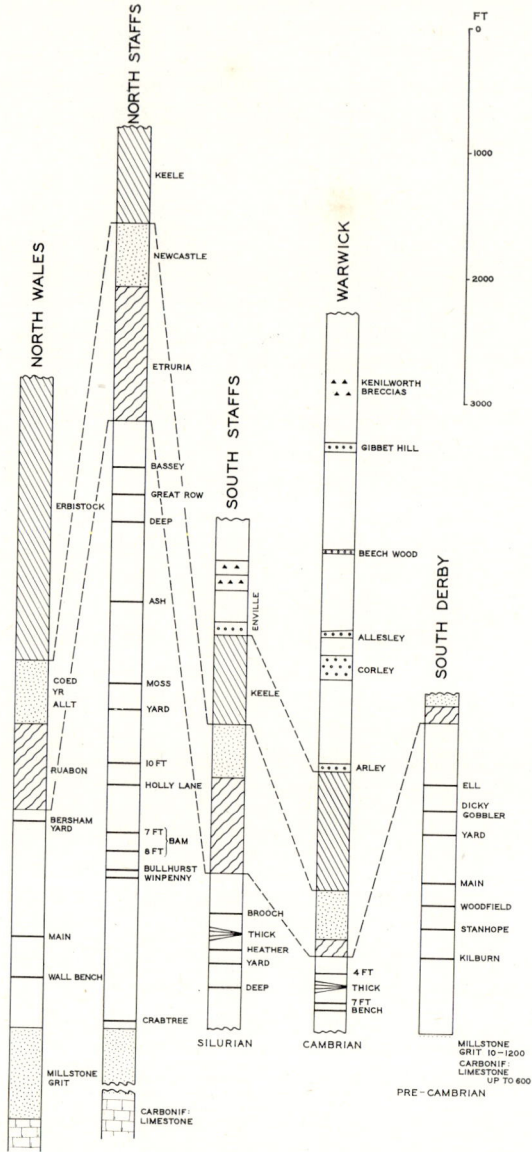

Figure 38. Vertical sections of the North Wales and Midland Coalfields
Note the development of conglomerates and breccias to the south indicating proximity
of land (St. George's Land) in that direction.

144

The Midland Coalfields have much in common for they show similar sequences of rocks (Fig. 38) and it is obvious that though now separate they were originally one. All have grey Productive Measures, in which shales and clays predominate over sandstones and contain the principal coal seams. In most fields Productive Measures are succeeded by Upper Coal Measures. These begin with multi-coloured clays and marls with rough sandstones or breccias (espley rocks) grouped under various names but mainly known as Etruria Marls (from Etruria in North Staffordshire) and of great importance for brick and tile making. Then there is a recurrence of grey measures, the sandstones and clays again with various names but here termed Halesowen Group (from Halesowen in South Staffordshire) followed, except in the east, by a thick series of red beds. The lowest 1,000 ft. or so of these are grouped as Keele Beds (from Keele in North Staffordshire). They are followed in the southern fields by similar red sandstones and shales but with the addition of conglomerates and breccias—the Enville or Corley Group named from Enville and Corley in South Staffordshire and Warwickshire respectively.

The lowest conglomerate contains many pebbles of Carboniferous Limestone; the higher conglomerates and breccias are richer in pebbles from older rocks mainly Silurian and igneous; breccias are better developed in the west (Clent Hills in South Staffordshire, for example) than in the Coventry–Kenilworth area. These facts indicate that somewhere to the south of the present fields there was high ground to provide the pebbly material some of which remained as angular scree stuff whereas some was rolled about in water until it furnished pebbles for the conglomerates. This high ground formed the limit of the coal swamp and therefore of the coalfields in that direction. The only direct evidence is that in South Staffordshire the Thick Coal splits and deteriorates south of Halesowen and that near Rubery a few miles farther south Halesowen Beds overstep on to the old rocks but it is believed that the barrier stretched right across the southern Midlands though perhaps breached at intervals by water channels. That some islands existed during coal times is evidenced by the banks of Silurian strata against which coal strata end in South Staffordshire and the breccias made of Cambrian shale in the Etruria Marls near Dosthill in north Warwickshire.

In the North Staffordshire area there are three separate coalfields, viz. the main or Potteries field with to the east the small ones of Shaffalong and Cheadle. To the north they are structurally connected via the East Cheshire coalfield with that of Lancashire.

The Pottery Coalfield is triangular in shape due to the fact that it is a syncline pitching south flanked by anticlines. The latter are so steep in places that the coals are almost vertical. The western anticline is faulted and this is partly responsible for the presence of Trias on that side. The eastern anticline brings up Millstone Grit to the surface but corresponding downfolds are responsible for the preservation of the Shaffalong and Cheadle coalfields. The main syncline is crossed by several faults of which the most important is the almost median north-south Apedale Fault (see Fig. 39).

The coals in the middle part of the Productive Measures are of better quality than those above and below but upwards the deterioration is compensated to some

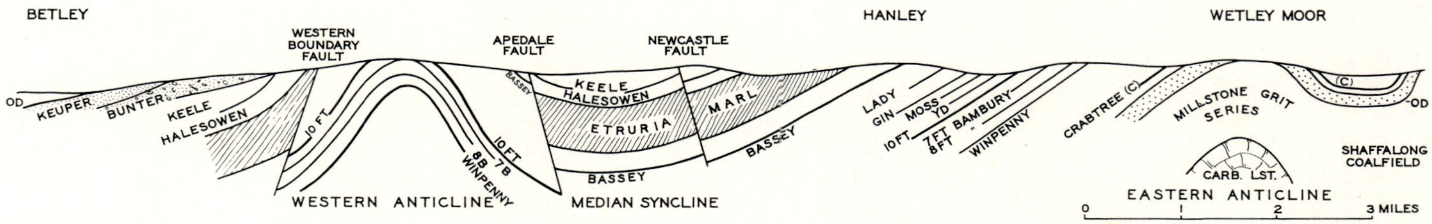

Figure 39. Section across the North Staffordshire Coalfields
(Based on the One-inch Geological Sheet 123)

extent by the development of a series of bedded carbonate ironstones (Black Band Series) extensively worked at one time and by grey clays used for the making of seggars (troughs in which pottery ware is fired), bricks and pipes.

Separating the Potteries Coalfield from that of North Wales is the Cheshire Basin with a great thickness of Trias rich in salt. Since the measures of the flanking coalfields dip inwards to this basin it is probable that they continue beneath the Trias but at considerable depth and too deep for coal working.

The North Wales Coalfield extends from the Point of Ayr along and under the Dee, whence it emerges in the little field at Neston in the Wirral, to a few miles south of Oswestry. In general the dip (see Fig. 41) is easterly and north-easterly off the Clwydian Hills—west of which there may be a downfaulted coal area in the Vale of Clwyd—but folds and faults cause some complication. The most important is the Bala Fault which south-west of Chester causes a block of Millstone Grit and Carboniferous Limestone to be brought against Productive and Upper Coal Measures. The others are of a roughly north–south and east–west pattern.

The Productive Measures are generally about 2,000 ft. thick but are thinner and have fewer coals in the south than in Flintshire where also there is a development of siliceous clays and purplish marls constituting the famous Buckley Fireclays in the top 100 ft. of Productive Measures.

The Etruria Marls are exposed in numerous brick pits between Wrexham and Ruabon; eastwards Halesowen and Keele Beds come on.

The southern end of the field is terminated by the uprise of Millstone Grit and the Carboniferous Limestone of Llanymynech but about 10 miles farther south Coal Measures come in again in the Shrewsbury Coalfield.

The Shrewsbury Coalfield and that of Lebotwood towards Church Stretton are of little economic value for the coals are few thin and impersistent. Their interest lies in the fact that they occur in the Upper Coal Measures which here rest directly on pre-Devonian rocks. To the east normal measures reappear in the Coalbrookdale Coalfield which is continued southwards by a narrow outcrop near Bridgnorth to the Forest of Wyre Coalfield.

In the Coalbrookdale Coalfield the grey Productive Measures with several 'sweet' coals were folded and denuded before Upper Coal Measures, which are here again coalbearing, were deposited; the resultant unconformable junction is known as the Symon Fault. South of Broseley the Upper Coal Measures rest directly on Silurian rocks.

In the Forest of Wyre there are again two series of coals; the lower are 'sweet' and the upper are sulphurous. The former are Middle Coal Measures which are the normal grey Productive Measures but here these include some red marls and espley rocks indicating that Upper Coal Measures types of sedimentation commenced earlier in the west than in the Midlands generally.

Farther west small outlying remnant coalfields cap Titterstone Clee and Brown Clee hills beneath a cover of dolerite (Fig. 36).

An area of Trias separates the Coalbrookdale and Wyre Forest coalfields from the more important field of South Staffordshire beneath which coal has so far only been found on the margins.

The South Staffs–Cannock Chase Coalfield extends from Rugely to Halesowen (see page 145); it is concealed on the north by the Triassic rocks of Cannock Chase; elsewhere, but particularly along the margins, Productive Measures pass under Upper Coal Measures, brought on either normally or by large downcast faults referred to as the Boundary Faults though coal is now worked beyond them and has been proved by boring to extend considerable distances. In several places the old Palaeozoic floor is brought to the surface by upfolds as, for example, in the Sedgley–Dudley area where, aligned with the north-west—south-east folding there is the basaltic intrusion of Rowley Regis, and also the larger Silurian outcrop near Walsall. Some portions of the 'floor' actually stood up as islands during coal formation and coal seams now end against them; there are several of these obstacles to mining in the West Bromwich area; they are often referred to as 'Silurian Banks'.

In the north there are about fourteen workable coals; southwards some of these about the middle of the sequence unite to form the famous 10 Yd. or Thick Coal. In the exposed field most of the coals are exhausted. In addition to coal the Productive Measures also contain valuable fireclays particularly in the Stourbridge area; the lower measures at one time furnished large supplies of clay ironstone on which the Black Country industries were founded; ironstone is now imported from the Jurassic ironfields.

The Warwickshire Coalfield is a relatively simple structure of a syncline pitching south with a subsidiary median anticline near Arley. The floor of Cambrian rocks emerges on the steeply dipping flanks between Atherstone and Bedworth and at Dosthill south of Tamworth. Most of the coal is now got beneath the Upper Coal Measures which the pitching dip causes to thicken southwards to over 3,000 ft. at Kenilworth (Fig. 40). On the west a great downthrow Boundary Fault introduces Trias and no coal had been found in that direction until the recent boring near Lichfield. There is also a north-east Boundary Fault but elsewhere Trias oversteps the Coal Measures. Beneath it coal is got at Binley east of Coventry.

There are exposures of Productive Measures, Etruria Marls and Halesowen Beds near Wilnecote and Nuneaton and of the various conglomerates in the red measures at Arley railway station, Corley, Allesley (north and west of Coventry) and at Gibbet Hill and Kenilworth (S.S.W. of Coventry).

The Productive Measures are about 1,000 ft. thick and, as in South Staffordshire, coals separate in the north unite southwards to form the 20-ft. Thick Coal in the south.

The Leicester–South Derby Coalfield is split into two portions by the north-west—south-east Ashby Anticline which brings to the surface the lower and relatively barren portion of the Productive Measures. Parts of both fields are concealed by Trias but particularly that on the east (Leicester Coalfield) which extends as far south as Desford (Fig. 40); this part is faulted against the old rocks of Charnwood Forest. There are differences in detail between the two fields which until recently could not be correlated with accuracy. High in the Productive Measures there is a series of Pottery Clays used in the manufacture of tiles and sanitary ware. Upper Coal Measures to the Halesowen Group are present.

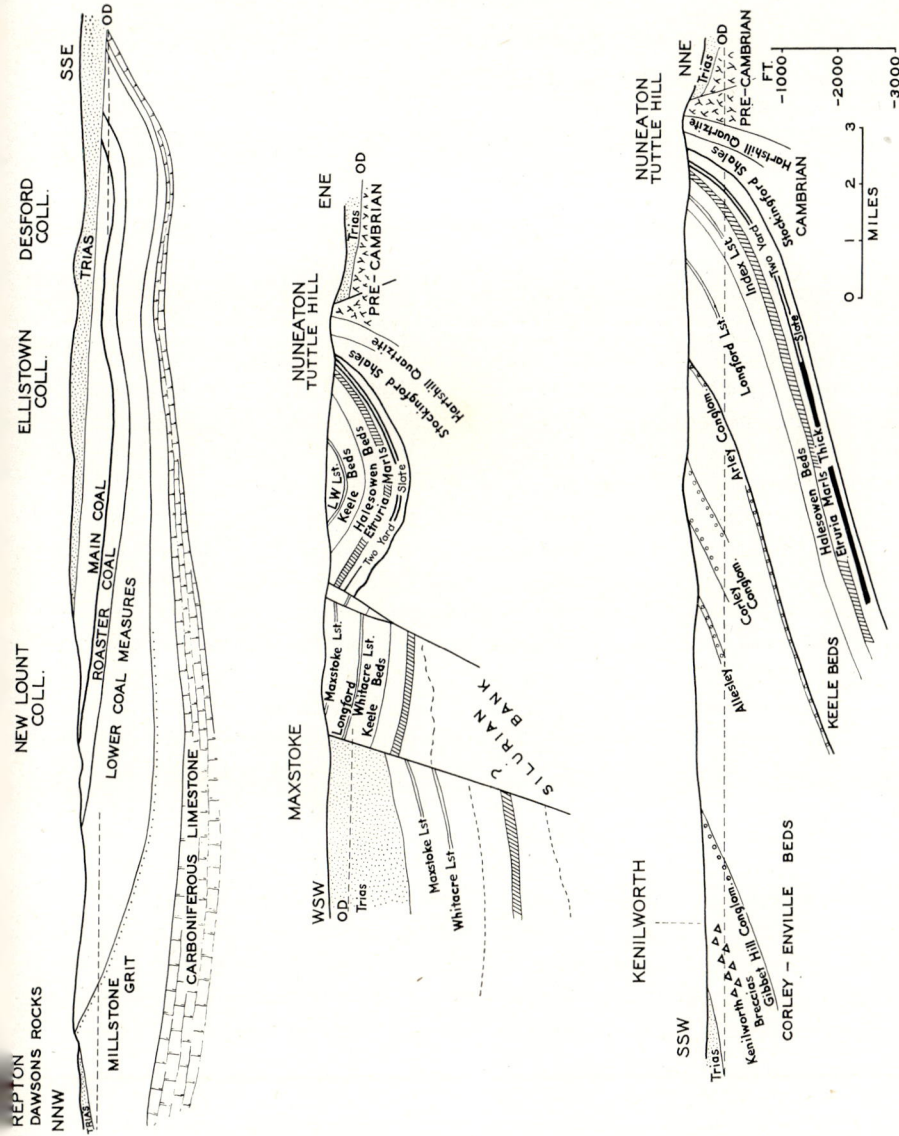

Figure 40. Sections in the Leicester and Warwickshire Coalfields

Note: (i) Thinning of Carboniferous rocks southwards and their crop against the Triassic cover near Desford. (ii) The broken syncline of Coal Measures bounded by faults in Warwickshire with Trias on pre-Cambrian near Nuneaton and on high Upper Coal Measures near Maxstoke. (iii) The syncline pitches southwards bringing on successively higher strata in that direction and also the union of seams to form the Thick Coal.

The Notts–Derby Coalfield is the southern part of the great York–Notts–Derby Coalfield; the exposed portion with a general dip east but with subsidiary upfolds lies north of Nottingham. Near that city the measures dip north-east and the field is brought to an end by the outcrop of lower strata. Similar conditions prevail for some miles east beneath the concealing Permo-Triassic rocks but borings in the Newark area disclose the presence of dome-like echelon folds (the Eakring Oilfield) and further indicate that still farther east beyond the Trent Productive Measures may rise against the New Red cover and thus bring to an end this coalfield.

PERMO-TRIASSIC ROCKS The Permo-Triassic rocks are of particular interest. Of undoubted Permian rocks the only representative is the Magnesian Limestone which is traceable from the Durham coast to Nottingham. It is true that it becomes sandy towards the southern end and has been equated by Sherlock with the Bunter. No Magnesian Limestone is present farther west though some basal breccias there are possibly of that age in the west but ranging up to Keuper in Charnwood. With rocks commonly accepted as Trias there are marked lateral changes from Cheshire to Charnwood. In Cheshire all members are well developed and may aggregate some 7,000 ft. in thickness of which about half is Bunter and most of the remainder Keuper Marl; in Charnwood Keuper Marl only is present and that but a few hundred feet thick. The south-easterly thinning of the subdivision is accompanied by overlap of higher members. Thus west of the South Staffordshire Coalfield the Lower Mottled Sandstone—a red and yellow false-bedded dune formation is present in force. On the eastern margin of that coalfield, at Barr Beacon, a thin breccia with fragments like those at Hopwas farther east has a matrix of sand similar to Lower Mottled Sandstone but no such sandstone is known farther east. The middle Bunter—the Bunter Pebble Beds—is well represented both in North and South Staffordshire as a reddish sandstone of even rounded grains with rounded pebbles of quartzite and quartz dispersed in sandstone or aggregated into shingle beds; it persists to Polesworth in north Warwickshire. The succeeding Upper Mottled Sandstone is usually a bright or a deep red soft sandstone of even smooth grains each with a thin pellicle of clay and iron oxide—characters which render the rock of value as moulding sand. Though 200 ft. thick on the west side of Birmingham it cannot be recognized east of the Birmingham Fault (a downthrow south-east ranging through Sutton Coldfield) and may have been overlapped by Keuper Sandstone. That sandstone is usually harder, more angular and irregular in grain than the Bunter; in colour it varies from red to white or buff and the pale shades are usually finer in grain and higher in the sequence. The base of the Keuper Sandstone may be conglomeratic and unconformable to the beds below but usually there is a passage upwards, by the incoming and thickening of marl bands, into the Keuper Marl.

The Keuper Marl is usually dull red in colour but there are greenish bands some of which are of dolomitic sand (the rock is then known as skerry) and normal quartz-grained sandstones as in the Upper Keuper or Arden Sandstone. Of great

import, however, are the thick beds of salt and of gypsum. One bed of salt in Cheshire is over 200 ft. thick; there the Keuper Marl exceeds 3,000 ft. in thickness in the centre of the basin; to the margins both marl and salt are thinner as at Stafford and Droitwich.

Gypsum in workable thickness is present at Tutbury south-east of Uttoxeter and from south of Derby up to Newark notably at Chellaston and Gotham. These places are not far from Charnwood Forest whose old hard rocks were eroded and then buried in Triassic times. This fossil landscape is now being revealed by modern denudation. North and north-east of Charnwood it may be remarked, too, that Lower Mottled and Bunter Pebble Beds are present but Upper Mottled is absent or not recognizable.

The uppermost beds of the Keuper are the Tea-green Marls (green and red marls) such as are to be seen in several places in the gypsum country followed by about 30–40 ft. of Rhaetic (dark shales with sandstones) which intervene between the Keuper Marl and the Lias. In addition to the main outcrop there is an outlier of Lias between Warwick and Birmingham and a larger one in the Cheshire Basin near Whitchurch.

The Trias of Central England is noteworthy in that fossils have been found therein. These include the shields of the minute bivalved crustacean *Estheria* from various horizons and the remains of plants, fishes and scorpions from the Keuper Sandstone at Bromsgrove. Reptilian remains have been got at Grinshill quarries near Shrewsbury.

Keuper Sandstone has furnished much building stone (see, for example, Lichfield Cathedral) and quarries are numerous. The Keuper Marl has been dug extensively for brickmaking particularly around Birmingham and Leicester.

REFERENCES

Geological Survey
 Regional Handbooks: Central England, ed 2, 1947; *Welsh Borderland*, ed 2, 1948; *North Wales*, ed 2, 1948.
 Charnwood Forest, Geology of the Ancient Rocks of, Watts, W. W., 1947, Leicester. 'Geology of South Shropshire', Whittard, W. F., *Proc. Geol. Assoc.*, vol. 63, 1952.
Excursions and Field Meetings
 International Geological Congress 1948.
 Long Excursions: A7 West Midlands; A9 Pennines; C6 North Wales and Shropshire; C1 England and Wales; C16 Vertebrate Palaeontology; A11 Geomorphology; A1 Economic.
Geologists Association, Proceedings or Circulars
 1925, South Shropshire. 1931, Minsterley; Bridgnorth; Birmingham. 1936, Birmingham. 1937, Oswestry. 1940, Midlands. 1945, Polesworth and Dordon; Wellington. 1946, Ashover. 1949, Nuneaton. 1950, North Staffs. 1953, Welshpool; South Shropshire. 1955, Birmingham. 1958, Welsh Borderland. 1962, Peak District.
Geologists Association, Guides
 1, Birmingham. 8, Stoke-on-Trent. 26, Peak District. 27, South Shropshire.

SHEET 12

NORTH WALES

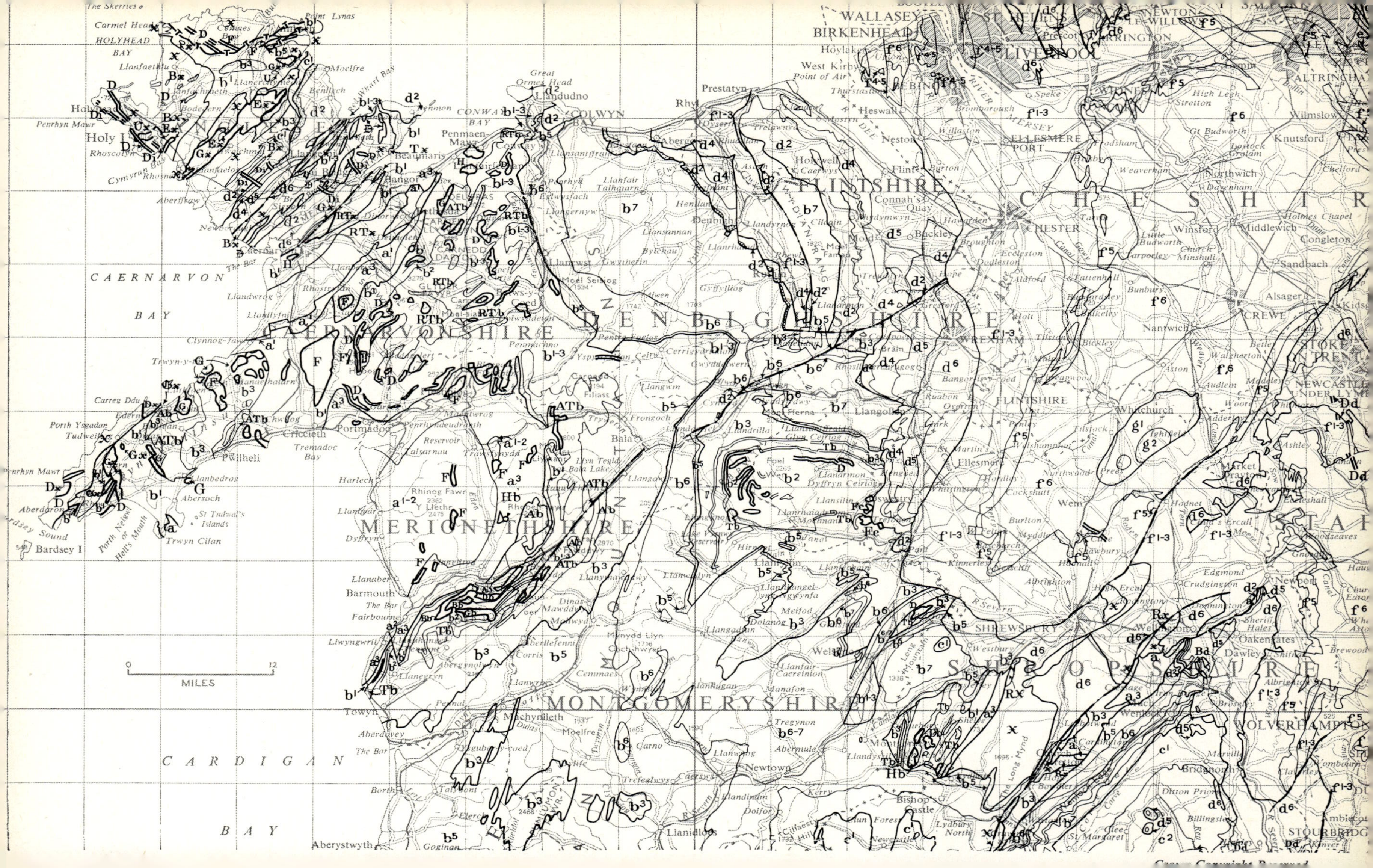

WALLASEY
BIRKENHEAD
LIVERPOOL
Hoylake
West Kirby
Point of Air
Prestatyn
Rhyl
Llandudno
Great Ormes Head
COLWYN BAY
CONWAY BAY
Penmaenmawr
Beaumaris
Bangor
Point Lynas
Moelfre
The Skerries
Carmel Head
HOLYHEAD BAY
Holy I.
Llanfaethlu
Rhoscolyn
Cymyran Bay
Penrhyn Mawr
Aberffraw
CAERNARVON BAY
CAERNARVONSHIRE
Llandwrog
Clynnog-fawr
Carreg Ddu
Porth Ysgadan
Tudweiliog
Porth Neigwl or Hell's Mouth
Aberdaron
Bardsey Sound
Bardsey I
Abersoch
St Tudwal's Islands
Trwyn Cilan
Llanbedrog
Pwllheli
Criccieth
Tremadoc Bay
Portmadoc
Harlech
Rhinog Fawr
Y Llethr
Dyffryn
Llanaber
Barmouth
The Bar
Fairbourne
Llwyngwril
Towyn
Aberdovey
Borth
Aberystwyth
CARDIGAN BAY
MILES
0
12
MERIONETHSHIRE
Bala
Bala Lake
Frongoch
Corris
Machynlleth
Cemmaes
Carno
Moelfre
Tregynon
Newtown
Llanidloes
Llanfair-Caereinion
Manafon
Meifod
Welshpool
MONTGOMERYSHIRE
DENBIGHSHIRE
Denbigh
Llangernyw
Llansannan
Moel Seisiog
Llangollen
Llandrillo
Ruabon
Wrexham
FLINTSHIRE
Holywell
Flint
Connah's Quay
Mold
Buckley
Heswall
Neston
Ellesmere Port
CHESTER
CHESHIRE
Whitchurch
Ellesmere
Oswestry
Wem
Nantwich
CREWE
Alsager
Sandbach
Congleton
Middlewich
Winsford
Northwich
Knutsford
Wilmslow
Shrewsbury
SHROPSHIRE
Long Mountain
The Long Mynd
Bishop's Castle
Oakengates
Dawley
Wellington
Bridgnorth
WOLVERHAMPTON
STOURBRIDGE
Newport
Market Drayton
NEWCASTLE UNDER LYME
Crown Copyright Reserved

NORTH WALES

This district extends as far south as Aberdovey and east to include Warrington and Shrewsbury. The western half is mainly of old rocks whereas the eastern part includes the North Wales Coalfield and Trias of the Cheshire Plain. Heights reach 3,560 ft. in the Snowdon area; outside that region they commonly range between 1,000 and 2,000 ft. though Anglesey and the Lleyn Peninsula are as low-lying as the Cheshire Plain. Much of the drainage is direct into the Irish Sea but some first goes east as in the case of the Dee and the headwaters of the Severn.

On the old rocks the population is scanty with some concentration in the coastal resorts. Hill farming is the rule with slate mining and quarrying; there are quarries for limestone and road metal on the coast and some lead mining in the Conway Valley. Copper mining at one time important in Anglesey is now extinct, though manganese has been raised recently near Pwllheli. A considerable amount of gold has been raised from veins between Barmouth and Dolgelly. In the north-east the coalfield is active but lead and iron mining in the limestone area there has declined. In addition to coal there is a considerable trade in bricks and tiles from the upper measures particularly about Ruabon. The population there and on the Cheshire–Shropshire borders is higher than in Wales generally and the Cheshire Plain provides excellent farming country.

The district has some magnificent scenery due largely to its diverse rocks and structures. In the old rocks the main structures are two somewhat complex synclines. One ranging through Snowdon from Conway to the Lleyn Peninsula introduces Ordovician strata between flanking masses of Cambrian and older rocks. The fact that the syncline is responsible for preserving the tough rocks which make up Snowdonia may seem startling at first sight. The other syncline lies east of the Harlech Dome and lets down the belt of Silurian strata about Lake Vyrnwy; this is part of the Central Wales Syncline. The other folds are mainly of Hercynian age (Permo-Carboniferous) which are fairly obvious in the anticline of the Clwydian Hills, though less so in the syncline of the Vale of Clwyd where it is masked by Trias, and in eastern Anglesey. There is also considerable faulting of which the most important examples are the Bala Fault and the Carmel Thrust; the latter bounds the pre-Cambrian at the northern end of Anglesey.

PRE-CAMBRIAN   The greater part of Anglesey and some of the adjacent mainland is made up of pre-Cambrian rocks. The oldest of these are gneisses which suffered considerable denudation before the succeeding bedded rocks were deposited. These range from the quartzite of Holyhead to grits, shales and limestones with which are associated some lavas and ashes. Lastly these were intruded by plutonic masses of which the most important is the coarse Coedana Granite though others

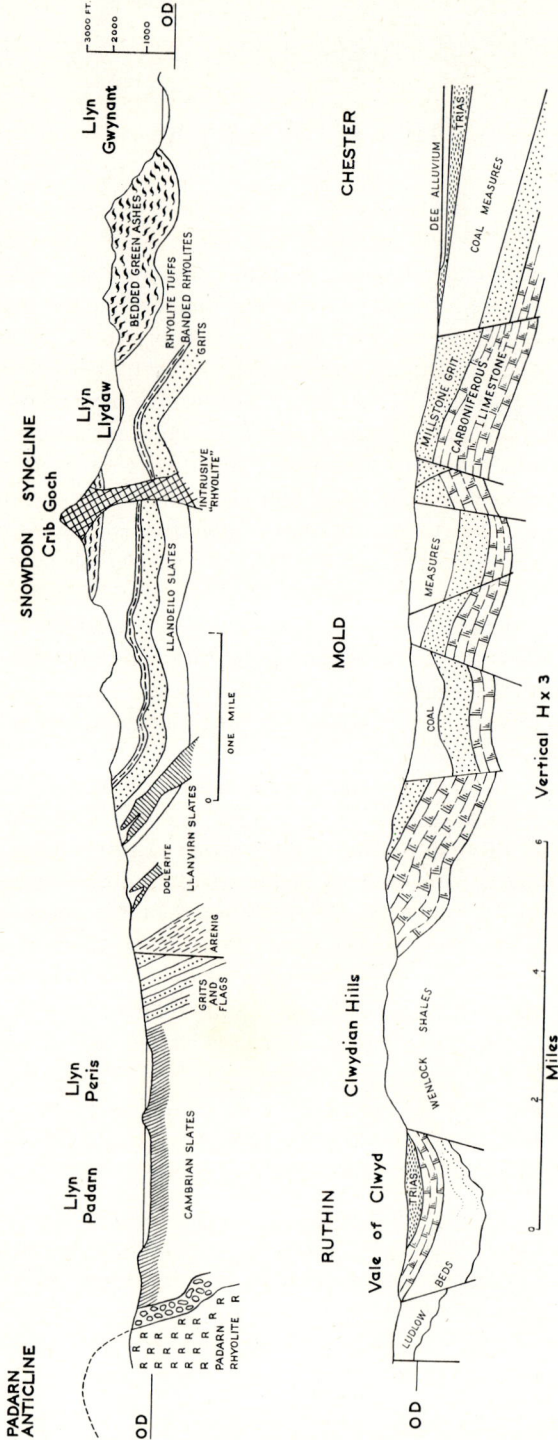

Figure 41. Sections to illustrate the structure of North Wales
(Snowdon section based on Fig. 3, H. Williams, Q.J.G.S. 1927, p. 337; the other on
One-inch Geological Sheet 108)

include gabbros and peridotite. All have been intensely folded and crushed as may be well seen in Holy Island. Similar rocks occur in western Lleyn but in Caernarvonshire they are mainly rhyolites occurring in two parallel ridges—one from Bangor to Caernarvon, with the granite of Twt Hill at its southern end, and the other, the Padarn Ridge, between Bethesda and Llanllyfni. At the eastern side of the district pre-Cambrian rocks of different type appear near Shrewsbury (see page 137).

CAMBRIAN   The Cambrian strata have a wider distribution; they crop out west and east of the Padarn Ridge giving rise to the slate country of Bethesda and occur in force in the Harlech Dome where they include the famous gold belt between Dolgelly and Barmouth with its veins of rich but erratic values. In the Harlech Dome, where the base is not seen, the beds are predominantly grits though inter-leaved with thick shales of which one includes a workable bed of manganese near Barmouth. These Harlech Beds, about 7,000 ft. thick and barren of fossils, are succeeded by 300 ft. of black pyritous mudstones, known as the Menevian or Clogau Shales, which yield many fossils including the trilobite *Paradoxides*. They are followed by 4,000 ft. of fine-grained flaggy sandstones interbedded with dark shales known collectively as the Lingula Flags; in addition to *Lingula* they carry such trilobites as *Peltura*. The Tremadoc Beds—mainly mudstones which cleavage has altered into poor slates associated with flags—complete the Cambrian sequence though in places overstepped by Ordovician. The many-branched graptolite *Dictyonema* characterizes a band near the base of the Tremadoc group.

A small inlier of similar beds from the Lingula Flags downwards occurs in St. Tudwal's Peninsula (the southern foot of the Lleyn).

In the Bethesda area the Cambrian commences with a coarse conglomerate, some 500 ft. in thickness, which rests unconformably on and contains pebbles of the Padarn rhyolite. This passes up into 2,000 ft. of fine grits and quartzites and these into the 2,300 ft. of mudstones (which now form the slate belt) interspersed with occasional thick beds of grit. The slates are mainly blue and purple though some are red and others green. A belt of green slates near the summit of the slate sequence has yielded a trilobite known as *Conocoryphe viola* indicative of Lower Cambrian. Coarse grits and conglomerates, 600 to 1,600 ft. thick, succeed the slate belt. Correlation with other areas is doubtful. In addition to the Penrhyn quarries near Bethesda the slate belt is also worked at Dinorwic quarries near Llanberis and at Nantlle south of Caernarvon.

ORDOVICIAN   This great belt of strata, which includes much volcanic material as lava flows and tuffs, succeeds the Cambrian unconformably; it is subdivided into series by means of trilobites and graptolites. The earliest series, the Arenig, begins with the andesitic lavas and ashes of Rhobell Fawr on the eastern side of the Harlech Dome. These are succeeded by the conglomeratic Garth Grit, only 200–300 ft. thick in the Dolgelly area but up to 3,000 ft. thick in Anglesey, which passes upwards into flags and shales carrying *Tetragraptus*. Around Arenig there are thin limestones and shelly beds carrying brachiopods and trilobites such as

Calymene and *Ogyia*. Thin ashy beds at Arenig represent the 1,000 ft. of rhyolites and ashes of Mynydd-y-Gader of Cader Idris.

The middle Ordovician consists of mudstones and shales (in part converted into slates, as at Blaenau Ffestiniog) characterized in the lower part by *Didymograptus bifidus* and in the upper part by *D. murchisoni* and therefore referable to the Llanvirn—true Llandeilo being thin or absent according to some authors. The thickness of these shales is variable and appears to be complementary to local great thicknesses of volcanic ashes, chiefly rhyolitic and andesitic, associated with lava flows of similar composition though in the Cader Idris district including the soda-rich types known as spilites. The group exceeds 4,000 ft. in the Arenig country but is only 1,500 ft. in the Snowdon Syncline where volcanic activity of this age is negligible as is the case also in Anglesey though recurring in western Lleyn.

The succeeding Bala Series begins with grey mudstones and blue shales reaching 4,000 ft. in thickness which furnish the slates of Corris. Thin siliceous bands are common but locally sandstones, often ashy, and limestones rich in brachiopods and trilobites are developed. At the top are black shales rich in *Dicranograptus* succeeded in the south by 5,000 ft. of mudstones and shales; these in the lower part are pale grey with dark mottling and yield *Dicellograptus*; The upper barren part is dark blue weathering rusty. Northwards they are thinner and include shelly limestones and sandstones.

In some areas, notably Snowdon and the Conway Valley, the Bala sediments are interrupted by great sheets of lava and ashes mainly rhyolitic.

Ordovician vulcanicity was accompanied by intrusions ranging from dolerites, such as Mynydd-y-Gader (near Dolgelly) and the dioritic rocks, as at Penmaenmawr, to granitic types as, for example, the granophyre on the scarp of Cader Idris.

Farther east there is a considerable outcrop of Ordovician rocks in the Berwyns (between Lake Vyrnwy and Oswestry) where Llandeilo and Caradoc strata rise as a dome amidst Silurian rocks. Dark cleaved mudstones are interspersed with bands of volcanic ash and with some limestones. There is a volcanic neck with lava and tuff about five miles N.W. of Llanymynech. Near that town Carboniferous Limestone transgresses on to the dome.

SILURIAN   The outcrop of the Silurian strata stretches from the Conway Valley and Clwydian Hills towards Llangollen and thence swinging southwards to curve back towards Welshpool. It thus separates the main outcrop of Ordovician from the smaller but still considerable one in the Berwyns west of Oswestry which is obviously anticlinal in form (page 140).

The Valentian or Llandovery Series at the base consists of blue, black and grey graptolitic shales usually about 300 ft. thick but becoming sandy and thicker southwards towards Plynlimmon and eastwards towards Welshpool. In the Berwyns, apart from a basal sandstone with shells, the Llandovery rocks are blue silty mudstones (650 ft.) and pale grey and purple shales (330 ft.) with graptolites but there is considerable thinning due to overstep in places. The junction with the Ordovician is unconformable but many graptolites survive the break to be accompanied by

various forms of *Monograptus* such as *M. priodon* and *M. sedgwicki*. A coarsening of sediment usually heralds shells and trilobites.

The Wenlock Series is mainly of grits and flags alternating with shales which carry *Cyrtograptus*. The series, known as the Denbighshire Grits, may reach 4,000 ft. in thickness. It flanks the Ludlow in the Conway Valley and occupies the syncline between the double outcrop of Llandovery strata at the head of Lake Vyrnwy; south-east of that lake Ludlow and Wenlock are not yet wholly differentiated.

Separation into Wenlock and Ludlow is dependant on the evidence provided by graptolites for the rocks are similar. In general the Ludlow strata are banded mudstones, siltstones and flags totalling over 5,000 ft. in thickness. Ludlow rocks occupy the Llangollen syncline, with Wenlock, Llandovery and Ordovician on both flanks. They also form much of the Clwydian Hills and are widespread on the Denbighshire Moors. Between Llansannan and Colwyn Bay the strata are much disturbed owing to contemporary slumping of the muddy sediments on the original sea bottom. A good section of this may be seen in a roadside quarry one and a half miles south of Llangerniew. Elsewhere there is considerable folding as may be seen in the Clwydian Hills, and about Llangollen.

No Upper Ludlow or Downtonian strata are known in North Wales and the next formation is Carboniferous though some authors wish to claim the basal conglomerate as Old Red Sandstone.

CARBONIFEROUS The Carboniferous Limestone forms a broken frame to North Wales for there are considerable masses in Anglesey and east of the Menai Straits, outliers on both sides of Llandudno Bay and from Colwyn an almost continuous stretch around the Vale of Clwyd and on the east side of the Clwydian Hills prolonged after faulting to beyond Oswestry. The eastern tract and succeeding strata are described elsewhere (page 143).

The limestones of North Wales fall almost if not entirely into the *Dibunophyllum* or uppermost zone of the Carboniferous Limestone (D_1 to D_3) indicating that up to D_1 times the region was land. In Anglesey the beds total about 1,600 ft. and are mainly pale limestone with occasional partings of shale and local sandstones. Dolomitization has affected the lower portion and tabular chert occurs in the upper beds which contain *Posidonomya*. In the south part of the island there are infolds of Millstone Grit and of Coal Measures but the latter are no longer worked. It is interesting to record that limestone from Anglesey is used in the walls of Caernarvon Castle.

The east end of Anglesey is mirrored in Great Orme with its magnificent cliffs of white limestone. In the mass east of Colwyn Bay there are many large quarries in thick bedded pale limestone with, to the south, numerous exposures of the basal conglomerate. Near St. Asaph the limestone is succeeded by Millstone Grit—here largely of shales and at one time thought to be Lower Coal Measures—and portions of the two formations emerge at intervals on the east side of the Vale of Clwyd (see Fig. 41).

The main mass of Carboniferous rocks, however, lies east of the Clwydian and Berwyn Hills. The basement beds of conglomerates with some shale and muddy limestone may reach 300 ft. but are usually thinner. The succeeding limestones are generally massive, grey or white with few shale partings and attain 3,000 ft. in thickness. In North Flintshire, however, these are succeeded by black muddy limestones followed by banded cherts parted by shale; southwards these pass laterally into sandy limestones, sandstones and dark shales. Between Oswestry and Llanymynech there is a considerable development of dolomite much quarried.

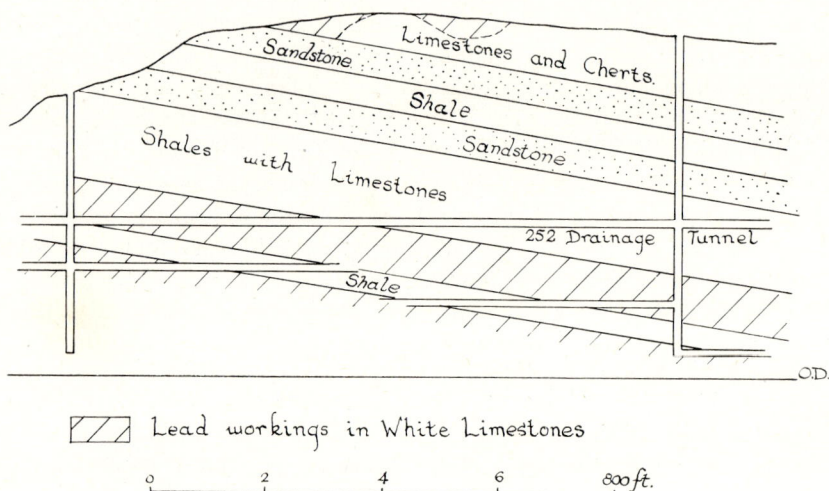

Figure 42. Section along Hendre Lode, Halkyn area, showing ore control by certain types of limestone.
Lode is nipped or barren in shales and sandstones. (Based on Fig. 24, *North Wales Lead and Zinc Memoir*)

Veins, mostly east–west, in the limestone of north-east Wales have produced large quantities of lead-ore with some zinc-ore and trivial amounts of fluor and barytes. Composition and structure often control deposition. Haematite replacing limestone was worked near Bodfari and lumps in clay in gash veins yielded ores of cobalt and nickel.

The Limestone Series are succeeded in the north by the dark Holywell Shales (400-600 ft.) followed by 300 ft. of fine-grained Gwespyr Sandstone. To the south these give place to the Cefn-y-fedw Sandstone 600 ft. thick about Ruabon but half that thickness near Oswestry. The age of these rocks was long in doubt but goniatites have now been found representative of all the Pennine zones of Millstone Grit.

Coal Measures at surface extend from the Point of Ayr (where they are worked beneath the Dee Sands) to beyond Oswestry but are divided into two fields by a great fault; the northern field is the richer in coal. The Productive Measures are

mainly grey shales but towards the top, about Buckley, include vari-coloured fireclays and silts of refractory quality. The succeeding Upper Coal Measures resemble those of the Midland fields in sequence and character and are dealt with elsewhere (page 147).

TRIAS AND LIAS   There are no Permian strata in the region. The main outcrop of Trias is in Cheshire where the formation attains its greatest development of over 5,000 ft.; of this the lower half is of sandstones mostly Bunter but including also some Keuper. The upper half, of Keuper Marl, includes vast deposits of rock salt (see Fig. 37).

In the Prees Heath area, near Whitchurch, the Keuper is succeeded by Lower and Middle Lias. The disposition of all these rocks indicates that they lie in a great shallow basin.

Trias also occurs in the Vale of Clwyd which is a deeply sunken trough floored with recent deposits on red Triassic sandstones that in the north may conceal Coal Measures.

GLACIAL AND RECENT   Much of the lower ground is obscured by glacial deposits. In addition there are considerable expanses of alluvium both marine and fluviatile, as for example, between Rhuddlan and Abergele, in Malltraeth Marsh in Anglesey, about Tremadoc and south of Harlech and about Towyn. Most of these places have, in addition, dunes of blown sand.

REFERENCES

Geological Survey
   Regional Handbooks: North Wales, ed 2, 1948; *Welsh Borderland*, ed 2, 1948.
Excursions and Field Meetings
   International Geological Congress 1948.
   Long Excursions: C6 North Wales and Shropshire; C7 Central and South Wales; C1 England and Wales; A11 Geomorphology.
Geologists Association, Proceedings or Circulars
   1920, Llangollen. 1927, Dolgelly. 1930, Snowdon. 1935, N.W. Denbighshire. 1939, Lleyn Peninsula. 1944–5, Dolgelly. 1955, Anglesey. 1957, Aberystwyth. 1958, Welsh Borderland. 1959, Snowdonia.
Geologists Association, Guides
   27, South Shropshire. 28, Snowdonia.

SHEET 13

YORKSHIRE COALFIELD

L I N C O L N S H I R E

THE WASH

LYNN DEEPS

BOSTON

MOUTH OF THE HUMBER

SPURN HEAD

GRIMSBY

CLEETHORPES

KINGSTON UPON HULL

HUMBER

SCUNTHORPE

GRANTHAM

NEWARK

N O T T I N G H A M S H I R E

DONCASTER

ROTHERHAM

SHEFFIELD

MANSFIELD

SUTTON-IN-ASHFIELD

KIRKBY-IN-ASHFIELD

ALFRETON

HEANOR

CHESTERFIELD

DERBY

D E R B Y S H I R E

LEEDS

BRADFORD

PUDSEY

MORLEY

OSSETT

BATLEY

DEWSBURY

WAKEFIELD

HUDDERSFIELD

BRIGHOUSE

HALIFAX

KEIGHLEY

BINGLEY

NELSON

BURNLEY

OLDHAM

HEYWOOD

ROCHDALE

STALYBRIDGE

MACCLESFIELD

C H E S H I R E

MABLETHORPE

SUTTON ON SEA

SKEGNESS

WOODHALL SPA

WORKSOP

WITHERNSEA

YORKSHIRE COALFIELD

THE district includes Bradford, Buxton, Derby and Nottingham on the west and south; on the north and east it includes the Humber and part of the Wash. The western part is the high ground of the southern Pennines ranging up to 2,088 ft. in the Peak but commonly 1,000–1,500 ft. and made up of bleak moorlands of Millstone Grit in the north and Carboniferous Limestone in the south. This thinly populated tract separates the industrial districts of Lancashire and North Stafford-shire from similar country on the east based on the Yorks–Notts–Derby Coalfield with its heavy iron, engineering, woollen textiles and clothing trades. Beyond the eastern edge of the exposed coalfield the ground is low embracing as it does the Vale of York and the broad valley of the Trent which together take the bulk of the Pennine drainage into the Humber. In the south-east Trent Vale is bounded by the Lincoln Cliff of lower Jurassic strata. Farther east lie the Chalk Wolds of Yorkshire and Lincolnshire and then the coastal plain. The great vales and the country to the east are agricultural but include also the large concealed coalfield, the ironfield centred on Scunthorpe, the great port of Hull and the fishing town of Grimsby.

The geological structure is relatively simple and is dominated by the anticlinal axis of the Pennines. Other folds are less obvious; of these the most important stratigraphically is the Market Weighton anticline north of the Humber. This operated throughout Jurassic times as a low ridge separating the two areas of deposition of north-east Yorkshire (page 187) and Lincolnshire though at times sufficiently submerged to permit deposition on it. The folds that give rise to the Eakring oil-field between Newark and Nottingham are concealed by the Trias; they were found by geophysical means supplemented by boring. The oil reservoir there is mainly in Millstone Grit. Other folds may be mentioned later but it may be noted that both folding and faulting are much less conspicuous than in the areas west of the Pennines.

CARBONIFEROUS   The strata fall into the usual threefold subdivision of Carbon-iferous Limestone, Millstone Grit and Coal Measures and all are well developed. The outcrops of Carboniferous Limestone are restricted to the south-west where the strata are brought to the surface by the broad Derbyshire Dome and by the subsidiary upfolds at Crich, Ashover and Kniveton. That the dome was operative during Carboniferous times is indicated by the fact that the shales which succeed the main mass of limestone thicken peripherally.

Some 1,500 ft. of limestones are exposed in the deeply dissected dome with a further 900 ft. disclosed by a boring near Matlock resting on pre-Cambrian vol-canic rock, (Fig. 37). They are mostly pale massive or thick-bedded limestones,

dolomitic in places as, for example, between the two lavas of Matlock Bath, but some of the lower beds are dark and thin-bedded, as in parts of the Wye valley, and the uppermost beds, as seen at Cawdor Quarry, Matlock, are nearly black limestones interleaved with shales; they there succeed about 60 ft. of pale limestone carrying *Lonsdaleia floriformis* which rests on a rotted toadstone (lava flow). Chert is present in some areas mostly in the higher beds. In addition to the normal limestones there is some development of reef knolls largely of brachiopod shells and corals though these are not so spectacular as in the Clitheroe and Craven areas (pages 186–7).

Most of the strata exposed are referable to the zone of *Dibunophyllum* characterized in the lower part, D_1, by *D. bourtonense* and *Cyathophyllum murchisoni*; *Lonsdaleia floriformis* marks the middle zone, D_2, which has a dark limestone at the base with the alga *Girvanella*. The uppermost zone, D_3, with *Cyathaxonia* also carries goniatites.

Associated with the limestones in many places there are igneous rocks usually spoken of as toadstones (possibly from their deadening effect on lead veins); some of these are sills and dykes of dolerite; others are basaltic lava flows and there are some agglomerate-filled volcanic necks. Examples of all may be seen in the Masson Hill–Via Gellia area near Matlock, where there are two main flows, and about Castleton and in Miller's Dale. The toadstones, normally black hard

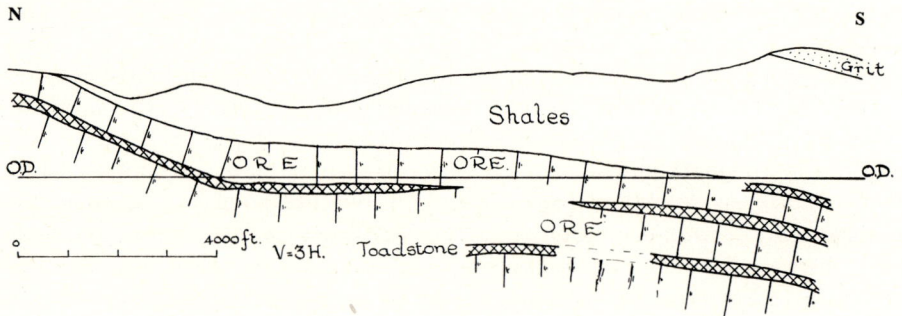

Figure 43. Section along Millclose Vein near Matlock
The vein is barren or pinched out in the shales and toadstone but bears lead ore in limestone. (After Trail, 1939)

rocks, show spheroidal weathering and often decay, even underground, into beds of clay. Such clays interfere with the circulation of water; they also impeded the upflow of mineralizing solutions with the result that deposits of lead frequently occur below them, but not in them, as, for example, the several in the famous Millclose Lead Mine at Darley Dale north of Matlock (see Fig. 43). A similar effect has been noticed at the junction of the main limestones with the overlying shales. The lead ore, galena, is accompanied by spar minerals; of these fluor occurs chiefly in the east with barytes to the west of it and that giving place to calcite farther west. Copper ore accompanied by lead, zinc, fluor and barytes at various

166

levels was worked at Ecton Mine in the extreme west in a pipe-like deposit. Most of the minerals, however, occur in veins, known as 'rakes', trending roughly east–west.

The Millstone Grit Series is made up of grits and sandstones separated by considerable thicknesses of shale. From a total of about 4,500 ft. in the north between Bradford and Skipton the measures thin southwards to about 750 ft. in the oilfield of Eakring and 200 ft. about Newark. Though traceable for miles most of the grits are lenticular; they are more persistent in the upper half of the series, i.e. from the Kinderscout Grit to the Rough Rock at the top, than in the lower part. The correlation of the grits by lithology has been placed on a firmer footing by the establishment of zones based on goniatites which usually occur in thin bands in the belts of shale. The zones are known by the initial letters of the goniatite genera. Thus E refers to *Eumorphoceras pseudobilingue* which characterizes the upper part of the Bowland Shales; these are dark shales with nodular thin or splintery black limestones containing the fossil and are succeeded by sandy shales and grits, as for example, the Skipton Moor Grits and at a higher level south of Skipton by Silsden Moor Grit; intervening shales carry *E. bisulcatum* accompanied by *Anthracoceras glabrum*.

In the succeeding group, H, characterized by various species of *Homoceras*, thin sandstones and grits occur in dark shales whereas in the next group, R, with *Reticuloceras*, grits are usually well developed. They include, for example, the thick Kinderscout Grit as well as others which are often grouped as the Middle Grits and of which the Chatsworth or Belper Grit is the topmost member.

In Derbyshire the black shales with thin dark limestones, that succeed the main mass of limestone are known as the Edale Shales; they carry goniatites indicating equivalence of the shales to upper E, and to H and lower R zones elsewhere. The lenticular grit of Mam Tor follows these shales and that by the Shale Grit and Grindslow Shales to the Kinderscout Grit.

The next belt of strata is characterized by two species of *Gastrioceras*; the lower part has *G. cancellatum*; the other species, *G. cumbriense*, ranges up into the lower Coal Measures of which the base is fixed at the upper surface of the Rough Rock. These upper beds of the Millstone Grit carry coal seams, locally workable, and occasional non-marine lamellibranchs, such as *Carbonicola*, giving further indication of the passage between the two formations.

In the Coal Measures the dominant rock is dark grey shale or mudstone though sandstones are by no means uncommon and several have received local names as, for example, the Elland Flags, the Woolley Edge Rock and so on. Some of the shales carry bands or nodular cakes of clay ironstone on which the iron trade was initiated though they are now no longer worked. Coals are fairly evenly distributed through the 5,000 ft. of strata but are thicker and of better quality about the middle of the sequence than elsewhere; they are all of the bituminous class. Most rest on fireclay though some have a seat of the very siliceous fine sandstone known as ganister which from its low alkali content is in demand for refractories. No seam

is workable throughout the coalfield. Correlation based on fossils as well as lithology indicates that many have received several different names while others with the same name are not the same seam.

The fossils include plants and non-marine lamellibranchs, both of wide distribution, and certain marine shells restricted to thin bands; of the latter the most famous is the Mansfield Marine Band. Zones based on the 'mussels' are indicated on Fig. 12.

The exposed coalfield extends from Bradford and Leeds to Derby and Nottingham. To the east Coal Measures pass beneath Permo-Triassic strata where they have been proved and partly worked for a breadth of 10–20 miles in some of the most modern collieries in the country. Beyond that again they are partly proved by borings and probably extend beyond Lincoln beneath a cover which ranges up to the Chalk.

PERMIAN AND TRIAS   Apart from a few feet at the base, of sands or breccia followed by marls, the Permian is made up of the Magnesian Limestone. The main or lower portion is usually a thick bedded creamy dolomite 100–300 ft. thick parted from an upper thin bedded dolomite (50–100 ft.) by red and grey marls with gypsum and salt (Middle Marls; 10–130 ft.) and succeeded by similar beds (Upper Marls; up to 100 ft. thick). The formation as a whole is usually about 400 ft. thick at outcrop but is nearly 700 ft. thick in parts of the concealed coalfield though only 300 ft. near Newark. Both limestones have been extensively quarried for building stone; to the south they become sandy as, for example, at Mansfield and die out near Nottingham though believed by some authors to pass laterally into sandstones classed as Trias.

The Bunter or lower portion of the Trias is of sandstones, fine-grained and red or mottled in the upper and lower portions, yellowish and coarser grained and locally pebbly in the middle portion but not everywhere distinguishable into Lower Mottled Sandstone, Pebble Beds and Upper Mottled Sandstone. The total thickness ranges from 200 to 600 ft.

The succeeding Keuper Sandstone (300 ft.) is red or brown; it has a pebbly base and may transgress on to older rocks; upwards it passes by alternation of marl into Keuper Marl (600 ft.) which includes beds of gypsum, as near Newark, but unlike Cheshire no salt.

Both Permian and Trias carry large quantities of water utilized for public and private supplies.

The dark Rhaetic shales followed by sandy and limy beds are seldom exposed.

JURASSIC   The Lower Lias, 800 ft. thick in south Lincolnshire, thins to 100 ft. at Market Weighton; it is mainly of shales but in the lower 200 ft. these carry many thin argillaceous limestones suitable for cement manufacture and in the upper part beds of ironstone of which the most important is the Frodingham Ironstone, 6–32 ft. thick, worked about Scunthorpe.

The Middle and Upper Lias from respectively 150 and 200 ft. thick in south Lincolnshire are absent on the Market Weighton axis but reappear northwards;

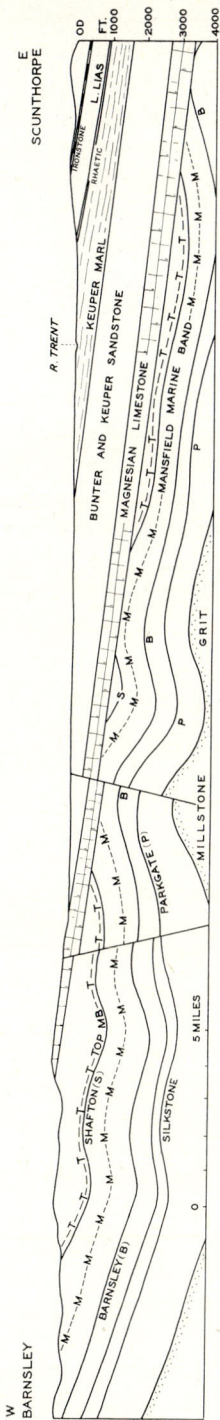

Figure 44. Section across the Yorkshire Coalfield
Note the easterly thinning of the Coal Measures and the marked unconformity of the Permian
(Based on Edwards, *Concealed Yorks-Notts Coalfield* G.S.M. 1951)

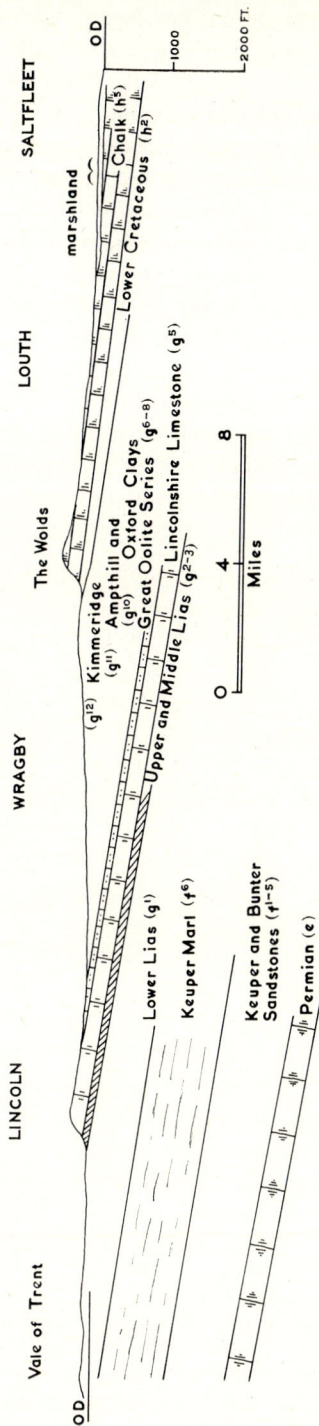

Figure 45. Section from Lincoln 'Cliff' to the sea, to illustrate structure and sequence of rocks

the clays of the former include thin and poor representatives of the Marlstone ironstone and limestone which form a step in the Lincoln Cliff; the latter is of shales and clays, black in the lower part, worked for bricks about Lincoln. Zoning of the Lias is based on ammonites but other shells are commoner.

The Inferior Oolite consists of the Northampton Ironstone, workable at Greet-well, Lincoln, but worthless farther north, followed by 10–20 ft. of the sands and clays of the Lower Estuarine Series and by the Lincolnshire Limestone up to 100 ft. thick. The limestone with shaly beds is worked for cement about Kirton while higher beds furnish the building stones of Ancaster; the rock ranges from compact to shelly and oolitic.

The Great Oolite of the Cotswolds is represented by up to 20 ft. of oolite, which disappears at Appleby, in dark shales and greenish clays the whole totalling about 100 ft. at Grantham but with the Inferior Oolite failing at Market Weighton.

A thin limestone represents the Cornbrash, some sandy clays the Kellaways Rock and the Ampthill Clay the Corallian so that the Upper Jurassic, about 600 ft. thick, consists almost entirely of clays referred to the Oxford Clay in the lower half and Kimmeridge Clay in the upper part. No higher Jurassic strata are present (Fig. 45).

CRETACEOUS The Kimmeridge Clay is succeeded by a very mixed series of sediments referred to the lower Cretaceous, which from 300 ft. on the south die out northwards. A basal Spilsby Sandstone is followed by the Claxby ironstones (mined at Nettleton) and the Tealby limestones in clays and marls which upwards give place to the sandy Carstone and to the Red Chalk. These are characterized by bivalves and ammonites. Near Market Weighton the Red Chalk rests with con-glomeratic base on Lower Lias.

The white chalk of Lincolnshire is only about 300 ft. thick fairly evenly divided between Lower, Middle and Upper Chalk for hundreds of feet of Upper Chalk have been removed by denudation leaving only that of its Holaster planus Zone. The Lower Chalk is mainly grey but is pinkish near the middle and top; at the base is a 6-ft. bed rich in *Inoceramus*; at the top is 2–3 ft. of marl with belemnites (Plenus Marls). There is no Melbourn Rock to mark the base of the Middle Chalk but the chalk there is grey and shelly with *Rhynchonella* and *Inoceramus labiatus*. Upwards the chalk is whiter, carries flint and is characterized by *Terebratulina lata*. The Upper Chalk, only found in Lincolnshire about Louth, is continued across the Humber to Flamborough (see page 190).

No strata higher than Chalk occur but there are widespread deposits of glacial material particularly on the low ground as well as much alluvium along the rivers and coastal tract. Blown sand extends as far inland as Scunthorpe and submerged forests in the Humber point to considerable oscillation of sea level.

REFERENCES

Geological Survey
  Regional Handbooks: Pennines, ed 3, 1954; *East Yorkshire and Lincolnshire*, 1948.
  Concealed Coalfield of Yorkshire and Nottinghamshire, ed 3, 1951.
  Mesozoic Ironstones of England: Northampton Sand Ironstone, 1951; Liassic Ironstones, 1952.

Excursions and Field Meetings
    Geology of Yorkshire, Kendall and Wroot, 1924.
    International Geological Congress 1948.
    Long Excursions: A9 Pennines; C4 East Midlands; A1 Economic; C1 England and Wales.
Geologists Association, Proceedings or Circulars
    1933, Holderness. 1940, Lincoln. 1951, Scunthorpe.
Geologists Association, Guides
    9, Sheffield. 11, Hull. 26, Peak District.
Yorkshire Geological Society see Proceedings for numerous short excursions.

SHEET 14

LANCASHIRE

BARROW IN FURNESS
MORECAMBE
MORECAMBE BAY
LANCASTER
FLEETWOOD
BLACKPOOL
St Anne's on the Sea
PRESTON
BLACKBURN
BURNLEY
NELSON
ACCRINGTON
KEIGHLEY
BRADFORD
LEEDS
HALIFAX
HUDDERSFIELD
DEWSBURY
WAKEFIELD
BARNSLEY
SOUTHPORT
CHORLEY
BOLTON
BURY
ROCHDALE
OLDHAM
WIGAN
MANCHESTER
SALFORD
STOCKPORT
ALTRINCHAM
LIVERPOOL
BOOTLE
CROSBY
WALLASEY
BIRKENHEAD
LIVERPOOL BAY
ELLESMERE PORT
CHESTER
FLINTSHIRE
COLWYN BAY
SHEFFIELD
CHESTERFIELD
MACCLESFIELD
Y O R K S
C H E S H I R E
0 12
MILES

LANCASHIRE

THIS sheet is mainly of Lancashire but includes a little of Westmorland and west Yorkshire, north Cheshire, a little of North Wales and of Derbyshire; it stretches from the northern shores of Morecambe Bay to North Wales and on the east includes Bradford and Buxton.

The anticlinal Pennine Chain runs north from the limestone of Derbyshire to that of the dale country but is mainly of Millstone Grit. This sparsely populated tract of high grit country separates the coalfields of Lancashire and Yorkshire with their important industries of cotton and wool respectively and to these regions it supplies abundant soft water from impounded reservoirs. Offshoots of the Pennines form the high grit country of Bowland Forest east of Lancaster and of Longridge and Pendle Hill near Blackburn with north-east—south-west anticlines bringing up the limestones as at Clitheroe (Fig. 46). Farther west is the drift-covered Trias of the Lancashire Coastal Plain which merges on the south into the Cheshire Plain. The coalfields are thickly populated; in addition to many sizable towns there are the cities of Manchester, dependent on cotton manufacture and merchanting, and the great port of Liverpool with shipbuilding across the Mersey at Birkenhead. Population is thinner elsewhere apart from coastal resorts, and Barrow with its heavy industries and shipbuilding. The chief town, Lancaster, is of no great size.

PRE-CARBONIFEROUS ROCKS   Whereas the bulk of the rocks are of Carboniferous and Triassic ages, some of the Silurian and Ordovician rocks of Lakeland just enter the district on the north, while in the south-west there is the Silurian of the Clwydian Hills. These are more conveniently described elsewhere (page 195 and page 158) but mention should be made of the inliers of pre-Carboniferous rocks in a syncline pitching east on the north side of the Craven Faults in the Settle area. The oldest of these rocks are coarse grits (locally known as Ingleton Granite) associated with slaty rocks, which crop out at Ingleton and at Horton-in-Ribblesdale. No fossils have been found in them; they bear some resemblance to Longmyndian rocks and have been claimed as pre-Cambrian.

Ordovician strata are represented by limestones in mudstone, correlated with the Coniston Limestone, followed by shales with conglomerate bands and volcanic ashes. Both groups yield trilobites.

Silurian strata commence with black shales with graptolites and with thin limy bands made up of trilobite fragments referred to the Valentian Series. The succeeding Wenlock Series are mainly of flaggy sandstones with shaly bands carrying graptolites such as *Cyrtograptus* and *Monograptus*. Ludlow strata, characterized

175

by *Monograptus nilssoni*, are also sandy but include the concentrically banded red and grey fine siltstones known as Moughton Whetstones at the head of Crummack-dale.

CARBONIFEROUS The broad threefold subdivision into Carboniferous Limestone, Millstone Grit and Coal Measures is obvious in this region where each member attains a thickness of about 5,000 ft. though there are considerable local differences in lithology and fossils attributable to unevenness in the long continued subsidence necessary for such an accumulation of sediments. Under these conditions a massive pure limestone marking clear and relatively deep water may form at one place, as in Furness, while at the same time thin-bedded dark clayey limestones with chert may be deposited elsewhere or shales with some thin limestones may occur as, in Bowland, yet all are included in the Carboniferous Limestone Series. Each facies carries characteristic fossils, the first with abundant corals, brachiopods and crinoids, the second with simple corals such as *Zaphrentis* and spiny brachiopods while the third has thin-shelled lamellibranchs and goniatites. A further phase and one characteristic of this region is the development, particularly about Clitheroe and Skipton, of thick lenses of shelly limestones, which give rise to prominent hills or knolls, amidst shales; these are known as reef knolls. All these types of sedimentation are marine whereas in the succeeding Millstone Grit and Coal Measures deltaic conditions prevailed with fewer and fewer incursions of the sea as the sequence is ascended and coal becoming greater in importance.

Carboniferous Limestone Series—The various regions show considerable differences in sequence and lithology but it is clear that all were not submerged at the same time. In Furness there are Basement Beds 300–800 ft. thick of shales, conglomerates, sandstones and limestones followed by the main mass of limestone of C_1 and later ages. Elsewhere there may be a few feet of conglomerate but limestone rests closely on the upturned edges of the older rocks as in the waterfall of Thornton Force at Ingleton and on Norber Brow near Austwick.

In Furness the main limestone begins with the Martin Limestone 150–450 ft. of tough grey and porcellanous (calcite mudstone) limestones capped by a 2 to 4-ft. Algal Limestone, followed by 170–200 ft. of the light grey Red Hill Oolite. Next come the Dalton Beds—thin bedded grey and dark grey limestones 380–850 ft. thick, followed by white or cream limestones. The lowest 400–450 ft. Park Limestone that follows is of S_2 age, is massive and its joints are seldom enlarged into 'grikes' whereas the succeeding Urswick Limestone (D_1) usually weathers in that fashion. The Yoredale group D_2–D_3 begin with 3 ft. of dark limestone (containing the alga *Girvanella* and well seen at Humphrey Head) followed by 1,400 ft. of black shales which in the lower 500 ft. carry dark cherty or coarsely crinoidal limestones and thin sandstones.

In the Clitheroe area the lowest or Chatburn Limestone, well bedded with shale partings, carries corals such as *Zaphrentis* and shells indicative of C_1. The succeeding limestone, which may be massive, or bedded crinoidal, or reef-like with shales, is followed by the Worston Shales (S_1) and the somewhat lenticular black and

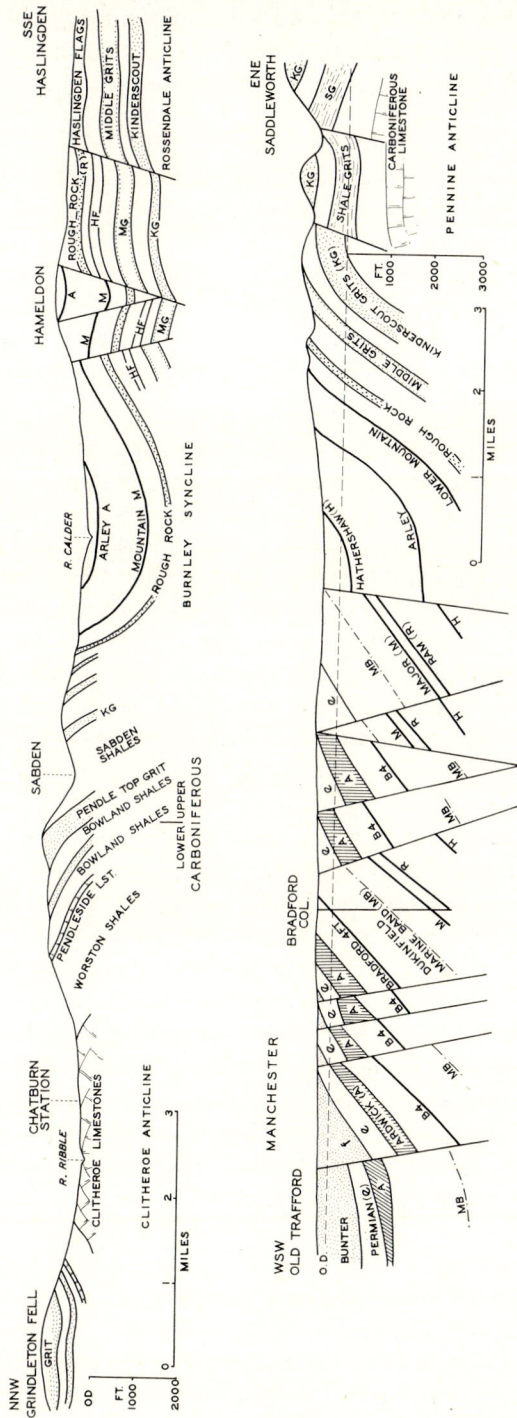

Figure 46. Sections across the Lancashire Coalfield
(Lower based on One-inch Geological Sheet 85)

177

cherty Pendleside Limestone (S_2–D_1) succeeded by the Bowland Shales of which the lower part is included in the Limestone Series while the upper portion is classed with the Millstone Grit Series. This division is an arbitrary one based on goniatites.

Similar measures prevail towards Skipton. North of the Craven Fault, however, the Pendleside Limestone is represented by the grey thick bedded Great Scar Limestone. This forms the basal bed there and is characterized by the corals *Michelinia grandis*, *Zaphrentis* and *Clisiophyllum* of S–D_1 age. To the south-east massive limestone gives place to the dolomitic and unbedded reef knolls of Malham, Cracoe and Burnsall. In place of the Bowland Shales come the Yoredale group of alternating limestones, shales and sandstones. Many of these beds, particularly the limestones, may be traced for miles and have been given local names. They characterize a great stretch of country in north Yorkshire and the name Yoredale is a corruption of Uredale of that district.

Millstone Grit—As the name implies this series comprises beds of grit some of which were formerly worked for millstones. There are many of these grits separated by considerable thicknesses of shale and though some, particularly the Rough Rock and the Kinderscout Grit lower down (Fig. 46), are of widespread occurrence they are in fact lenticular and this has often led to false correlations. Some of the grits are coarse-grained, as for example the Rough Rock which also has pebbles of quartz and feldspar up to an inch in length, while others, such as the Haslingdon Flags a few hundred feet below the Rough Rock, are fine-grained. The top portion of many of the grits is often fine-grained and may be a ganister and this in turn may give place to fireclay; either may underlie a coal, as, for example, in the Holcombe Brook district near Bolton or east of Lancaster or north of Pateley Bridge, Yorkshire.

Fossils comprise plants rather similar to those of the Coal Measures and various shells of which the most important are the goniatites which are utilized for sub-dividing and correlating this great series. These shells may occur fairly evenly distributed through thick shales, as in the lower part of the sequence, but more often are concentrated into or restricted to thin bands. These may be of dark shale, thin beds of impure limestone or the splintery limy nodules known as 'bullions'. The classification based on goniatites (largely the work of Bisat) has resulted in placing the base of the series in the Bowland Shales where *Eumorphoceras* first appears whereas formerly the base of the much higher Kinderscout or Fourth Grit was often regarded as the base. Beginning with *Eumorphoceras* (E Zone) succeeding zones are respectively characterized by the goniatite genera *Homoceras* (H), *Reticuloceras* (R) and *Gastrioceras* (G). (Fig. 12). These zones are sub-divided according to species and it may be noted that G is continued up into the Coal Measures.

Many of the grits and some of the thick shales have received local names, as for example the Kinderscout, Mam Tor and Chatsworth grits of Derbyshire, the Sabden Shales of north-east Lancashire and the Edale Shales of Derbyshire, while the names of others are based on some character, such as the widespread Rough Rock or the Bearing Grit from the lead mining region of Grassington. The grits

frequently cap high ground whereas the shale belts are eroded into hollows but sections of both are common in the steep-sided ravines, known as cloughs, cut by cascading tributaries to the main streams of the Pennines as, for example, in the Todmorden–Burnley area.

Coal Measures—Millstone Grit passes upwards conformably into Coal Measures the base of the latter being arbitrarily chosen at the bottom of the Six-Inch Mine— a coal with a marine roof that rests on the Rough Rock. In the succeeding 5,000 ft. of measures sandstones are common in the lower part, some of them being free-stones and others flaggy, formerly worked to a considerable extent for building purposes including roofing. The bulk of the measures, however, are grey to dark grey shales and mudstones; some of them contain bands and nodules of clay iron-stone. Seams of coal are fairly evenly spaced; most of them rest on a seatearth of fireclay or, particularly in the lower part, of the very siliceous fine sandstone known as ganister. The coals (known in Lancashire as 'mines') are of the bituminous class suitable for general purposes and gas; there are no true steam coals or anthra-cites; cannel was formerly important in the Wigan area. Though coals persist over wide areas few continue unchanged over a coalfield for somewhere they generally thin, pass into worthless shale or split into thin bands amidst shale. The Arley, (Fig. 46) however, is a persistent 3 to 5-ft. seam about 1,500 ft. above the base of the Lancashire Coal Measures and is correlated with the Better Bed of Yorkshire; it was chosen as the dividing plane between Lower and Middle Coal Measures. The latter contain most of the workable seams of coal. The Upper Coal Measures consist of fireclays, mudstones and sandstones, with thin bands of Spirorbis lime-stone but barren of coal, long known as the Ardwick Series in Lancashire and referable to the Phillipsi-tenuis Zone. Though often red this is no longer regarded as characteristic for similar colouration locally affects all the Upper Carboniferous strata to depths of as much as 1,600 ft.

Plant remains are common as are the fresh water lamellibranchs but marine fossils are restricted to a few thin bands. Of these in addition to the Six-Inch Mine there are three about midway between the Six-Inch and Arley associated with the Mountain Mines, another about 1,200 ft. above the Arley equated with the Clay Cross band of Yorkshire, and the Dukinfield Marine Band, about 1,500 ft. still higher, regarded as the equivalent of the well known Mansfield Marine Band. The lowest group of three is characterized by *Gastrioceras* the others by *Anthra-coceras*; in addition to these goniatites there are shells such as *Dunbarella* (*Pterino-pecten*) *papyracea*.

The non-marine lamellibranchs or mussels are more widely distributed and form the basis for zoning with the zone of *Anthraconaia lenisulcata* up to the Arley, *Carbonicola communis* for about 1,000 ft. to the Trencherbone Coal, *Anthraconaia modiolaris* for another 1,000 ft. to the Rams Mine, that of *Anthracosia similis* and *Anthraconaia pulcra* to some distance above the Dukinfield Marine Band, then *Anthraconauta phillipsii* followed by *A. tenuis*. Fossil plants are common at many horizons.

The Lancashire Coalfield is roughly triangular in plan with the measures dipping steeply south-east from the Millstone Grit on the flank of Clitheroe anticline and west from the Pennines (Fig. 46); on the west and south the measures pass beneath Trias and it is in these areas that reserves lie for the exposed field is approaching exhaustion. In the middle of the exposed field Millstone Grit is brought to the surface by upfolds and faults but there are many other folds and faults of great magnitude. South of Manchester the field is continued towards North Staffordshire by a narrow strip and Coal Measures emerge again in North Wales so that it is likely that they exist beneath the Cheshire Plain though the thickness of Triassic cover there exceeds 4,000 ft. usually regarded as the limit of working.

The Yorkshire Coalfield is dealt with elsewhere (page 165) but passing mention may be made of the small coalfield at Ingleton with its two workable seams.

PERMO-TRIASSIC ROCKS Between the deposition of this New Red Sandstone formation and that of the Coal Measures there was considerable folding, faulting and erosion so that it is not surprising that the Permian rests unconformably on Coal Measures, Millstone Grit and Limestone Series. That conditions were unsettled during Permian times is shown by marked differences in lithology. Thus the thick Magnesian Limestone of east of the Pennines is but feebly represented west of those hills and even then in Lancashire only near Barrow in Furness as a mappable band. There much of its place is taken by breccias and by red shales with gypsum. Bordering the Lancashire Coalfield on the south and west is the Collyhurst Sandstone (up to 1,100 ft. thick but very irregular in thickness) followed by 50 to 150 ft. of Manchester Marls. The former are red sandstones (with breccia bands) resembling Penrith Sandstone; the latter are red and variegated marls. Small patches of sandstone occur near Clitheroe and at Ingleton.

In Triassic times conditions became more settled with thick sandstones in the lower half followed by red marls with beds of salt the whole perhaps between 5,000 and totalling 7,000 ft. Much of the sandstones is relegated to the Bunter beginning with the Lower Mottled Sandstone (400–1,200 ft.) with rounded (millet seed) grains; this is well developed in the Wirral area and in South Lancashire. Next come the Pebble Beds 700 to 1,200 ft. of yellow buff and red sandstones of coarser grain in which there are beds of shingle and scattered pebbles of quartzite though these die out northwards of the Ribble. The Upper Mottled Sandstone (500 to 800 ft.) is a red fine-grained soft but coherent sandstone.

The next sandstone, the Keuper Sandstone, usually about 400 ft. thick, may have a hard coarse, even conglomeratic, bed at its base but in West Lancashire there appears to be a passage from the Bunter. Keuper Sandstone has been much used for building. There appears to be a perfect passage via the Waterstones made up of sandstones and marls into the Keuper Marl. This formation reaches 3,000 ft. thick and is particularly valuable in that it contains thick beds of salt some 2,000 ft. above its base in central Cheshire. Farther north the Marl is thinner but there is a salt basin near Fleetwood and another in Walney Island near Barrow.

IGNEOUS ROCKS There are igneous rocks in North Wales and in Derbyshire

(see pages 157 and 166) but in the Lancashire area activity has been confined to small dykes of dolerite such as occur near Grindleton (Clitheroe) and near Gleaston in Furness.

DRIFT DEPOSITS   Over most of the area up to altitudes of about 500 ft. much of the solid geology is obscured by thick deposits of glacial drift mostly boulder clay but including some sands and gravels. At higher elevations, particularly on the grit outcrops of the Pennines, thick beds of peat occur. Peat also occurs at low level as, for example, Chat Moss west of Manchester and near Formby; at the latter place it is associated with an ancient blown sand (Shirdley Hill Sand) in much demand for glass making. Recent blown sand fringes most of the Lancashire coast between Blackpool and Formby. There are broad stretches of marine and fluvia- tile alluvium alongside the Ribble up to Preston and bordering the coast in the Fleetwood–Lancaster area, and farther north in Furness, while remains of sub- merged forests in the Wirral and Formby areas indicate further oscillations of sea level.

REFERENCES

Geological Survey
    Regional Handbook: Pennines, ed 3, 1954.
Excursions and Field Meetings
    International Geological Congress 1948.
    Long Excursions: A9 Pennines; C1 England and Wales.
Yorkshire Geological Society, Proceedings
    1955 and 1956, Cliviger Valley near Burnley. 1956, Settle. 1961, Clitheroe.
Geologists Association, Proceedings or Circulars
    1925, N.E. Lancashire. 1955, Settle. 1958, N.E. Lancashire.
Geologists Association, Guides
    7, Manchester.

SHEET 15

NORTH-EAST YORKSHIRE

NORTH-EAST YORKSHIRE

THE district extends from Hartlepool on the north to include Bradford, Leeds and Beverley on the south while on the west it embraces some of the Dale country between Grassington and Middleton in Teesdale. It thus includes much of the Mid Pennines (and the consequent easterly drainage via Tees and Humber of the Millstone Grit and Carboniferous Limestone) as well as the Cleveland and other hills of the Jurassic country north of the Vale of Pickering and the Chalk Wolds swinging in a great arc from Flamborough Head. Permo-Triassic country mainly lies low, between the Jurassic and Carboniferous outcrops, in the Vale of Mowbray. Heavy industries are confined to the north with engineering, shipbuilding, originally based on the iron ores of Cleveland, of Middlesbrough and Hartlepool and chemical plants of Billingham with its salt and anhydrite and to the southern margin based on coal, wool and engineering; both of these tracts are more fully dealt with elsewhere (page 207 and page 165). In the Dale country there was formerly considerable lead mining but this has now dwindled to the raising of the accompanying spars of fluor and barytes previously regarded as waste products. There is some fishing but the major industry is agriculture with mixed farms on the low ground and sheep and cattle raising on the higher country.

In addition to the broad topographic elements based on solid geology there are, however, certain seemingly anomalous tracts of country and of drainage due largely to the interference caused by ice during the glacial epoch. For example, the Derwent rises a few miles north-west of Scarborough but instead of seemingly obvious outlets north of Scarborough and near Filey it turns its back on the sea and swings round by the foot of the Chalk Wolds to join the Ouse between Goole and Selby. There is low ground too, south of Darlington where a Swale of earlier days may have joined the Tees instead of turning south as now to join the Ouse. Unfortunately the present maps to not permit drift deposits to be shown but the Filey outlet is blocked by glacial drift which also floors the wide Vale of Pickering and the great Vale of York. These two vales are also the sites of lakes held up by ice. A similar hold up by ice caused the forerunner of the Derwent to spill over the hills and so cut the Forge Valley.

The rocks range from Carboniferous Limestone to Chalk. In the former the structure is relatively simple in the north with a gentle seaward dip but interrupted by folds in the southern part. Structures affecting the Jurassic are mentioned later.

CARBONIFEROUS Three groups of strata are represented: the Carboniferous Limestone Series, the Millstone Grit and the Coal Measures though an account of the last is given elsewhere (page 167). The Limestone Series extends well to the west

of the Sheet line with the result that the lowest strata are not always included. The series is of two main facies which are sharply divided about the line of the South Craven Fault between Settle and Pateley Bridge. In both there is thick limestone in the lower part (though not of the same age) known as the Great Scar on the north and as Clitheroe Limestone on the south. The latter is followed by the thick shales, some sandstones and grits and thin limestones of Bowland-Pendle Hill; the former by the rhythmic series of limestones, shales and sandstones known as the Yoredales (from the Yore or Ure of Wensleydale) which give rise to a characteristic stepped topography. The Great Scar Limestone, underlain by a few feet of conglomerate filling in hollows in the rigid basement platform of folded Ordovician–Silurian rocks which emerge as inliers in the valleys about Settle, is a pale grey pure and massive limestone with the basaltiform coral *Nematophyllum minus*, the single coral *Cyathophyllum* and brachiopods such as *Cyrtina*, *Chonetes* and *Productus* which indicate a position ranging from S_2 to D_1 in the zonal classification. This limestone is well developed in Ribblesdale and Wharfedale and there are inliers of it in the northern dales. West of Wharfedale Yoredale strata occur as outliers capped by Millstone Grit but east of the Wharfe present a continuous outcrop. In both areas limestones and sandstones stand out as bold crags and steps, giving rise to waterfalls, and are easily followed across miles of country. Many of these limestones have received individual names which indicate localities, position or thickness, from their importance in the lead mining fields about Reeth and Gunnerside; the chief in upward sequence are the Hardraw Scar, Simonstone, Middle, Five Yard, Three Yard, Underset and Main (the last being equivalent to the Great Limestone farther north). They carry such corals as *Lithostrotion*, *Orionastraea* and *Dibunophyllum* and shells such as *Productus*.

The Limestone Series south of the Craven Fault is dealt with elsewhere (page 176), but it may be said that the limestones of Clitheroe are mainly dark; and that though some knoll-like masses occur in Craven they are more frequent around Clitheroe; that the succeeding Bowland Shales are dark and carry goniatites of which those in the upper part of the conformable sequence are regarded as characteristic of the Millstone Grit Series.

In the Dale country north of the Craven Faults the Millstone Grit appears to be unconformable to the limestone measures. At the base is the Grassington or Bearing Grit of the Grassington–Pateley Bridge leadfield. At higher levels there are the Follifoot and Brimham grits of the Pateley Bridge–Harrogate area and others still higher but all appear to be lenticular developments amidst shales. The latter carry some marine fossils including goniatites in limy bands as, for example, the Colsterdale Marine Band and the Cayton Gill Shell Bed (Colsterdale is west of Masham; Cayton Gill near Ripley about 4 miles north of Harrogate). Both are traceable across miles of country about Nidderdale. In that same area coals of workable thickness also appear. On the north the outcrop of the Millstone Grit swings east through Richmond. North of that town to Teesdale it is concealed by the Permo-Trias; southwards it continues as a broad belt until it splits into three parts which lie north of the Yorkshire Coalfield, about Otley, north-west of the

Lancashire Coalfield about Pendle and between these coalfields in the main Pennine uplift.

The Millstone Grit is followed by the Coal Measures of which three portions appear on the map. In the north there is part of the Durham Coalfield about Bishop Auckland with outliers to the south-west; on the south the northern fringes of the Lancashire and Yorkshire coalfields separated by Millstone Grit of the Brontë country between Keighley and Hebden Bridge.

PERMO-TRIAS This group, sometimes known as the New Red Sandstone, consists of the Magnesian Limestone with associated red marls in the lower or Permian portion and of red sandstones followed by a considerable thickness of red marls (Keuper Marl) in the upper part. The Permian rests discordantly on the Coal Measures east of Leeds, on various members of the Millstone Grit to Richmond, thence on the Yoredale Series to the Tees where Millstone Grit and then Coal Measures reappear as part of the Durham Coalfield (see page 210). In places, at the base there is a few feet of rough sand filling in hollows in the Millstone Grit as below Knaresborough Castle; elsewhere the limestone rests on a clean swept platform. The limestone is divided by the Middle Marls (red marls with gypsum) and followed by similar Upper Marls with gypsum and anhydrite. Collapse of the strata due to solution of the gypsum in places lets down considerable masses of soft red sandstones as, for example, about Ripon; some 16 ft. of contorted gypsum in the Upper Marls may be seen in the bank of the Ure at Ripon Parks four miles north of the city. The limestone with the characteristic shell *Productus horridus* may be seen in quarries just north of Tanfield near Masham.

The sandstones above the Magnesian Limestone and the Keuper Marl and the Rhaetic are poorly exposed for, owing to their softness, they were deeply eroded by the glacier coming south between the Jurassic hills and the Pennines and then largely buried by ice-borne debris. Red sandstone, however, is visible in a quarry at Bilbrough (between Tadcaster and York) and some 42 ft. of beds referable to the Rhaetic were proved in a shallow boring at Northallerton mainly as black shales with the shell *Avicula contorta*.

Borings in the neighbourhood of Whitby have proved interesting. Beneath about 1,240 ft. of Lias and 60 ft. of Rhaetic nearly 900 ft. of red marl intervened before about 1,100 ft. of sandstone largely Bunter was pierced. This rested on about 400 ft. of Permo-Triassic marls which succeed the Magnesian Limestone that here contains not only thick beds of anhydrite and salt but also beds of potash minerals. The borings are interesting also in that they proved for the first time that there is here a thick bed of common salt near the base of the Keuper Marl (see Fig. 47).

JURASSIC The Jurassic and Cretaceous rocks of North Yorkshire present resemblances to and differences from those of the rest of England. The former point to continuity of areas of deposition the latter to interruptions and barriers though these may not be obvious. For example, there is a zone of upfolding at Market Weighton (between Hull and York) which persisted from Liassic times until the

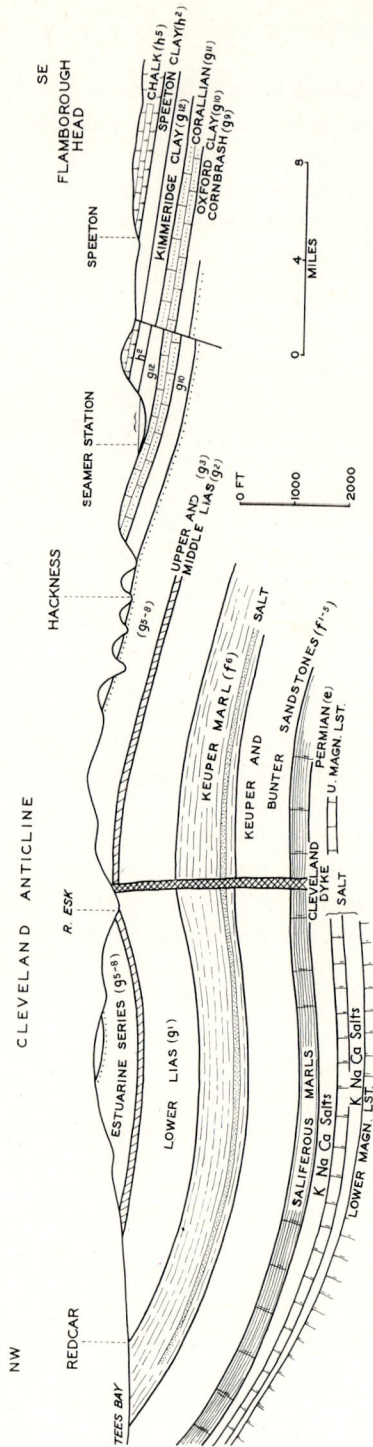

Figure 47. Section across the Cleveland Anticline

Chalk almost on to the Trias but as it is approached the Lower Lias thins and shows evidence of shallow water, the Middle Lias is absent and the Upper Lias almost so. On higher strata the effect is even more marked for the various subdivisions not only thin on or against that ridge but are widely different in character on the two sides indicating a real barrier in the form of a broad low-lying ridge at times above water and at others submerged. All its effects are beyond the scope of the present work but enough has been said to indicate that correlation of deposits to the north and south of it based on lithology alone would present some difficulties.

The main area of Jurassic rocks lies between Redcar, Thirsk and Filey much of it forming a dissected plateau reaching in the west heights of over 1,000 ft. and on the east providing magnificent coast scenery. Whereas the general structure of the Jurassic rocks of Britain is that of strata dipping gently to the east and south-east in North Yorkshire it is obvious from the many inliers of Lias that some other structures are involved. These take the form of a dome elongated E.S.E.–W.N.W. in the Cleveland Hills (Fig. 47) with subsidiary uplifts and troughs to the east of it. One of these subsidiary domes is well displayed by the Lias in Robin Hood's Bay; rather less obvious is a basin at Whitby.

The Lower Lias, about 900 ft. thick in the northern tract, consists of soft dark shales with occasional thin bands of limestone and clay ironstone. The various zones characterized by ammonites may be seen on the coast. Middle Lias, up to 260 ft. thick, is comprised of a sandy series—sandstones and micaceous silts, well exposed between Redcar and Staithes and with abundant shells—and an Ironstone Series of clays and shales with beds of ironstone up to 11 ft. thick. The ironstones are oolitic, grey when fresh but weather reddish brown; they carry about 30 per cent iron; have been extensively quarried and are still mined.

The Upper Lias, up to 300 ft. thick, is of dark clays and shales with thin limestones towards the base and elsewhere septarian limestone nodules, often enclosing fossils; ammonites are common and three are shown on the arms of Whitby town council. From 30 to 120 ft. up the shales are black and bituminous with lenses of jet (Whitby jet has been prized for ornaments from the Bronze Age onwards though less popular now than during the reign of Queen Victoria). The succeeding Alum Shales are soft and micaceous with pyrite nodules, particularly at the base, and calcareous nodules towards the top; the latter were used in cement manufacture at Mulgrave near Sandsend; the former were quarried near the cliff tops at Peak, Saltwick, Kettleness and Boulby. In addition to alum they yielded many saurian remains, such as *Ichthyosaurus* and *Plesiosaurus*, as well as an abundance of ammonites including *Dactylioceras* and *Hildoceras*. Higher beds exposed at Blea Wyke Point, comprise sandy shales followed by soft yellow sandstone.

The Middle Jurassic of Yorkshire, totalling about 700 ft., resembles Coal Measures more than rocks of the same age in southern England—the Inferior and Great Oolites; it makes the moorlands north of Scarborough. Like the Coal Measures it is of deltaic origin though termed, unfortunately the Estuarine Series; it includes coal seams on seatearths and some of the coals reach workable thickness as for example, near Coxwold; moreover, it too has washouts and marine interludes.

The first and lowest of these marine phases and known as the Dogger, is from 2 to 40 ft. thick, mainly of green sandstone with a sandy oolite rich in *Terebratula trilineata* at the junction with the Lias and a shelly bed nearer the top; it is well exposed at Blea Wyke Point. The next band, about 200 ft. up, is the Ellerbeck Bed—about 15 ft. of ferruginous sandstones rich in shells.

A third about 300 ft. above the base is the Millepore Bed—about 14 ft. of calcareous and ferruginous sandstone seen off Yons Nab north of Gristhorpe Bay and rich in bryozoa though represented by oolite in the Howardian Hills. Another, some 70 ft. higher, comprises up to 100 ft. of impure grey limestone beds interleaved with sandstones and shales; *Gervillella* is a common fossil. These limestones occur at Blea Wyke and at Hundale Point north of Scarborough and south of that town at White Nab disappearing in Gristhorpe Bay beneath the Upper Estuarine Series which reach 200 ft. thick and have at the base 40 ft. of the current-bedded Moor Grit. The deltaic measures include thick current-bedded ferruginous sandstones with shales and thin coals resting on fireclays. Plants such as *Equisetales* are not uncommon at Cloughton, Hayburn Wyke and Gristhorpe and there are shells of *Unio* a freshwater mussel.

The Cornbrash, important in southern England, is here only a few feet thick; it may be seen at Filey.

The Upper Jurassic begins with the Kellaways Rock, 50 to 90 ft. thick, of which the lower part may be shales, as in Gristhorpe Bay, or nearly the whole may be thick bedded sandstone, as beneath Scarborough Castle.

The Oxford Clay up to 150 ft. thick has a sandstone, the Hackness Rock, at the base as may be seen at Castle Hill and between Scarborough and Filey.

A mixed series of calcareous grits and oolites, 150–600 ft. thick represents the Corallian. They may be seen on Filey Brigg, capping the Oxford Clay in Cayton Bay, on Scarborough Castle Hill and at many places in the Hambledon and Hackness hills. Some beds contain fossil sponges, as at Hackness, but corals and shells prevail.

Little is seen of the Kimmeridge Clay, which is up to 400 ft. thick, apart from the coast though it floors much of the alluvial filled Vale of Pickering. No Portland or Purbeck strata are known in this part of England.

CRETACEOUS The Lower Cretaceous is represented by the Speeton Clays, about 300 ft. thick, that occur in the cliffs about Speeton to the north of Flamborough Head (Fig. 47). At the base is a coprolite bed containing worn casts of Kimmeridge ammonities. The clays proper, both light and dark, carry some ammonites which permit correlation with other localities but belemnites are commoner.

The Chalk begins with a few feet of Red Chalk following Speeton Clays but the bulk of the formation is of white chalk. The total thickness may exceed 1,700 ft.; of this 1,300–1,400 ft. is exposed either on the coast or just inland and at least 1,000 ft. is referable to the Upper Chalk. Fossils used for zoning the chalk in southern England are rare in Yorkshire and recourse has been made to other forms as, for instance, *Hagenowia rostrata* in place of *Micraster coranguinum*. The cliffs

from Speeton to Sewerby provide the following uninterrupted sequence. The Lower Chalk, characterized by *Holaster* is about 130 ft., mostly grey and marly but pinkish above a midway band, 1½ ft. thick of shelly chalk, which represents Totternhoe Stone; a thin marl at the top is the equivalent of the Plenus Marl but a Melbourn Rock is not developed. The Middle Chalk is about 400 ft. thick mostly white and flint-bearing apart from a basal grey chalk carrying *Inoceramus labiatus* and *Rhynchonella cuvieri*. This Middle Chalk may be seen about North Landing, Flamborough. Fossils are not common in the Upper Chalk, which is a white chalk with tabular grey flints in the lower part. In the Planus Zone in addition to the sea urchin there is a thick band of *Ostrea vesicularis*. The zones with *Micraster cortestudinarium*, *Hagenowia rostrata* and *Uintacrinus*, each about 100 ft. thick, may be seen on the south side of Flamborough Head and it may be noted flint in them dies out upwards. Next come the zone of *Marsupites testudinarius*, 120 ft. of blocky and flaggy chalk with nodules of marcasite, and that of *Inoceramus lingua* with rather more bands of marl; only 180 ft. of this is seen on the coast where it contains siliceous sponges.

POST CRETACEOUS   Tertiary strata are not represented in the area but the Cleveland Dyke, one of the Mull swarm of diorites or dolerites which penetrates Jurassic rocks about Egton and Trias farther to the west–north–west, is referred to this era.

No account of the district would be complete without some reference to glacial phenomena. Boulder clays and glacial sands and gravels are common on the low ground both on the coast and inland but it is certain that most of the Jurassic country was not invaded by ice. Ice from the North Sea deflected some of the Pennine and Lake District ice southwards through the Vale of Mowbray and also ponded back drainage to form lakes in Cleveland, Vale of Pickering, Vale of York and elsewhere. The lake waters escaped by cutting channels in the cols as, for example, in the Forge Valley (about 4 miles west of Scarborough). Moraines in the neighbourhood of York have really determined the site of that city by providing trackways across what were formerly swamps of alluvium and peat.

REFERENCES

Geological Survey
    Regional Handbooks: Pennines, ed 3, 1954; *East Yorkshire and Lincolnshire*, 1948.
    Mesozoic Ironstones of England: Liassic Ironstones, 1952.
Excursions and Field Meetings
    Geology of Yorkshire, Kendall & Wroot, 1924.
    International Geological Congress 1948.
    Long Excursions: A9 Pennines; C2 N.E. Yorkshire; A1 Economic; C1 General.
Yorkshire Geological Society, Proceedings
    1949, Grassington; Stainmore; Whitby. 1950, Filey. 1951, Reeth. 1952, Upper Eskdale.
      1955, Helmsley–Coxwold. 1957, Teesdale; Mallerstang. 1958, Coverdale and Colsterdale.
      1959, Grassington; Malham. 1960, Robin Hood's Bay. 1961, Weardale.
Geologists Association, Proceedings or Circulars
    1933, Yorkshire Dales. 1934, East Yorkshire. 1938, Harrogate. 1954, East Yorkshire.
Geologists Association, Guide
    11, Hull.

SHEET 16

LAKE DISTRICT AND ISLE OF MAN

LUCE BAY
BURROW HEAD
WIGTOWN BAY
Whithorn
Kirkcudbright
Castle Douglas
Dalbeattie
CRIFFEL
Gatehouse of Fleet
Newton Stewart
56(d2, LOWER)
51(b6-7)
50(b5)
SOLWAY FIRTH
CARLISLE
Annan
Maryport
WORKINGTON
WHITEHAVEN
St Bees Head
CUMBERLAND
WESTMORLAND
HELVELLYN
HIGH STREET
SKIDDAW
Penrith
CROSS FELL
Windermere
Bowness
Kendal
BARROW IN FURNESS
MORECAMBE BAY
MORECAMBE
Heysham
LANCASTER
Grange
Carnforth
WHERNSIDE
Settle
Preston
POINT OF AYRE
ISLE OF MAN
Ramsey
Maughold Head
DOUGLAS
Santon Head
Jurby Head
Kirkmichael
Peel
MILES
0
12

LAKE DISTRICT AND ISLE OF MAN

ON THE north the sheet boundary ranges by Newton Stewart and Annan to an eastern margin including Haltwhistle and Kirkby Stephen while the southern limit is near Lancaster. From motives of economy the Isle of Man is moved eastwards. The area north of the Solway, however, is dealt with elsewhere (page 215) as is Alston (page 209). This account, therefore, is mainly concerned with the Lake District and its borderland the Vale of Eden, Furness and West Cumberland and with the Isle of Man, of which a separate account is given. On the mainland the counties involved are Cumberland and Westmorland with parts of Yorkshire and Lancashire.

The interior of the district provides some of the finest scenery in the country in a small compass comprising as it does clusters of mountains rising to 3,210 ft. in Scafell, 3,118 ft. Helvellyn and 3,054 ft. in Skiddaw, with deep valleys and lakes, pastoral and wooded country and harsh craggy heights. An inspection of the map will show that the old rocks of the Lake District are partially rimmed by Carboniferous and Trias and that the valleys and lakes radiate from a narrow tract between Scafell and Kirkstone Pass. This arrangement is related to a dome-like uplift of the district in Tertiary times which initiated a drainage that has persisted in spite of many differences in lithology to the present day. It may be remarked that a similar uplift affected the Wealden area (page 23) and that these movements were but the marginal efforts of the upheaval that produced the Alps. Some modification of the water drainage erosion has been effected by ice smoothing and rounding certain portions, over-deepening main valleys thereby causing tributary valleys to hang hundreds of feet and so causing waterfalls such as Lodore. In this connexion it may be mentioned that the bottom of Wastwater is well below sea level.

This interior country is mainly devoted to sheep, forestry, water supply and tourists; its fringe supports cattle while the coastal tract and the Vale of Eden permits mixed farming. Other industries are quarrying for road metal, slate and limestone, the mining of coal and ironstone on the west coast, of gypsum in the Eden Valley and at St. Bees Head, of barytes in the interior, where lead, zinc, copper and tungsten were formerly also wrought. There are ports dependent on these trades such as Whitehaven, Workington, Maryport and Silloth as well as the great shipbuilding and engineering centre of Barrow.

ORDOVICIAN   The oldest rocks of the district are the Skiddaw Slates with a main outcrop about ten miles wide and twenty-five miles long from Dent near Cleator Moor to about ten miles east of Keswick where they occupy the crest of a major anticline through Skiddaw (Fig. 48). There are numerous subsidiary folds some of which with faults are responsible for the inliers of Ullswater and near Haweswater

and of Cross Fell. The exact thickness is unknown but amounts to several thousands of feet. Slates is a misnomer for although the rocks are cleaved they seldom produce slates. The formation includes grits and sandstones, such as may be seen about Bassenthwaite, while higher strata comprise flags, siltstones, banded and dark shales with grey the prevailing colour. Fossils are not common; the most important are graptolites such as *Didymograptus extensus* and *D. bifidus* indicative of Arenig age. There are good localities for fossils about Bassenthwaite, Braithwaite near Keswick and Buttermere.

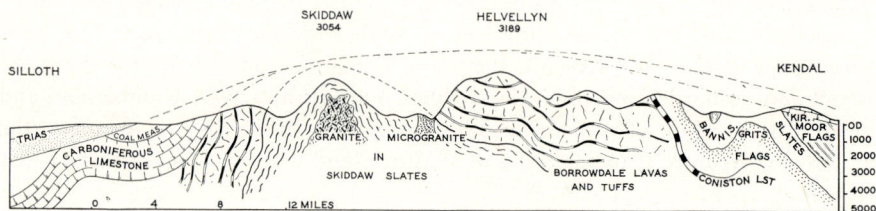

Figure 48. Diagrammatic section across the Lake District

Note (i) Skiddaw Anticline in the old rocks, with granite core (the resulting land persisted into Lower Carboniferous times), (ii) the upfold separating the north and south Carboniferous outcrop and (iii) the effect of the Tertiary dome.

Next come the Borrowdale Volcanic Series, about 10,000 ft. thick, made up of great lava flows, with some intrusive rocks of similar nature and interspersed with ashes. These flank the outcrop of Skiddaw Slates giving more rugged and craggy scenery and build up Scafell, Helvellyn and Coniston Old Man. Most of the lavas are andesites usually bluish and rather fine-grained, as about Thirlmere, but more basic and porphyritic low in the sequence, as on Eycott Hill (about 9 miles west of Penrith) and on Binsey near Bassenthwaite. Rhyolites, however, are not uncommon as flows and some similar rocks are intrusive. They may be seen in the Gosforth–Wastwater area and about Ambleside.

The ashy rocks, greenish in colour range from fine tuffs to coarse agglomerates. Many of them show alternate bands of coarse and fine material especially on cleaved faces. Some of the thicker beds provide good roofing slates as in Borrowdale, at Honister and about Elterwater and Coniston.

No fossils have been found in these rocks but their general equivalence to the Llandeilo of Wales is indicated by their position for the succeeding unconformable Coniston Limestone Series represents the Caradocian. This series (300–800 ft.) begins in Lakeland with an ashy conglomerate, split in places by a rhyolite flow, and is succeeded by calcareous shales with limestones and ashy beds. Brachiopod shells and trilobites are common. In Drygill (north of Carrock) and in the Cross Fell area the sequence is mainly of shales.

The conformable Ashgill Series (100 ft.) with a 12-ft. limestone at the base carrying *Staurocephalous* followed by shales completes the Ordovician.

SILURIAN The Llandovery Series is represented by the Stockdale Shales of

which the lower 50 ft. are black with thin pale bands and the upper 200 ft. are greenish with dark bands; the dark bands carry such graptolites as *Cyrtograptus* and *Monograptus*.

Wenlock strata are represented by blue-grey laminated mudstones with gritty partings, known as the Brathay Flags (1,000 ft.); these have provided flags and tilestones. The succeeding Ludlow Series is a monotonous one of flags, grits and mudstones, grey to olive in colour, totalling about 12,000 ft. in thickness. Fossils are not common but shells such as *Cardiola interrupta, Chonetes striatella* and *Rhynchonella nucula* occur as well as some trilobites and graptolites. The strata are grouped as follows: Coldwell Beds, 1,500 ft. of olive flags; Coniston Grit, 4,000 ft. of coarse grit with some flags near the middle; Bannisdale Slates, 5,000 ft. of cleaved leaden grey mudstones; Kirkby Moor Flags, 1,500 ft. of micaceous greenish flags with some rusty-weathering calcareous bands carrying fossils. These flags complete the Silurian for no Downton strata are recognizable.

The main outcrops of the Silurian rocks are on the south side of Lakeland and in the Howgill Fells. On the north their outcrop may be concealed by Carboniferous rocks (Fig. 48) for large fragments of them and of Coniston Limestone occur in the basal Carboniferous Conglomerate at the foot of Ullswater.

In the Cross Fell inlier the Lakeland rocks are repeated on a miniature scale near the foot of the great faulted Pennine escarpment.

IGNEOUS INTRUSIONS   The Ordovician and Silurian rocks are invaded by some large igneous masses and many smaller stocks and dykes which together present a great variety of rocks though granitic types predominate.

One of the largest masses is the Eskdale Granite on the west; it occurs in two outcrops one small at the head of Wasdale and the other extending from the foot of Wastwater to Bootle. The usual type is coarse with much smoky quartz and may be pink or grey in colour. It is interesting to record that cobbles of it occur in the Sand Rock Mine—a coal at the top of the Millstone Grit—at Bacup in Lancashire.

Adjoining the outcrop of the Eskdale Granite at the foot of Wastwater, though the contact is not visible, is that of the Ennerdale-Buttermere Granophyre. The normal rock is a pinkish, fine-grained mixture of quartz and feldspar.

Skiddaw Granite invades Skiddaw Slates near the crest of the main anticline. It reaches the surface in three small outcrops, in Sinen Gill, in the Caldew valley and in Grainsgill, but is presumably one mass at no great depth since there is a wide area of metamorphism where slates are converted to hard hornfels near the contact and chiastolite spots appear in the soft outer zones. The granite in Grains-gill has been altered to greisen by late stage irruptions of magmatic solutions and quartz veins have been formed bearing the tungsten ores wolfram and scheelite, as well as blende, mispickel, traces of molybdenite etc.

The adjoining Carrock Complex to the north forms a tract a mile broad and four miles long in Borrowdale rocks flanked on the south by Skiddaw Slates and on the north by the shales of Drygill. It includes a suite of gabbros (on the south) a median rib of diabase and the several granophyres of Carrock Fell, Great Lingy

and Harestones. The most accessible section is on the east end of Carrock at Furthergill Syke.

Other interesting rocks in the Keswick area are the picrite at Dash, the diorites of Embleton, the Sale Fell minette, the dolerite of Castle Head and Friars Crag (Keswick), the Amboth dyke west of Thirlmere and the microgranite of Threlkeld and St. Johns. Farther to the south-east there is a small outcrop of gabbro near Haweswater and, near the Borrowdale–Coniston series contact, the Shap Granite. The latter is a biotite granite with large crystals of pink feldspar and is much used as an ornamental stone as well as for road metal. Fragments of this stone occur in the nearby basal conglomerate of the Carboniferous thus proving the age of in-intrusion to be Old Red Sandstone. On analogy a similar age is presumed for the other masses.

CARBONIFEROUS   The strata fall into the usual three subdivisions but the middle one, of Millstone Grit, is here of little consequence. On the other hand the Carboniferous Limestone Series presents many features of interest for the lower measures, the Tuedian (page 209), in Northumberland and North Cumberland, were not deposited over the site of the Lake District and of Alston while farther south in Westmorland they are represented by thick limestones. Furthermore, when deposition had started over the site of Lakeland it followed a rhythmic Yoredale succession of limestone shales and sandstones north of Penrith and Cockermouth whereas south of that line limestones predominate in the lower part of the sequence.

Basement Conglomerate is present in many places including the foot of the Pennines. One of the best and most accessible sections is by the roadside at the north end of Ullswater. It is hundreds of feet thick at Great Mell Fell near Ullswater but thins unevenly round the northern rim of Lakeland to disappear at Cockermouth though there are patches of it in south Cumberland and Furness, and near Kendal and Sedbergh. It reappears in force about Tebay to link up with the Ullswater outcrop. Some of its pebbles have already been noted.

For the Limestone Series the Shap–Ravenstonedale area is a classic one for north-west England. The Basal Conglomerate is followed by dolomites with some bands which are oolitic or pebbly or algal. The fossil marking this zone (C) is th brachiopod *Athyris glabristria*. Next come hundreds of feet of normal limestone with *Lithostrotion* corals and several genera of brachiopods though the limestone sequence is interrupted by the thick Ashfell Sandstone. Most of these rocks are referable to the S Zone characterized by the shells of *Productus corrugata-hemisphericus* and *Cyrtina carbonaria* and the basaltiform coral *Nematophyllum minus*. It was during the middle period of this zone that the Lake District island or peninsula was submerged beneath the Carboniferous sea and deposition of limestone took place throughout northern England. These limestones have the *Girvanella* algal band in the middle of D Zone which is itself characterized by such corals as *Lonsdaleia floriformis*, *Dibunophyllum* and *Cyathophyllum* and species of *Productus* including the large *P. giganteus*.

In Furness and South Cumberland the sequence begins with 300–800 ft. of

shales, conglomerates, sandstones and limestones (Basement Beds) followed by the main mass of limestones. These, roughly 2,000 ft. thick and mostly light grey or cream in colour are referable to zones C, S and the lower part of D. The next 1,400 ft. of beds are dark shales with thin cherty or crinoidal limestones.

In West Cumberland there is about 700 ft. of solid limestone apart from thin shale partings and one thick sandstone (Orebank Sandstone) which serve to divide the sequence into 1st to 7th Limestone; the 1st Limestone at the top is the equivalent of the Great Limestone of the Alston district (page 210). Above it come shales and sandstones which farther north have thin limestones similar to some about Alston.

From Cockermouth northwards flows of basalt (Cockermouth Lavas) intervene between the Basal Conglomerate and the 7th Limestone and the partings between the limestones thicken until the sequence about Caldbeck is of Yoredale facies.

The Millstone Grit is thin and poorly developed lithologically. Goniatites indicate the presence of the topmost G. (Gastrioceras) Zone; the middle zones of R and H are absent but some authors claim limestone-bearing measures down to the Great Limestone as lower Millstone Grit.

The Coal Measures consist of 1,000 ft. of grey Productive Measures with many coal seams followed by Whitehaven Sandstone—a group of purplish sandstones and shales, over 1,000 ft. thick, equivalent to the Barren Red Measures of Scotland and part of the Upper Coal Measures of the Midlands. The Productive Measures continue for short distances only beneath the Permo-Trias but persist under sea where coals are worked five miles from the coast. Coal mining in this field is rendered difficult by considerable faulting though this same factor has led to the deposition of haematite iron ore in the Carboniferous Limestone (see page 202 and Fig. 50).

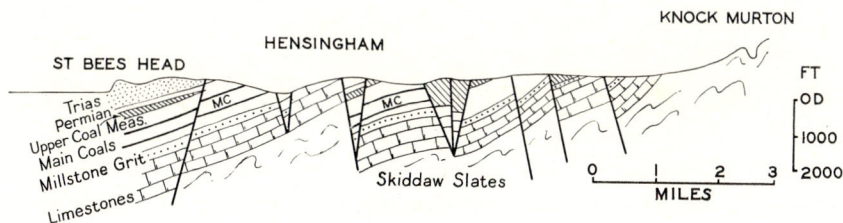

Figure 49. Section across the Cumberland Coalfield

This section, almost at right angles to previous one, shows the (i) seaward dip of the strata resulting from the Tertiary dome, (ii) the faulted nature of the field, and (iii) the unconformity of the Permo-Trias. (Based on One-inch Geological Sheet 28)

PERMO-TRIAS   In the Vale of Eden the Penrith Sandstone forms the basal member and may reach 3,000 ft. thick. For the most part it is a coarse pinkish rock with well rounded (millet-seed) grains of quartz but thick brockrams (breccias) occur at the base and towards the top in the Appleby area. The stones are mainly Carboniferous though the upper brockram includes rare fragments of Whin Sill.

In the Appleby area grey or yellow dolomitic shales and sandstones (Hilton

Plant Beds) succeed the Penrith Sandstone and are followed by a thin magnesian limestone. Farther north these beds die out and Penrith Sandstone grades upwards into the red St. Bees Shales which carry workable beds of gypsum. Southwards Penrith Sandstone and brockrams die out and in Furness there is a Magnesian Limestone, 63 ft. thick, at the base of the series followed by St. Bees Shales though near Millom borings found grey strata suggestive of Hilton Plant Beds.

On the north side of St. Bees Head, at Barrowmouth, there is a conformable passage upwards from a thin coarse brockram filling hollows in Whitehaven Sandstone to about 30 ft. of Magnesian Limestone and over 100 ft. of St. Bees Shales into the red St. Bees Sandstone of the Headland. Inland the Magnesian Limestone dies out and near Egremont hundreds of feet of brockram replace St. Bees Shales and perhaps part of the St. Bees Sandstone. The brockram is evidently a scree deposit washed by torrents into a sea or lake; wide differences in pebble content point to derivation from different valleys. As a rule, however, pebbles of the lower part of the brockram are of Carboniferous Limestone while higher parts include Borrowdale and Skiddaw fragments indicating progressive denudation of the hill country. Northwards the brockram is but a thin pebbly base to the St. Bees Shales which about Maryport and Aspatria are more sandy than usual. In the Barrowmouth area the St. Bees Shales include a bed of gypsum and anhydrite.

St. Bees Sandstone is generally red though some portions are grey buff or orange in colour, often then with grains well rounded. About Carlisle the latter may be segregated into an upper or Kirklinton Sandstone but in the south, about Seascale where the formation is over 3,200 ft. thick, such material is interdigitated with normal red sandstone. In the Carlisle–Silloth area the sandstone formation is thinner and is there succeeded by the red Stanwix Shales equivalent to Keuper Marl elsewhere, and these in the centre of the Carlisle basin by the dark shales with thin limestones of the Lower Lias. So far no Rhaetic has been recognized but it may be hidden by the widespread deposits of glacial drift.

In the south Stanwix Shales are present in Walney Island near Barrow; they there contain beds of salt.

DRIFT DEPOSITS   Much of the ground below the 1,000-ft. contour is mantled by glacial deposits chiefly of boulder clay but with sand and gravel also, as for example in the Brampton, Wigton and Gosforth areas. From the erratics in the boulder clays it is clear that an ice stream traversing the Southern Uplands drove on to the Cumbrian coast and hemmed in the Lake district ice. That some of the latter went via Stainmore Pass to Scarborough is shown by the trail of Shap Granite erratics.

In the coastal tracts there are widespread deposits of alluvium both fluviatile and marine. These include the silty muds known as warp and the sand and shingle of the raised beaches. Several stages of uplift of both kinds of deposit may be recognized. The deposits are well developed in the Maryport–Silloth–Carlisle area and in the drowned valleys of Furness. There are dunes of blown sand about Silloth, Ravenglass and Barrow.

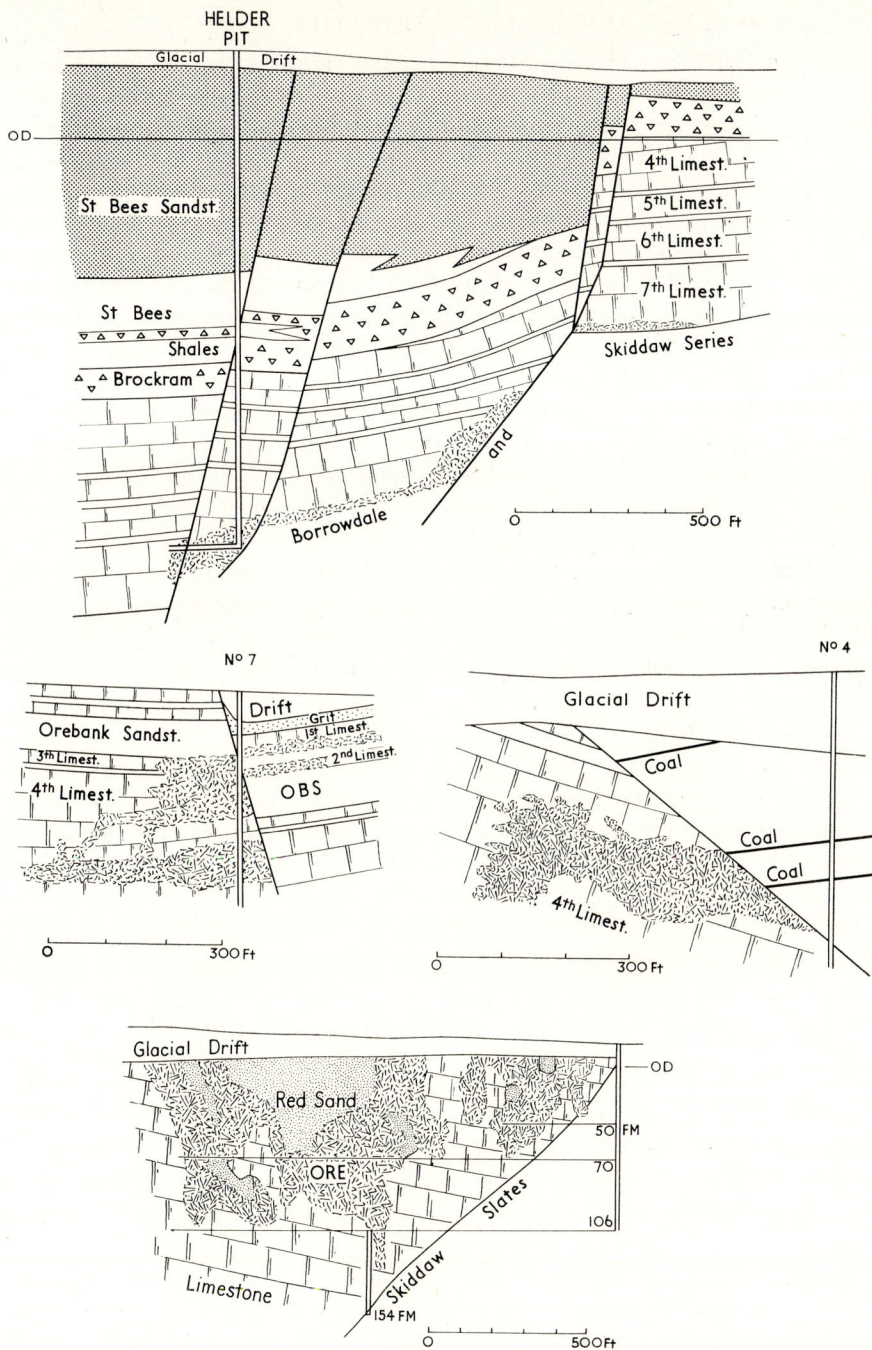

Fig. 50. Sections to illustrate Haematite Deposits of W. Cumberland and Furness

Helder Mine, Egremont: replacement of 7th Limestone. *Bigrigg No. 7 Shaft*: replacement of 1st–4th Limestones. *Montreal Mine, No. 4 Shaft*: coal and iron worked from same pit across Coal Fault. *Park Mine, Furness:* 'sop' infilling a swallow hole. (Based on Plate V, Figs. 9, 16 & 23 of Geol. Surv. *Haematite* Memoir)

MINERAL DEPOSITS Mention has been made of the tungsten deposits of Carrock. Better known perhaps is the graphite formerly got from a pipe-like deposit in the Borrowdale rocks near Seathwaite south of Derwentwater which formed the basis of the Cumberland pencil works. Much more important, however, were those of copper, lead and zinc. These occur in both Borrowdale rocks and Skiddaw Slates— the copper chiefly in east-west veins, the lead zinc lodes ranging roughly north–south. The Caldbeck Fells and Coniston provided most of the copper; the head of Ullswater and the Keswick area most of the lead and zinc. With the latter are associated barytes worked at Force Crag and south of Caldbeck. Oddly enough fluorspar is comparatively rare in the district.

The west coast and Furness have long been famous for haematite iron ore (see Fig. 50). Most of it occurs as irregular masses replacing certain beds of Carboniferous Limestone intersected by faults but some in the Furness area, now worked out, occurred as soft ore in ancient solution chambers that were known as 'sops'. Some haematite also occurs as veins in the Skiddaw Slates in West Cumberland and in the granite area of Eskdale.

Gypsum provides a major industry in the Eden Valley; some is got at Barrowmouth, St. Bees Head and there is a deposit at present unworked of gypsum and anhydrite east of Barrow.

Countless other mineral species are present in the Lake District but are of no economic value.

ISLE OF MAN

Most of the Isle of Man is made up of much folded Manx Slates. These resemble the Skiddaw Slates and like them have flaggy and gritty portions. By some authors they are thought to represent the lower concealed part of the Skiddaw sequence and are classed as Cambrian but no fossils of diagnostic value have been found.

In addition to dykes of dolerite and felsite the Manx Slates have been invaded along the major anticline by the two granite masses of Foxdale and Dhoon; the latter is a porphyritic microgranite with steep walls whereas the Foxdale mass of coarse, grey, muscovite granite shelves gradually beneath the slates.

The Carboniferous Limestone Series is represented at both ends of the island beginning with a basal conglomerate. Thereafter the resemblance ceases for the rocks about Castletown are of limestones followed by the basaltic lavas and tuffs of Scarlet Point whereas those at the north end of the island, deeply buried under glacial drift include no volcanic rocks, exhibit a Yoredale sequence and are more akin to those of Cumberland than to the Castletown rocks thus indicating the presence of some kind of a barrier during deposition.

Reddish sandstones with bands of conglomerate and lenses of impure limestone occur about Peel. Their age is uncertain but they probably represent Basement Beds of the Carboniferous.

About 3,000 ft. of Permo-Triassic strata are concealed by glacial, raised beach deposits and blown sand at the north end of the island. There is a brockram at the base followed by some red marl and this by thick sandstones which give place

upwards to red marls with salt and gypsum. The sequence therefore resembles that of West Cumberland and Barrow.

A considerable amount of lead ore was at one time raised, the principal mines being at Laxey and at Foxdale. Farming is the chief industry today but thousands of tourists are attracted yearly by the varied coastal scenery.

REFERENCES

Geological Survey
    Regional Handbook: Northern England, ed 3, 1954.
    'Geology of the Lake District', Hollingworth, S. E., *Proc. Geol. Assoc.* vol. 65, 1954, pp. 385–411.
    'Geological History of the Lake District', Mitchell, G. H., *Proc. Yorks. Geol. Soc.*, vol. 30, 1956, pp. 407–463.
Excursions & Field Meetings
    International Geological Congress 1948.
    Long Excursions: A2 N.W. England; A1 Economic; C1 England & Wales.
Geologists Association, Proceedings
    1921, Lake District. 1925, Whitehaven & West Cumberland. 1936, Cross Fell. 1954, Lake District. 1955, Cross Fell. 1963, Lake District.
Yorkshire Geological Society, Proceedings
    1950, Sedbergh. 1951, Ravenstonedale; Reeth. 1956, Dunfell. 1959, Furness. 1960 Sedburgh.

SHEET 17

CHEVIOT—DURHAM

North Berwick

Bass Rock

Dunbar

Barns Ness

ST ABB'S HEAD

St Abb's
Eyemouth
Burnmouth

Black Law

BERWICKSHIRE

Berwick upon Tweed
Tweedmouth

57 (d^2 UPPER)

Holy Island

Farne Islands

Bamburgh

Sea Houses

Coldstream

MERSE

Beadnell
Beadnell Bay

57 (d^2, UPPER)

THE CHEVIOT

ROXBURGHSHIRE

Amble

58 (d^4)

Druridge Bay

NORTHUMBERLAND

Redesdale Forest

Newbiggin by the Sea

ASHINGTON

BEDLINGTON

BLYTH

59 (d^5)

WARK FOREST

WHITLEY BAY

62 (e')

GOSFORTH
TYNEMOUTH

NEWCASTLE
SOUTH SHIELDS

BLAYDON
GATESHEAD
HEBBURN

WHICKHAM

SUNDERLAND

STANLEY

CONSETT
CHESTER le STREET

HOUGHTON
SEAHAM
HARBOUR

e' (62)

DURHAM

d^4

d^5

f$^{1.5}$

CROSS FELL

Penrith

BISHOP AUCKLAND

WEST HARTLEPOOL
Hartlepool

f$^{1.5}$

BILLINGHAM

STOCKTON ON TEES

THORNABY on TEES
MIDDLESBROUGH

DARLINGTON

d^2

0   MILES   12

CHEVIOT–DURHAM

THIS area extends from St. Abb's Head on the north to Middlesbrough on the south and its western boundary runs by Selkirk; it thus includes the Cheviots and the wild Border country and the Northern Pennines—all very sparsely populated and with few roads—as well as the Northumberland–Durham Coalfield with its collieries, ports and shipbuilding yards, great engineering and chemical works. In the north-west it embraces much of the Scott country. Heights range from 2,676 on The Cheviot to the 2,930 of Cross Fell and apart from the coastal belt much of the country lies between 800 and 1,500 ft.

On the north drainage is mainly via the Tweed; on the west the most important streams are the Eden and Liddel Water but much more water goes easterly, chiefly by the Tyne, from the dip-slope of the Carboniferous rocks east of the Pennine escarpment. The groups of strata range from the Ordovician and Silurian of the eastern part of the Southern Uplands to the Permo-Triassic rocks of the Eden Valley and of the coastal tract but Carboniferous rocks predominate. They provide vast quantities of coal and formerly yielded rich ores of lead and zinc and some iron from the veins of Alston, Weardale and Teesdale. These veins today are worked for fluor, barytes and witherite, the spars which accompany lead, but the glory of the mining fields has departed.

ORDOVICIAN—SILURIAN The oldest rocks are those of the Southern Uplands which reach the coast between Dunbar and Berwick. On the north-west, brought by the Southern Uplands Fault against the Old Red Sandstone and Carboniferous rocks of Dunbar (see page 224 and Sheet 19), there is a narrow wedge of Ordovician forming part of the Lammermuir Hills. To the south of this there is a broad outcrop of Llandovery strata that reaches the coast at St. Abb's Head followed south of Hawick by Wenlock rocks which to the east are transgressed by Old Red Sandstone lying unconformably across the denuded innumerable folds that affect the older strata.

In the main outcrop of Ordovician the Arenig strata are vari-coloured radiolarian cherts in mudstones; thin seams of black shale carry *Tetragraptus* and horny brachiopods.

The succeeding strata are rusty and grey sandy and micaceous shales and mudstones in place of the black (Glenkiln) shales of the Moffat area and the black Birkhill Shales are replaced by flags and grits with conglomerates though interleaved shales still carry some graptolites. The rocks become even coarser upwards and the dominant type in the Llandovery is of massive grits and greywackes with some shales, such as may be seen between Cocksburnspath and St. Abb's Head repeated by innumerable flexures. Shales half a mile south-west of Siccar Point carry *Monograptus priodon*.

Wenlock and Ludlow strata do not reach the east coast but are present near Hawick where they are overspread north and east by Old Red Sandstone and Lower Carboniferous rocks respectively. Grey mudstones, shales and greywackes with graptolitic shale bands predominate though green mudstones with nodular limestones occur at the top. The graptolites include *Cyrtograptus* and *Monograptus*; shells in the limy beds recall those of the western Midlands (Sheet 11).

Farther south a small inlier in Teesdale (near Cowgreen Mine 9 miles W.N.W. of Middleton) indicates that Ordovician strata constitute the platform on which rests the Carboniferous rocks. The larger inlier of Cross Fell is mentioned elsewhere (see page 197).

OLD RED SANDSTONE   The middle portion of this formation is absent in Southern Scotland and Upper Old Red sediments not only rest unconformably on Lower Old Red but transgress the outcrops of the Silurian and Ordovician rocks. Lower Old Red Sandstone sediments appear at surface only in the coastal belt about St. Abb's Head where they are red, feldspathic sandstones interspersed with conglomerates and associated with andesitic lavas and beds of coarse tuff. Near Eyemouth there are several agglomerate-filled vents.

The Upper Old Red Sandstone, up to 2,000 ft. thick, usually has conglomerate at the base though higher conglomerates occur in the red sandstones which are cleaner looking and less feldspathic than those below. Locally there are beds of red shale and of the concretionary limestones known as cornstones; lavas of this age, however, are rare. Some of the conglomerates contain fragments of the Cheviot granite and lavas thus establishing the age of that igneous complex.

The Cheviot massif consists of the deeply dissected remains of a volcano intruded by a mass of granite and traversed by numerous dykes. The volcanic episode began with an explosive phase that produced the thick series of ashes and tuffs known as the Basal Agglomerate. This is up to 200 ft. thick, is restricted to the south and has fragments up to 5 ft. across of rhyolite and smaller pieces of Silurian shale.

The explosive phase was quickly followed by a great outpouring of lavas beginning with reddish porphyritic rhyolites, sometimes called Biotite Lavas or Mica-Felsites, followed by the main mass of lavas. These are chiefly brown andesites but include some pitchstones and trachytes. Occasionally the lavas include or are intercalcated with some red marl and sandstone.

The granite mass is believed to be a laccolith, rather than a plug with steep sided contacts, for though the junction with the lavas is sharp on the south elsewhere granite and lavas are interleaved and a considerable area of lavas, believed to be roof, is much metamorphosed. The normal rock is a pink granophyric granite but is basified in places by assimilation of lavas.

The next phase was the intrusion of dykes cutting both granite and lavas followed by some effusion which led to the development of much tourmaline but unlike similar effusion in Cornwall and Cumberland did not produce tin and wolfram ores.

CARBONIFEROUS   The strata fall into the usual tripartite division of Limestone Series, Millstone Grit and Coal Measures though the Millstone Grit is relatively thin and unimportant. On the other hand the Limestone Series exceeds 8,000 ft. in Northumberland; of this great thickness, however, relatively little is of limestone especially in the lower part of the sequence known as the Tuedian. The outcrop of this subdivision, about eight miles wide in the north-east but broader to the west largely owing to relatively low dip, stretches from Berwick to the Solway and to Brampton.

On the Scottish side of the Border the sequence begins with a volcanic phase of basaltic lavas, known as the Kelso Traps, which may have emerged through such agglomerate-filled vents as those between Melrose and Selkirk. Although some cornstones, sandstones and marls of Old Red Sandstone aspect are intercalated with the lower lavas the sedimentary sequence begins with the Cementstone Group 3,000 ft. thick. In this group grey and reddish shales with innumerable thin bands of impure freshwater or estuarine limestone predominate though sandstones are not uncommon in the upper and lower portions; at the base there is a conglomerate east of the Cheviots (Roddamdene Conglomerate) and a cherty dolomite (Carham Stone) in the Tweed area. Fossils link the group with the Oil Shales of the Central Valley of Scotland (page 226). In north-east Cumberland marine shells indicate C_1 subzone.

Next comes the Fell Sandstones—a group of pink, coarse, false-bedded and massive sandstones, 600 to 1,000 ft. thick, which gives rise to bold escarpments. A volcanic episode then intervenes in the north about Glencartholme with 300 ft. of basic lavas and tuffs; shales and cherts interbedded with the latter have yielded crustacea, arachnids and fish remains.

In Northumberland the succeeding division of the Lower Carboniferous is known as the Bernician. It begins with the Scremerston Coal Group which shows a recurrence of cementstone conditions being made up of shales with thin impure limestones but accompanied in this case by coal seams. At Berwick the group is 1,000 ft. thick and has at least ten workable coals, some over 6 ft. thick. Southwards it thins to 300 ft. at Alnwick, with only four thin coals, but regains its thickness to the west where marine limestones appear in a Yoredale type of sequence though workable coals die out.

All the subdivisions described above are absent in the Alston country but farther to the south-west are represented by the thick limestones of Westmorland (page 198). At the base in both areas there is a conglomerate claimed by some as Old Red Sandstone but by others regarded as basal Carboniferous.

The Dun Limestone and its equivalents has been adopted as the base of the Limestone Group and of D Zone. Above it throughout the area there is a Yoredale type of sequence with limestone, shale and sandstone rhythmically repeated. The limestones, often succeeding a coal seam, recur at intervals of about 100 ft. and retain their characters over hundreds of square miles of country. The thickest, apart from the area of the Pennine Escarpment, is the Great Limestone (50–60 ft.) but the others and some of the sandstones and shales have also received individual

names chiefly as a result of lead mining. The main outcrop from the Berwick and Alnmouth coastal tract swings inland alongside the Tyne to the Pennine Escarpment near Brampton. The great breadth of outcrop east of that escarpment is due to the fact that the gentle dip of the measures nearly coincides with the seaward slope of the country. Thus one may travel many miles along the valleys bordered by the outcrop of a particular bed such as the Great Limestone. There are, however, patches of limestone measures let down by faulting or folding amidst lower strata as, for example, in the Border country north of the Solway and to the south of Berwick. In the latter region the synclinal fold partly responsible for the outlier is well displayed on the shore at Green's Haven.

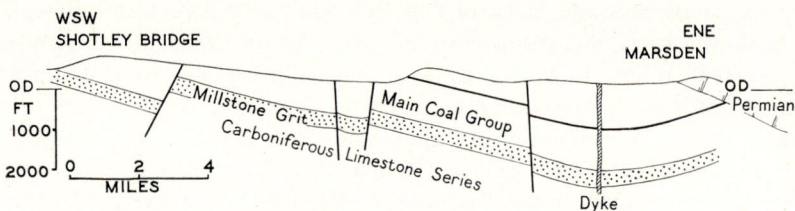

Figure 51. Section across the Durham Coalfield
Note the violent unconformity of the Permian to the Coal Measures. (Based on Fig. 17 Northern England Geol. Surv. Handbook)

The Millstone Grit is not well developed and its limits are open to doubt. Some workers would adopt the Great Limestone as the base, though there are many limestones above that horizon, whereas others would fix the base at a thick sandstone succeeding the highest limestones as has been Survey practice to date and the one chosen here for expediency. The upper limit is the lowest coal of the Coal Measures. Within these bounds the formation ranges from 600 ft. with little shale in Northumberland to 300 ft. in Durham made up of three grits parted by considerable shales.

About 1,800 ft. of Coal Measures are present in which the principal working coals are restricted to the 700 ft. or so from the Brockwell Coal up to the High Main. In Durham the 200 ft. of measures below the Brockwell include ganisters of which the most famous is that of Tow Law at the base. Above the High Main massive sandstones predominate and include the 120-ft. Newcastle Grindstone and the Seventy Fathom Post—local developments about the same horizon respectively south and north of the Tyne.

The Barren Red Measures of Scotland and the Whitehaven Sandstone of Cumberland do not appear to be present, but the non-marine lamellibranchs provide correlation with these and other coalfields.

In addition to the main field there are outliers of Coal Measures as far west as Midgeholme let down by the Stubbick Fault, and also near Barnard Castle.

Whereas it is true that in general the measures dip gently seawards it is known

that as the coast is approached in south Durham the strata turn up and the coals crop against the Permian cover (see Fig. 51). Similar conditions prevail off the mouth of the Tyne and are likely to continue northwards undersea to beyond Amble thus completing the eastern rim of a basin elongated north-south, hidden partly by the sea and partly by Permian rocks, the latter lying discordantly with a dip to the east and south-east.

PERMIAN AND TRIAS   Apart from the small outlier at Cullercoats the outcrop of Permian strata is continuous southwards. Most of it, about 800 ft., consists of the Magnesian Limestone; this passes down into 15 ft. of Marl Slate, famous for fish, amphibian and plant remains, which in turn rests on the Yellow Sands a deposit filling in hollows in the Carboniferous rocks and consequently of irregular thickness but not exceeding 100 ft. The lower part of the Magnesian Limestone is a blue-grey evenly bedded rock fossiliferous only in south Durham. Next comes the Shell Limestone—reef-like masses with many shells and bryozoa—flanked to the west by bedded dolomites and to the east by brecciated dolomites and buried in part by concretionary limestones. Overlying these are the massive oolitic Hartlepool and Roker dolomites succeeded by the flaggy dolomites of Billingham. The Shelly Limestone may be seen at Blackhall Rocks east of Castle Eden and on Beacon Hill, the brecciated dolomites in Frenchman's Bay near Tynemouth and the concretionary limestones at Fulwell near Sunderland.

Near Middlesbrough Triassic rocks are brought against Magnesian Limestone by faulting. The rocks are largely concealed by drift but red sandstones representing Bunter and Keuper pass downwards into marls associated with salt and gypsum deposits and upwards into the Keuper Marl which is succeeded by the Rhaetic and Lias of Redcar. These are the youngest rocks in the district apart from some of the dykes.

The Permo-Trias of the Eden Valley is dealt with on p. 199; here it may suffice to state that Magnesian Limestone is virtually absent from that tract.

WHIN SILL AND DYKES   There are two systems of dykes: one of E.N.E. or east-west trend which do not cut Permian rocks and the other ranging W.N.W. to link up with the Mull swarm which cut Permian and later strata and are presumed to be of Tertiary date. With the former are associated various sills affecting strata from Carboniferous Limestone to Coal Measures; of these the most famous is the series of lenses collectively known as the Great Whin Sill and seen at intervals throughout the limestone country. Bamburgh Castle stands on such a sill and there is another fine exposure at Castle Point, Embleton; on the escarpment High Cup Nick may be mentioned with farther east both sides of Teesdale and the waterfall of High Force. A thickness of about 100 ft. is common but the sill is 240 ft. thick at Burtree Pasture Mine in Weardale. Hett Whin Dyke traceable for 20 miles in south Durham is the best-known pre-Permian dyke and the Acklington Dyke ranging from south of Amble through Hawick the best of the Tertiary suite. Both dykes and sills are dolerites but the more recent set is the less basic and has a glassy matrix.

MINERAL DEPOSITS Two classes of mineral deposits other than coal make this district famous: the lead–zinc–iron–fluor–barium deposits occurring in veins and associated flats (where the mineralizing fluids have replaced certain beds of limestone) and those of salt, gypsum and anhydrite. The former are mainly in the limestone country particularly the Great Limestone of Alston, Weardale and Reesdale though a few extend into the Coal Measures with the result that some collieries in Durham work barytes and witherite as well as coal. These barium minerals tend to predominate in veins at the periphery of the orefield; inwards from this zone galena (PbS) and blende (ZnS) or chalybite ($FeCO_3$) become abundant giving place interiorly to fluor.

The bedded deposits are confined to the Permo-Trias with gypsum in the Eden Valley and anhydrite and salt respectively in the Billingham and Hartlepool areas of the east.

REFERENCES

Geological Survey
   Regional Handbooks: Northern England, ed 3, 1953. *South of Scotland*, ed 2, 1948.
   North Pennine Orefield, vol. 1, 1948.
Excursions and Field Meetings
   International Geological Congress 1948.
   Long Excursions: C9 N.E. Coast; A1 Economic; A19 Scotland, General.
Geologists Association, Proceedings
   1931, Newcastle and Durham.
Yorkshire Geological Society, Proceedings
   1952, Durham. 1960, Durham.

SHEET 18

GALLOWAY

ROXBURGH

SELKIRKSHIRE

DUMFRIESSHIRE

KIRKCUDBRIGHTSHIRE

AYR

WIGTOWN SHIRE

CARLISLE

WORKINGTON

DUMFRIES

New Galloway

Castle Douglas

Dalbeattie

Kirkcudbright

Gatehouse of Fleet

Girvan

Ballantrae

Whithorn

Port William

Stranraer

Portpatrick

LOCH RYAN

LUCE BAY

BURROW HEAD

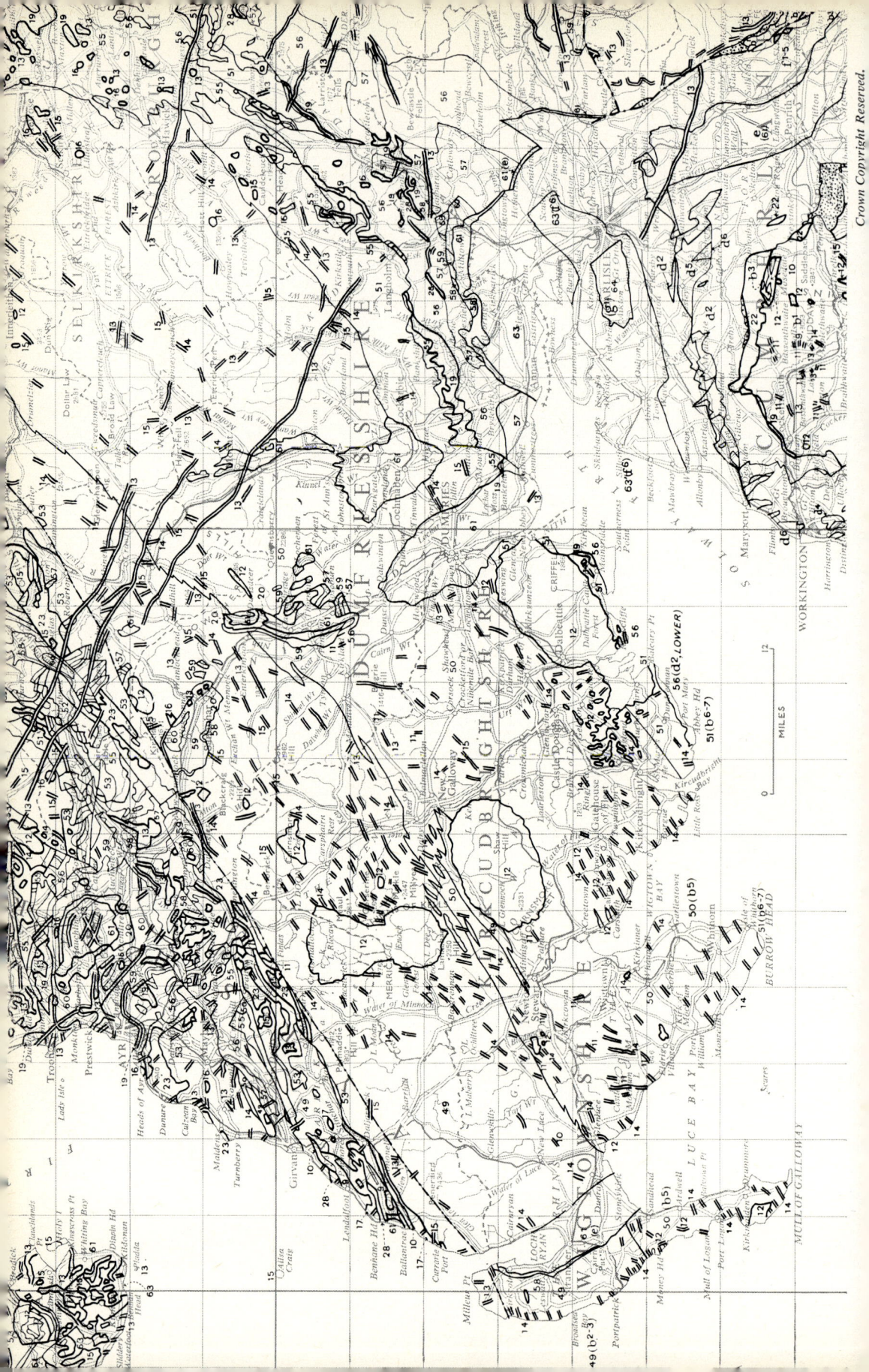

MULL OF GALLOWAY

SOLWAY FIRTH

WIGTOWN BAY

Ailsa Craig

Turnberry

Benbane Hill

MILES

0   12

GALLOWAY

ON THE north, this sheet, which may be described as of the Burns country, takes in Galston and Biggar, on the east just omits Hawick and on the south includes Cockermouth though the Cumbrian portion is dealt with elsewhere as is also the southern half of Arran and part of the northern fringe. It therefore covers much of south-west Scotland—fairly thickly populated on the north in the coalfields but much less so to the south and even there most of the people are concentrated into such places as the port of Stranraer and manufacturing and market towns such as Annan, Dumfries and Moffat with industries dependent on wool, agriculture, sheep and cattle raising. Being part of the Southern Uplands most of the country, as may be expected, lies high apart from the coastal tracts. Heights range from 2,680 ft. on Dollar Law and 2,695 ft. on White Coomb north of Moffat to the 2,000–3,000 ft. mountains about New Galloway though such hills as Criffel rising from the coastal plain are much more conspicuous. There is considerable drainage to the south by the Dee, Nith, Annan and Liddel, some goes westerly, as by the Ayr, and east via the Tweed but much goes into the Clyde which rises near Wanlock-head.

Slaty Ordovician and Silurian rocks dominate the country with Carboniferous mainly in the north-west about Ayr partly connected by outliers, such as at Sanquhar and Thornhill, to the fringes of Carboniferous rocks along the Solway and the Border country. There is Old Red Sandstone about and east of Maybole and New Red Sandstone east of Ayr, at Stranraer, and along the Solway, but much more conspicuous on the map are the outcrops the Galloway Granites. Not shown on these maps but of some importance are the recent marine and estuarine deposits. These have filled in former broad estuaries—such as that from Newton Stewart to Wigtown Bay, those up to Gatehouse of Fleet, to Kirkcudbright, to Dalbeattie and to Dumfries with broad fringing sea marshland and sands, particularly about Annan—to match those across the Solway. On the west similar deposits in a tract four miles wide connect Loch Ryan and Luce Bay where there is a considerable area of blown sand. There are also fringes of marine alluvium north of Girvan and about Prestwick with sand dunes in the latter area.

The old rocks of the Southern Uplands are closely folded along axes of N.E.—S.W. trend; of similar trend is the Great Southern Upland Fault which separates most of the old rocks from Carboniferous and associated rocks occupying the Midland Valley of Scotland.

ORDOVICIAN—SILURIAN These rocks occupy a belt about forty miles wide in the Southern Uplands; of this belt about the northern third are Ordovician, the rest Silurian. The oldest rocks recognized are referred to the Arenig Series. These

are black shales, with cherts of various colours, partly interbedded with tuffs and associated in the lower part with lavas of a peculiar nature poured out on a sea bottom and known as spilites. The lavas, dark green and decomposed, are particularly well developed about Ballantrae. Sections there at Bennane Head reveal 700 ft. of lavas followed by 800 ft. of coarse agglomerates and tuffs and these by 70 ft. of red, green and grey radiolarian cherts interstratified with tuffs. Thin black shales in the tuffs yield graptolites such as *Didymograptus*. These lavas may be seen in the railway cutting at Killochan station and in quarries at Craighead both north-east of Girvan and similar rocks to those of Bennane Head are brought up in the folds of anticlines east of New Cumnock.

In addition to the lavas there are intrusions of serpentine, gabbro and granite in the Girvan–Ballantrae area where they may be seen along the coast.

The Arenig rocks of Girvan are there succeeded by 3,000 ft. of massive conglomerates, grits, shales and mudstones with limestones; these rocks carry corals, shells, trilobites and some graptolites. About 60 ft. of mudstones with limestones may be seen between thick conglomerates in Benan Burn a tributary to the Stinchar six miles S.E. of Girvan. The whole constitutes the Barr Series equivalent to the thin Glenkiln Shales (named from Glenkiln midway between Thornhill and Locker-bie) where there is a shale sequence upwards from radiolarian cherts to the Gala Group of the Silurian.

The succeeding Ardmillan Series of the Girvan area is mainly of flags but included thin shales with graptolites as well as shells and trilobites denote equivalence with the 100-ft. dark Hartfell Shales of Moffat (see page 224) and of a broad belt of rocks intermediate between these two types in the intervening tract.

There is some doubt as to whether the Glenkiln and Barr Series should be referred to the Llandeilo or to Lower Caradocian but it is accepted that the Ardmillan and Hartfell groups should be divided between Upper Caradocian and Ashgillian.

The succeeding Silurian rocks show similar lateral differences in lithology. The Lower Llandovery Series of Girvan comprises 700 ft. of conglomerates, sandstones and shales with limestones; the fauna is mainly of corals, shells and trilobites but again includes some graptolites enabling correlation to be made with 150 ft. of the black graptolitic Birkhill Shales of Moffat (page 224). On the other hand the Upper Llandovery of both areas is largely of sandstone and is 3,000–4,000 ft. thick.

Llandovery strata occupy a broad median belt in the Southern Uplands ranging from fifteen to twenty-five miles wide; nearly the full sequence is present in Luce Bay. Apart from some inliers north of the Southern Uplands Fault (see page 225) the outcrop of Wenlock and higher strata is confined to the south in a strip up to five miles wide ranging from Abbey Head (near Kirkcudbright) to south of Hawick where the Ordovician–Silurian outcrop is transgressed by Old Red Sandstone.

Lithologically the transition from Llandovery to Wenlock is not marked for grits and shales with conglomerates again are common. The lower or Riccarton Group, 1,000 to 1,500 ft. thick, is well exposed in Burrow Head where seams of dark shales yield graptolites such as *Cyrtograptus murchisoni*, *Monograptus priodon*, etc.

The succeeding Raeberry Castle group, 500–750 ft. thick, includes green shales with nodules of limestone carrying shelly fossils. There is a narrow strip of these beds at the end of Burrow Head and a two-mile wide belt at the seaward ends of Kirkcudbright Bay with sections near Abbey Burnfoot, Gipsy Point and Raeberry Cliffs. At White Port near Abbey Head they are overlain unconformably by the basal conglomerate of the Carboniferous.

Ludlow strata appear to be absent in south-west Scotland but with Downtonian beds may be present north of the Southern Upland Fault (see page 225).

OLD RED SANDSTONE   Allusion has already been made to the extensive folding affecting the Ordovician and Silurian rocks which is responsible for the great breadths of outcrop of various members having high dips and no great thicknesses. When most of this folding had been completed Old Red sediments were then laid down across the denuded folds. The sediments of the Lower Old Red Sandstone, feldspathic sandstones and conglomerates, are mainly confined to the area north of the Southern Uplands Fault north and east of Girvan where they are associated with lava flows. Upper Old Red Sandstone lies mainly east of the present district though there are patches about Ecclefechan, Langholm and near Riccarton Junction, mainly of red sandstone. Of much more importance, however, are the great igneous masses of Lower Old Sandstone age though the youngest rocks into which they are visibly intruded are Silurian strata.

IGNEOUS ROCKS   The principal intrusions are those of Loch Doon, Cairnsmore of Fleet, and Criffel.

The Loch Doon mass, extending eleven miles from Loch Doon on the north to Loch Dee on the south and about four miles wide, has invaded Ordovician strata comprising grits and shales which have been considerably metamorphosed. The mass includes several types of rock but three predominate; these are the moderately coarse biotite granite with white feldspars of the central ridge with a grey tonalite or granodiorite on its flanks and two masses of norite (hypersthene gabbro) which occur on the south and in the north-western corner of the complex. All contain clots of dissimilar rocks. As against the older concept of plutonic intrusions some authors invoke extreme alteration of sediments by invading magmatic material for this complex mass of apparently igneous rocks.

The Cairnsmore of Fleet mass is roughly oval in outcrop and is a fairly typical coarse grey granite though most of the mica is black biotite rather than silvery muscovite. On the north-west it is in contact with Ordovician rocks brought up on the crest of an anticlinal fold; elsewhere at surface it lies wholly in Llandovery rocks.

The Criffel mass rises boldly from the coastal tract of the Solway through Llandovery and Wenlock strata. It is a coarse grey granite with biotite and hornblende but with a little muscovite. There are quarries at Dalbeattie and near Creetown. On the eastern side of Criffel the granite is foliated.

The smaller granite masses of Carsphairn and of Crammag Head in the Mull of Galloway call for little comment but the island of Ailsa Craig is made up of a

peculiar fine-grained riebeckite granite (rather similar to that of Arran, page 234), pebbles of which serve as an indicator of ice movements in the drifts bordering the Irish Sea. There are small masses of porphyry north of Kirkcudbright and innumerable north-east dykes, mainly of diorite.

There are also some dykes of north-west trend, as for example, that through Moffat cutting Permian Sandstone. These are regarded as of Tertiary age and as part of the Mull swarm (see page 250).

The intrusion of the larger masses of granite has induced considerable alteration in the invaded sediments. Shales develop chiastolite and the flags and grits become hard hornfels with biotite, cordierite and garnet while cherts are recrystallized into quartzites. The metamorphic effect of the small masses and dykes is negligible.

CARBONIFEROUS The Carboniferous rocks fringing the northern shore of the Solway commence with conglomerates on Abbey Head but farther to the north-east there are basaltic lavas at the base. These are well developed about Ecclefechan but less so beyond Langholm. They are followed upwards by about 700 ft. of Whita Sandstone—pink below, yellow gritty and false-bedded above—and these by over 1,000 ft. of shales and mudstones with thin limestones, carrying lamellibranch shells and algal fossils, referable to the Cementstone Group. Next comes about 500 ft. of sandstones (Fell Sandstone) and about 300 ft. of tuffs and lavas (Glencartholme Volcanic Group) followed by about 400 ft. of mixed measures of sandstone, shale and marine limestones with coal seams. The coals, usually thin and poor, are locally workable on the English side of the Border. The strata up to this level are referred to the Calciferous Sandstone Series (see pages 226 and 235).

The succeeding 1,200 ft. of the Limestone Series, as in the rest of Scotland, has a median coal-bearing group though the coals here are of little value. The limestones are thicker than those below and contain such corals as *Dibunophyllum* and *Lithostrotion* with large shells of *Productus*; there are good exposures at Penton Linn in Liddel Water. Reddish limestones occur in the Thornhill outlier.

Apart from about 600 ft. of sandstones in a boring near Canonbie and referred to this group the Millstone Grit is not developed in this part of Scotland other than as thin bauxitic clays such as occur in the Sanquhar Coalfield between the Coal Measures and the floor of thin limestones on Ordovician strata. This transgression is in great contrast to the full sequence of rocks about New Cumnock just over the Southern Uplands Fault and to those in the next inlier to the south about Thornhill with Limestone Series and Coal Measures partly concealed by Permian sandstones. In the Sanquhar Coalfield there are three good coals and a representative of Skipsey's Marine Band followed by some Barren Red Measures.

Similar measures are present in the small coalfield of Canonbie. On the English side of the Border (in Jockies Syke) the Barren Red Measures resemble those of the Keele Beds of the Midlands both in appearance and in fossil plants.

NEW RED SANDSTONE This formation includes Permian and Triassic strata. The former consists of red false-bedded sandstones interleaved with bands of breccia and towards the base in Sanquhar and Thornhill associated with lava flows.

The rounded polished grains in the sandstones and the interleaved breccias invite comparison with the Penrith Sandstone. Footprints of reptiles believed to be Permian are found in sandstone quarries at Corncockle Muir (north of Lochmaben and near the centre of the Annan outlier). In Nithsdale there is a considerable tract of Permian with numerous sandstone quarries about Dumfries, and there are smaller patches to the north about Thornhill and Sanquhar.

Farther to the west the hollow between Lock Ryan and Luce Bay is floored by Permian sandstone and breccia largely concealed by recent deposits; similar rocks fringe the coast between Ballantrae and Bennane Head.

Triassic rocks are confined to the Solway from about Annan eastwards. Except in the upper part they are less false-bedded than the Permian sandstones and the constituent grains more angular. In place of breccias there are some shale beds though locally there is a basal conglomerate where the beds transgress on to Carboniferous rocks.

ECONOMIC PRODUCTS   Apart from building stones, of which the most important are the red sandstones of the Permo-Trias and the granites quarried about Dalbeattie and Creetown for dock work and road stones, there is little of economic value outside the coalfields with the exception of the lead deposits of Wanlockhead and Leadhills situated midway between Dumfries and Biggar. These were worked until recently and may be reopened. The galena associated with some blende, calcite and quartz occurs in several N.N.W. veins in Ordovician strata. Other minerals include haematite on the east side of the Loch Doon Granite and minor occurrences of copper, antimony, barytes, etc.; gold occurs in some alluvial deposits in the Leadhills; silver accompanies lead.

REFERENCES

Geological Survey
  Regional Handbooks: South of Scotland, ed 2, 1948; *Midland Valley of Scotland*, ed 2, 1948.
  Silurian Rocks of Britain, vol. 1, 1899.
Excursions and Field Meetings
  International Geological Congress 1948.
  Long Excursions: A15 Arran and S.W. Scotland; A19 Scotland, General.
Geologists Association, Proceedings
  1933, Girvan–Ballantrae. 1938, Dumfries.

SHEET 19

EDINBURGH AND GLASGOW

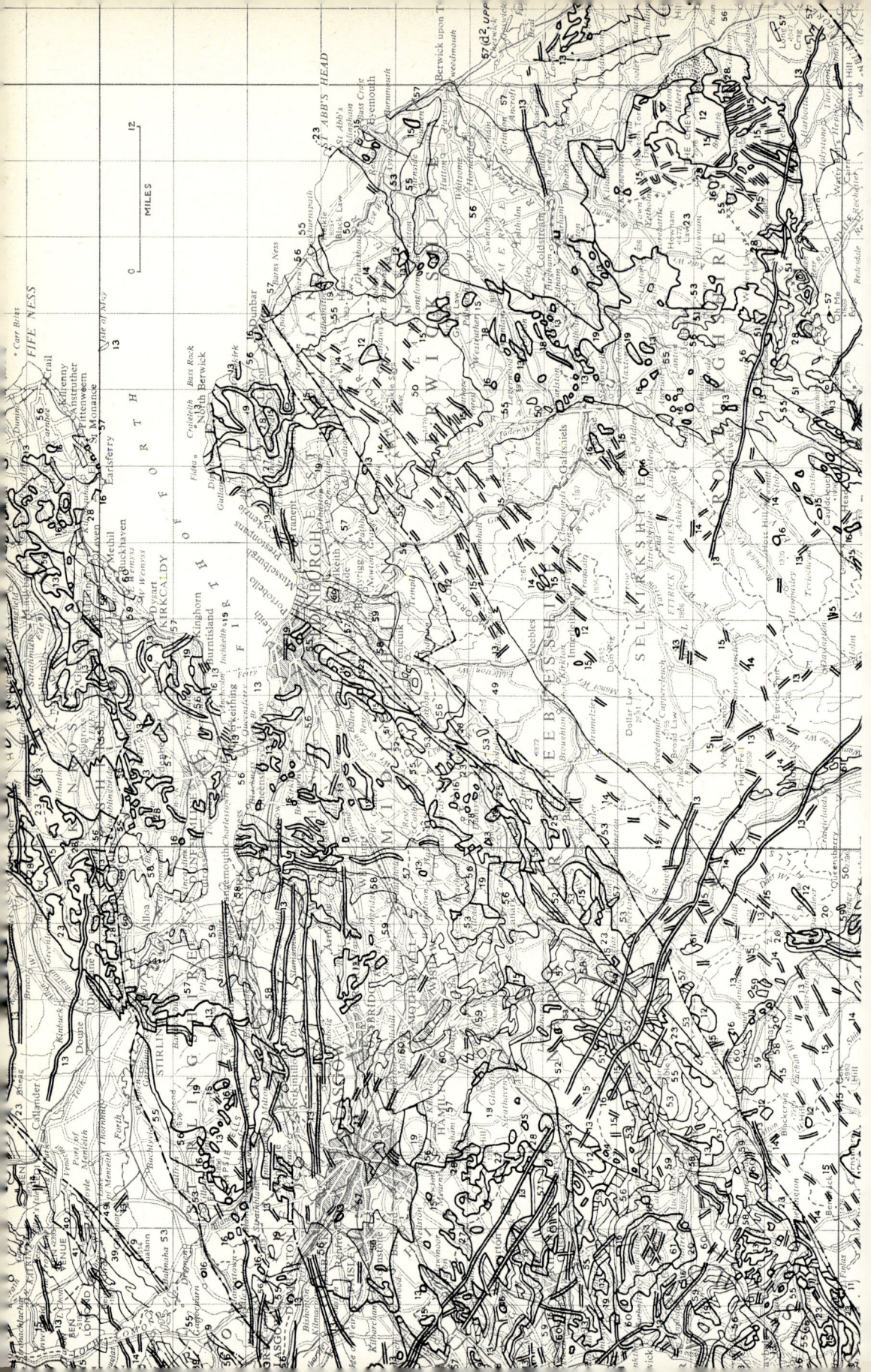

EDINBURGH AND GLASGOW

THIS sheet extends from Fife Ness to Lock Katrine thence southwards to Dalmellington and eastwards via Moffat to a meridian through Berwick. It thus includes the greater part of the Central Valley with its thick population engaged in coal mining and the engineering and shipbuilding based on the iron and steel trade as well as much of the thinly populated Southern Uplands and the Cheviot country though an account of the latter is included with that of the Northumberland–Durham Coalfield region. The Central Valley (Fig. 52) occupies a trough fault of which the northern member is the Highland Boundary Fault, between the Firth of Clyde and Stonehaven near Aberdeen, and the southern member is the Southern Uplands Fault between Ballantrae and Dunbar. The trough was obviously initiated in very early geological times for some of its rocks, which range upwards from the Lower Old Red Sandstone, transgress its boundary faults as, for example, the Coal Measures of Sanquhar. In general, however, to the north of the trough lie the Dalradian schists of the Highlands and to the south of it Ordovician—Silurian strata whereas the trough itself is occupied by Old Red Sandstone, chiefly on the

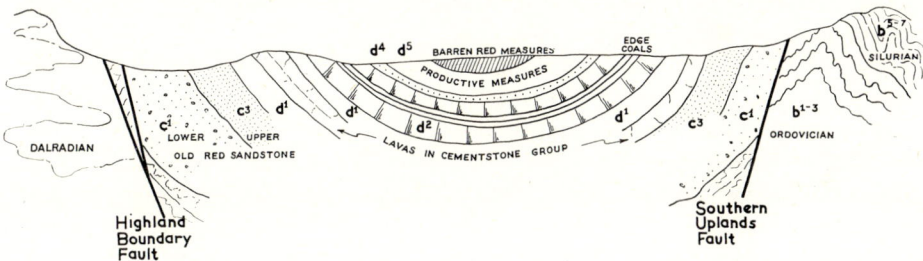

Figure 52. Diagrammatic section across the Central Valley to show sequence and simplified structure

Older Palaeozoic rocks are caught up in the Highland Boundary Fault but their relation to the Ordovician and Silurian south of the Southern Boundary Fault is unknown. The Edge Coals occur in the Limestone Series and are separated from the Productive Coal Measures by barren Millstone Grit and the Upper Limestone Group.

flanks, Carboniferous and Permian rocks. The counties involved include Fife and Stirling, the Lothians, Lanark, Berwick, Roxburgh, Selkirk, Peebles and part of Ayrshire. Much of the drainage is to the west via the Clyde but in the eastern tract there are the Forth and the Tweed and to the south rivers running to the Solway, such as the Nith, Annan and Liddel. Apart from the Central Valley and that is well diversified and by no means low-lying most of the country is ground above

1,000 ft. and often exceeds 2,000 ft. with hills aligned chiefly north-east—south-west.

LOWER PALAEOZOIC ROCKS Apart from the small area of schists and slates, included in the north-western corner of the Sheet near Loch Lomond and dealt with elsewhere (see page 245), the oldest rocks of the area are the slaty rocks constituting the Southern Uplands. These comprise Ordovician strata, cropping out in a strip commencing near Dunbar and widening south-westwards to over ten miles, and rather similar Silurian rocks occupying a much broader belt to the south between Peebles and Hawick. Both are highly folded and both are transgressed on the east by Old Red Sandstone between Hawick and Dunbar indicating that the principal folding was of Caledonian age. There are two primary folds made up of numerous parallel flexures. In the northern fold area mainly affecting the Ordovician rocks the flexures dip inwards giving the appearance of a syncline; in the southern fold belt the flexures dip outwards as if anticlinal.

The oldest members of the Ordovician are referred to the Arenig Series and are mainly dark mudstones with black shales and cherts of various colours. In the area to the south-west these strata are associated with submarine lava flows and other igneous rocks (see page 216). In the Moffat area these are represented by the tuffs of Trowdale.

There is some divergence of opinion as to the presence or otherwise of Middle Ordovician strata as certain diagnostic graptolites have not yet been found but the sequence upwards in some places is still of black shales and cherts, totalling about 200 ft., though in the Lammermuir Hills and the Leadhills there is over a thousand feet of grits and conglomerates.

The succeeding Silurian strata begin with about 150 ft. of black shales (named Birkhill Shales from a locality of that name north-east of Moffat) followed by 3,000–4,000 ft. (Gala Group) mainly of grits and flags but with some shales. These, referable to Valentian (Llandovery) Series, make up the greater part of the broad outcrop of Silurian rocks; south of Hawick they are succeeded by conglomerates, grits and shales of the Riccarton Beds which represent part of the Wenlock Series.

The type area for these Ordovician and Silurian rocks is Dobb's Linn, near Birkhill Cottage at the head of Moffat Water and about 9 miles N.N.E. of Moffat, a region made classic by the researches of Lapworth. Along the valley runs a north-south fault with a throw of about 50 ft. bringing crumpled Hartfell Shales on the east against Glenkiln Shales on the west where the latter occupy the foot of the Main Cliff and yield *Didymograptus superstes*. The succeeding Hartfell Shales (100 ft. thick and named from a fell north of Moffat) include about 40 ft. of barren mudstone in the upper half but provide such graptolites as *Climacograptus*, *Dicranograptus* and *Dicellograptus* lower down. Next and quite conformably come the black Birkhill Shales with *Diplograptus*, *Monograptus* and *Rastrites* in sequence followed by grits and flags of the Gala Group.

Similar beds are brought up in the cores of minor anticlinal folds.

As mentioned above some of the uppermost Ordovician strata are grits and conglomerates. These at Leadhills and Wanlockhead provide the favourable

country rock to lead veins whereas the black shales brought in by folds and perhaps by thrusting have a deadening effect on the veins. Both groups of mines were extensively worked until recent years.

In addition to the main outcrop there are inliers of Silurian rocks. Of these, one of the largest occurs between Lesmahagow and Muirkirk south-west of Lanark; it comprises greywackes, flags and shales totalling near 3,000 ft. of which the upper half that contains beds with *Ceratiocaris* is assumed to be Ludlow, while the lower part may be Wenlock. These are followed by about 2,700 ft. of red sandstones and mudstones, with a fish bed and median conglomerate zone, assigned to the Downtonian. To the south is the smaller inlier of the Hagshaw Hills and Little Cairn Table. The strata here yield typical Silurian fossils including trilobites such as *Calymene blumenbachi*. There are inliers of similar rocks to the north-east in the Tinto Hills and in the Pentland Hills.

OLD RED SANDSTONE   The Old Red Sandstone, violently unconformable to the underlying beds, falls into two subdivisions of Lower and Upper Old Red Sandstone. Both are represented in the great trough of the Central Valley along its northern and southern flanks and outside that trough south of Dunbar. In the Lower Old Red Sandstone conglomerates and grits are abundant, especially in the lower part; they are followed by softish red sandstones. In the north-western tract the conglomerates contain many pebbles of Highland rocks. In the south the stones are mainly derived from the Southern Uplands and include greywacke, slate, chert and jasper; here the sedimentary rocks may reach a thickness of 2,000 ft. and they are overlain by thick volcanic rocks.

The volcanic rocks of Lower Old Red Sandstone age are mainly lavas though there are some intercalated tuffs, mostly coarse, along with ashy sandstones and some volcanic agglomerates filling necks. Olivine basalts predominate in the lavas but there are some andesites, as near Dalmellington and in the Pentland Hills, and rocks approaching rhyolites. The so-called Scotch Pebbles of agate represent silica amygdales weathered out of the lavas to form with other rocks pebbles in river gravels.

In addition to the volcanic rocks there are many intrusives. These are chiefly of felsite which, being hard, gives rise to prominent hills such as Black Hill in the Pentlands south-west of Edinburgh, Tinto south-east of Lanark and farther west the fells of Garleffin and Glenalla near Straiton (Sheet 20). In addition there are many sills of diorite and dolerite. One of the most interesting masses is that of Distinkhorn which occurs on the west side of the Silurian inlier of Muirkirk; this includes a variety of rocks ranging between granites and diorites. Another noteworthy locality is furnished by the Pentland Hills (south-west of Edinburgh) which not only show strata ranging from Ordovician to Carboniferous but also various types of lavas and tuffs interbedded with Old Red Sandstone, vents with agglomerates, and intrusions of felsite and diorite.

During Middle Old Red Sandstone times the area in common with most of the Scottish mainland was subject to folding, uplift and denudation with the result that Upper Old Red Sandstone not only rests unconformably on Lower Old Red but

transgresses on older strata. Upper Old Red Sandstone occurs about Kinross where it succeeds Lower Old Red lavas and west of Stirling where it follows Lower Old Red sediments. On the south side of the trough it reappears on similar strata north-east of Lanark and outside the trough occurs in force between Dunbar and Hawick mostly resting on various members of the Ordovician and Silurian though south of St. Abb's Head succeeding Lower Old Red Sandstone strata.

There is usually some conglomerate near the base of the series but the greater part of the sequence is made up of clean bright red sandstones though these become paler (even yellow and white) towards the top of the formation. There are sub-ordinate bands of cornstone (impure limestone) and of shales and marls. The formation is estimated to be 1,500 ft. thick about Kinross.

The sandstones furnish excellent building stones as, for example, in the Craig-millar Quarries, Edinburgh and quarries near Dunbar. There are no outstanding fossil fish localities in the area though *Holoptychius* has been got from Salisbury Crags Edinburgh (Fig. 54).

The absence of lava flows is in marked contrast to Lower Old Red Sandstone.

CARBONIFEROUS   In Scotland the Carboniferous falls into the subdivisions tabled below (see also Fig. 52).

Coal Measures	⎧ Barren Red Measures: reddish sandstones and marls ⎨ Productive Measures: grey shales and sandstones with ⎩ valuable coal seams; some ironstones
Millstone Grit	: Massive sandstones
Limestone Series	⎧ Upper Limestone Group: thin marine limestones alter- ⎪ nating with shales and sandstones ⎨ Limestone or Edge Coals: similar to Coal Measures but ⎪ ironstones commoner ⎩ Lower Limestone Group: similar to Upper Group
Calciferous Sandstone Series	⎧ Oil Shale Group: oil shales intercalated with shales, ⎪ sandstones and occasional thin freshwater limestones ⎨ Cementstones: rapid alternations of shales and thin ⎩ argillaceous dolomites

The Lower Carboniferous is unlike that of most of England and Wales but has some affinity with that of Northumberland and North Cumberland in its lower part and with its Yoredale facies of alternating limestones, shales and sandstones with the Dale Country of Yorkshire in its upper part. The Millstone Grit is not strictly comparable with that of England in that the lower third of it, below a palaeontological break, is deemed equivalent to the uppermost part of the English Lower Carboniferous. The Coal Measures are more nearly of the English type and greatly resemble those of Cumberland. At all stages up to and including the Millstone Grit there are volcanic episodes where lavas take the place of sediments either wholly or in part. These volcanic outbreaks tend to occur at higher horizons in the sequence when traced from east to west. The strata of all the subdivisions are affected by igneous intrusions mainly in the form of dykes and sills. Some of

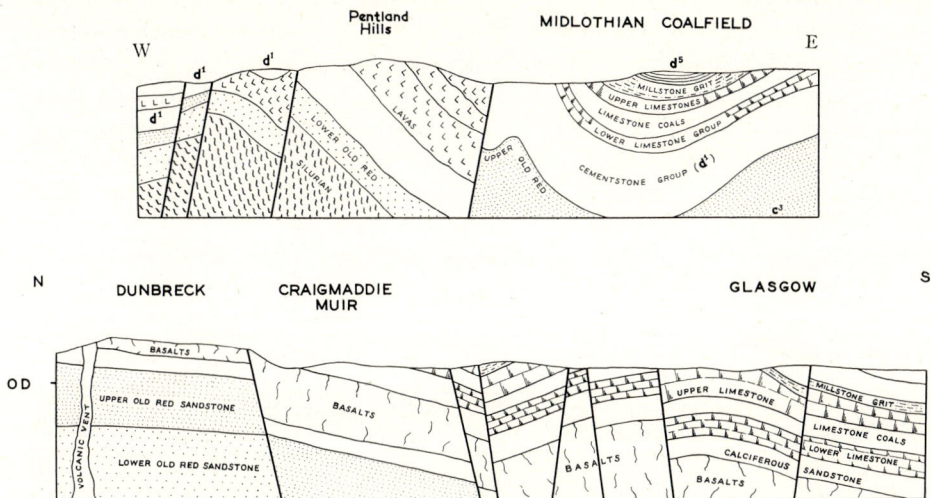

Figure 53. Sections in the Edinburgh and Glasgow areas to show variations in sequences

The Pentland lavas include rhyolites, trachytes, andesites and basalts. (Based on the respective One-inch Geological Sheets)

these have destroyed large areas of coal though it is interesting to record that in the vicinity of intrusions the ordinary bituminous coals are in places converted to anthracite.

There are not only marked variations in the kinds of rocks from place to place but also great variations in thickness of individual groups and of the whole. The maximum of 7,000 ft. is attained in East Fife decreasing westwards to 2,500 ft. in North Ayrshire. The thickness of individual groups will be dealt with under detailed accounts but although much of Ayrshire falls into another region some comments are given hereunder for the sake of completeness.

The Cementstone Group with normal sediments is about 500 ft. thick in East Fife and there is about 4,000 ft. of the Oil Shale Group. To the west the place of sediments is taken more and more by lavas until in the Glasgow and Ayrshire districts they may locally replace the whole though elsewhere in those districts up to about 1,000 ft. of sediments of the Oil Shale Group may be present. It may be mentioned that the volcanic rock of Arthur's Seat Edinburgh (Fig. 54) is near the junction of the Cementstone and Oil Shale groups. The beds of oil shale from which mineral oil is distilled are best developed in Midlothian, West Lothian and parts of Fife.

The Lower Limestone Group begins, with a change of flora, at the Hurlet or Main Limestone and extends to the top of the Hosie Limestones; its variations in thickness are somewhat erratic from 610 ft. in Fife, 380 ft. in north-east Stirling, 700 ft. in Kilsyth, 480 ft. in Glasgow to 120 ft. in North Ayrshire.

The Limestone Coal Group ranges from 1,600 ft. in Fife to 650 ft. in Ayrshire; its valuable coals are worked in many places but the ironstones on which iron trade of Scotland commenced are now but little wrought.

The Upper Limestone Group extending from the Index to the Castlecary Limestone decreases from about 1,600 ft. in the north-east to 900 ft. in Glasgow and 260 ft. in Ayrshire. Sandstones abundant in the upper part of the Coal group now predominate.

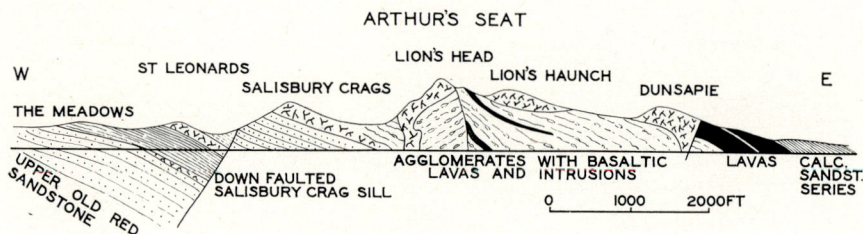

Figure 54. A section through the volcanic complex of Arthur's Seat
(Based on Fig. 4, *Edinburgh*, Geol. Surv. Mem., 1910)

The Millstone Grit is mainly massive coarse sandstone but there are some ganisters and fireclays of value though coals are thin and poor. It decreases from over 1,000 ft. in Fife to 300 ft. in Glasgow; in Ayrshire it is largely represented by volcanic rocks. About a third of the way up in the Millstone Grit great changes in flora and fauna set in; with respect to the former a fairly obvious change is that the ribs of *Calamites* alternate at the nodes above this horizon whereas below many do not; there is also a marked change in fishes but with invertebrates the change occurs at or near the Castlecary Limestone.

It has been stated already that the lower Scottish Millstone Grit is referable to the upper part of the English Limestone Series; the zones of the latter are not fully recognizable in Scotland but the limestone groups there appear to range upwards from D_2.

The Productive Measures thin from 1,700 ft. in Fife to 700 ft. in Ayrshire. The coals are mainly of the bituminous class; those of Lanarkshire are now nearly exhausted but there are large reserves in the north-east.

Skipsey's Marine Band at the top of the Productive Measures affords correlation with the English and Welsh coalfields. Beneath it occur respectively the 'mussel' zones of Similis-Pulchra, Modiolaris and Communis while above it in the Barren Red Measures are those of Phillipsi and Tenuis. Fossil plants, of less importance for zonal correlation, are well represented.

The Barren Red Measures over 1,000 ft. thick in Fife are only 300 ft. thick in Ayrshire where they are succeeded by up to 500 ft. of Permian lavas and these by 1,500 ft. of bright red and orange sandstone—the Mauchline Sandstone. Some of the volcanic necks in other districts are regarded as of Permian age.

IGNEOUS ROCKS   These include lava flows, intrusive sills and dykes, some tuffs and agglomerate filling vents or volcanic necks. As it is impossible to determine the precise age of some intrusions other than as Permo-Carboniferous they are included here.

The bulk of the lavas are basalts; most are olivine-bearing and some of these carry large crystals of feldspar whereas others are fine-grained throughout. There are, however, some trachytes, as for example, the large spread from the Garleton Hills near Haddington to the coast west of North Berwick, and also some rhyolites. In that district they are associated with trachytic tuffs but, as one may expect, most tuffs are of basaltic type such as may be seen about North Berwick. The tuffs here are associated with strata of Calciferous Sandstone age; at higher levels tuffs are less common.

There are many volcanic necks filled with basaltic agglomerates often threaded by basaltic intrusions. These stumps of old volcanoes often form hills, as, for example, Arthur's Seat of Edinburgh (Fig. 54), the Saline Hills (north-west of Dunfermline), Binn Hill (Burntisland), Largo Hill (near Leven), the Campsie Fells (north of Glasgow); of a neck completely filled with basalt the Castle Rock Edinburgh may be quoted.

There are also plugs of trachytic rocks as, for example, Bass Rock and North Berwick Law while east of Haddington there are large sills exposed, for example, at Pencraig Quarry.

More completely denuded vents may be studied on the shore about North Berwick.

Farther west Lower Carboniferous basaltic lavas are present in force in the Bathgate Hills and north-west of Strathaven while still farther west are Permian lavas, up to 500 ft. thick, beneath the Mauchline Sandstone. Associated with the latter are numerous volcanic necks.

Quartz dolerite, similar to the Whin Sill south of the Border, is the prevalent type of rock in the numerous dykes and sills. Some of the sills attain a thickness of 300 ft. and the longer dykes a breadth up to 150 ft. but most are smaller. Stirling Castle stands on the cragged scarp of a thick sill and the northern parts of the Forth Bridge are supported by another.

Tertiary Dykes—These are of north-west trend and a prominent group of them extends from beyond Moffat to the Firth of Clyde and thence to Mull. They are of doleritic type often with a glassy rather than finely crystalline matrix.

REFERENCES

Geological Survey
  Regional Handbooks: Midland Valley of Scotland, ed 2, 1948. *South of Scotland*, ed 2, 1948.
  Coalfield Memoirs.
  Silurian Rocks of Britain, vol. 1, 1899.
Excursions and Field Meetings
  International Geological Congress 1948.
    Long Excursions: C13 Edinburgh and St. Andrews; C15 Glasgow District; A19 Scotland,
      General; C16 Vertebrate Palaeontology.
Geologists Association, Proceedings
  1927, Edinburgh.
Yorkshire Geological Society, Proceedings
  1955, Edinburgh. 1961, Glasgow.
Edinburgh Geological Society
  1960, Edinburgh.

SHEET 20

GLASGOW, SOUTH-WEST HIGHLANDS
AND ISLANDS

NORTH

STIRLING

GLASGOW

AYR

SOUND OF BUTE

FIRTH

COLONSAY
(Argyllshire)

SOUND OF ISLAY

SOUND OF GIGHA

MULL OF KINTYRE

BENBANE HEAD

RATHLIN SOUND BENMORE HEAD

MILES

West Reef

GLASGOW, SOUTH-WEST HIGHLANDS AND ISLANDS

WITHIN this sheet lie Colonsay, Jura and Islay, separated from Arran by the long peninsula of Kintyre, and the mainland bordering the Firth of Clyde. It may be described as Scotland in miniature for the principal rock types of Scotland are there represented, and the country ranges from the sparsely populated islands and highlands to the coalfields of Ayrshire and the western part of the Central Valley with the great shipbuilding and engineering works based on the Clyde about Glasgow.

The account that follows is based on localities rather than on rock sequences as elsewhere.

ISLANDS AND PENINSULAS Some of the oldest rocks in the district emerge in south-west Islay where for about ten miles north of Rhinns Point the country is made up of Lewisian Gneiss which includes some hornblende schists. There is a small outlier of Torridonian Sandstone near Portnahaven but the main mass of that formation lies north of the Lewisian and east of Loch Indail as well as making up the islands of Oronsay and Colonsay. The rest of Islay is less simple though it may be described as having a rim of quartzite to schists and slates with some bands of limestone; the latter are important for correlation with other parts of Scotland extending through the Grampian Highlands and as a basis for working out detailed structures. These rocks are classed as Dalradian. To the north-east almost the whole of Jura is made up of a similar quartzite though at the north slates link up through the island of Scarba with those of Easdale near Oban.

The long peninsula is almost bisected by West Loch Tarbert. To the south of that sea loch the country is mainly of quartzose mica schist though through it runs two well-marked bands—one of limestone and the other of epidote–chlorite–hornblende schists known as the Green Beds (see page 246). South of Campbeltown, however, there is a considerable spread of the much younger Lower Old Red Sandstone and to the west of that town about Machrikanish there is some Carboniferous Limestone and a little coalfield.

North of Loch Tarbert there are quartzites and slate-schists similar to those of east Islay. The slaty beds form a central tract about Loch Gaolisport or Killisport and are continued along the north side of Loch Fyne. South of Loch Fyne to the mouth of the Clyde the country is mainly of quartzose schists though with a well marked slate belt extending from the neck of Bute and the foot of Loch Long through Aberfoyle where the slates have been worked extensively for two hundred years. South of this slate belt the schists soon give place to Lower Old Red Sandstone let down by the great Highland Border Fault which ranges from the Clyde to Stonehaven near Aberdeen.

The Isle of Arran differs considerably from the country hitherto described and is to be linked with the islands farther north for like them it has been the scene of Tertiary igneous activity. The northern half of it is made up almost entirely of granite set in a nearly complete circular frame of Dalradian schistose grits bordered in turn by Old Red Sandstone, on the south and east, and by Carboniferous and Permian rocks, in the eastern semicircle.

In the centre, surrounded by Old Red Sandstone and Permian rocks, is a smaller circular outcrop of granite enclosing vent agglomerates and felsites, and associated with diorite and gabbros. Farther to the south-east is a small granite and diorite ring complex amidst felsites and diorites which rise through the Permian and Triassic sediments of the southern half of the island.

The northern granite rises in craggy heights to the summit of Goatfell (2,866 ft.). It is made up of an outer coarse granite against which is chilled a fine-textured granite; both are biotite granites. The surrounding rocks though obviously re-arranged by the intrusion show little alteration.

The earliest members of the central complex are believed to be the gabbro and diorite exposed at the head of Glen Dubh. These are succeeded by a fine-grained granite richer in biotite than the northern granite and containing hornblende in addition. Both are pierced by the vent agglomerates which form a rough ring inside the complex. The rock fragments include much Old Red Sandstone as well as material derived from the Rhaetic, Lias and Chalk along with Tertiary basalts. The whole has been veined by felsites and granophyres. In addition to basaltic lavas there are others of rhyolite; both may be seen on Ard Bheinn.

Lastly there is the microgranite of Tighvein (1,487 ft.) amidst augite-diorite forming part of a rock complex. North-east of Tighvein thick sills and masses of analcite-olivine dolerite partly encircle Lamlash Bay, towards which they decline, from Clauchlands Point to Kingscross Point and the south end of Holy Island (though most of that island is made up of a sill of riebeckite trachyte similar to that of Ailsa Craig). Farther south there is another semicircle of similar dolerites near Dippin Head and to the west of this there are the large sills of quartz dolerite of Auchenhew and Auchareoch hills. Farther west again are the quartz porphyry sills of Bennan Head—Meall Buidhe (726 ft.), Drumadoon Bay and other places. With these are associated thin sills of greenish pitchstone though these are not restricted to the southern part of the island.

The sedimentary rocks of Arran include the Dalradian bordering the northern granite; this series is made up of schistose grits with intercalations of slate. Both Upper and Lower Old Red Sandstone are well represented; the latter has sills of dolerite but is more remarkable in containing a workable vein of barytes (in Glen Sannox). Members of the Scottish Carboniferous from the Calciferous Sandstone to the Coal Measures are represented in the outer rim of the northern granite and coal was at one time worked in the Limestone Series about a mile south-east of Cock of Arran; tuffs and sills of dolerite are also present.

The Permian is of wide distribution and comprises breccias and dune-bedded sandstones; both may be seen about Brodick. The Trias, represented by marls

with sandstones, is well developed in the south; on the south coast it is invaded by countless dykes of olivine dolerite. Later solid formations are represented only by fragments in vents.

MAINLAND The old rocks north of the Highland Border Fault have already been mentioned. South of that fault is another one bounding the Ordovician and Silurian rocks of the Southern Uplands from Ballantrae to Dunbar. The country occupying the trough between these major faults, and known as the Central Valley, contains the chief coalfields (see page 228) but this account is concerned only with the western part. Old Red Sandstone emerges on the sides of this trough and Upper Old Red Sandstone flanks the Clyde in the Rothesay area and between Gourock and Ardrossan.

The Carboniferous rocks lie mainly in two basins both rather badly broken by faulting. The concern here is with the Ayrshire Coalfield for only the western rim of the other enters the sheet near Glasgow.

In the Lower Carboniferous most of the Calciferous Sandstone Series is represented by volcanic rocks—chiefly basaltic lavas. As in other areas the limestone-bearing measures are subdivided by a median coal group the whole ranging from about 1,000 ft. down to less than 100 ft. due to attenuation of the measures; of the higher total about 120 ft. and 260 ft. may be referred respectively to the Lower and Upper Limestone groups of shales, sandstones and limestones. Some of these limestones though seldom exceeding 20 ft. in thickness have proved exceedingly valuable as a source of lime and for iron smelting; they have been extensively quarried and some have been got underground by mining. The Limestone Coal Group, up to about 650 ft. thick, contains useful coal seams though these are less regular in their occurrences than higher coals. The succeeding usually arenaceous series, the Millstone Grit, is represented in most of this district by basalts and the weathering of these lavas has given rise to the Ayrshire Bauxitic Clays used in the manufacture of refractory products.

The Productive Coal Measures, of grey shales and sandstones, are the chief repository of coal seams though many of these are spoiled by intrusions of dolerite. They also contain valuable fireclays and the one time valuable ironstones in the form of bands and nodules. The total thickness of these measures is about 700 ft. They are succeeded by the Barren Red Measures, up to 500 ft. thick, of red and purplish-grey sandstone and shales with occasional thin bands of Spirorbis limestone.

Permian rocks occupy a considerable area in Central Ayrshire. They consist, in the lower part, of about 500 ft. of lavas, mainly olivine-rich basalts, though there are some tuff and desert sand layers between flows and more especially at the base and top of the volcanic series. With these lavas are associated a great series of volcanic necks which pierce both Barren Red Measures and the lavas but not the overlying Mauchline Sandstone Series. The latter, up to 1,500 ft. thick, is of bright red to orange colour, markedly false-bedded, and built up of rounded and polished sand grains. With such characters it is obvious that desert conditions prevailed at

the time of its formation. It has been worked extensively for building purposes at Ballochmyle Quarries, Mauchline, Ayrshire.

REFERENCES

Geological Survey
    Regional Handbooks: Midland Valley of Scotland, ed 2, 1948. *Tertiary Volcanic Districts*, ed 2, 1948.
Excursions and Field Meetings
    International Geological Congress 1948.
      Long Excursions: C15 Glasgow; A15 Arran and S. W. Scotland; A16 South-west Highlands; A19 Scotland, General.
Geologists Association, Proceedings
    1924, Arran.
Geologists Association, Guides
    32, Arran.
      Glasgow District (Bassett, D.A.), 20 excursions.

SHEET 21

DUNDEE

KINCARDINESHIRE
PERTHSHIRE
ANGUS
Stonehaven
Inverbervie
Johnshaven
Milton Ness
Montrose
Scurdie Ness
Lunan Bay
Arbroath
East Haven
Carnoustie
Buddon Ness
Broughty Ferry
Tayport
Newport
MILES
Inchcape or Bell Rock
ST ANDREWS BAY
St Andrews
Kingsbarns
FIFE NESS
Crail
Kilrenny
Anstruther
Pittenweem
St Monance
Isle of May
Earlsferry
Methil
Buckhaven
Dysart
KIRKCALDY
Kinghorn
Burntisland
Inchkeith
Bass Rock
North Berwick
Dunbar
Barns Ness
FIRTH OF FORTH
Brechin
Kirriemuir
Forfar
Coupar Angus
Alyth
Newburgh
Cupar
Crieff
Callander
Doune
Alloa
STIRLING
Grangemouth
Charlestown
Inverkeithing
Kinross
Peter Hill
LOCHNAGAR
Balmoral Forest
Pitlochry
Aberfeldy
Killin
BEN LOMOND
BEN ALDER
Meagaidh
Kinloch Laggan
Dalnaspidal
Uglamain
Bridge of Gaur
Port of Menteith
Thornhill
Laurencekirk
Catterline
Gourdon

DUNDEE

THIS sheet extends from Stonehaven in the north-east to the foot of Loch Lomond in the south-west involving chiefly the counties of Kincardine, Angus, Perth, Fife, Kinross and Stirling. It is bisected diagonally by the Highland Boundary Fault (see Fig. 52) which separates the old and foliated rocks on the north-west, that build up the Grampian Highlands, from the Old Red Sandstone and Carboniferous rocks of the northern part of the Midland Valley including the Fifeshire Coalfield. The foliated rocks give rise to barren high ground, much of it ranging to well over 3,000 ft., with small and scattered communities in the deep valleys which drain mainly into the Firth of Tay. On the other hand the younger rocks, often with a drift cover, provide better soils and carry a larger population mostly in towns of considerable size; this country is by no means flat for it includes the Campsie Fells, the Ochil Hills and the Sidlaw Hills though in general the heights seldom exceed 1,000 ft. Industries range from farming and coal mining, with slate quarrying at Aberfoyle, to general manufactures including jute at Dundee; lochs and reservoirs in the west are utilized for electric power. Apart from these activities there is the university at St. Andrews and the area caters for a considerable tourist trade.

ANCIENT ROCKS On the north side of the Highland Border Fault there is an almost continuous outcrop, about five miles broad, of schistose grits and similar rocks are caught up in folds east of Loch Rannoch. Separating the two is a broad belt of quartzose mica schists interspersed with slates, mica schists and graphitic schists and with narrower bands of limestone and of the epidote–chlorite and hornblende schists that make up the so-called Green Beds. The limestone bands and the Green Beds constitute the chief horizon markers in this thick series of rocks classed as Dalradian. Farther north come the Moine Schists or Central Highland Granulites as yet largely undifferentiated. These are threaded by a series of dykes

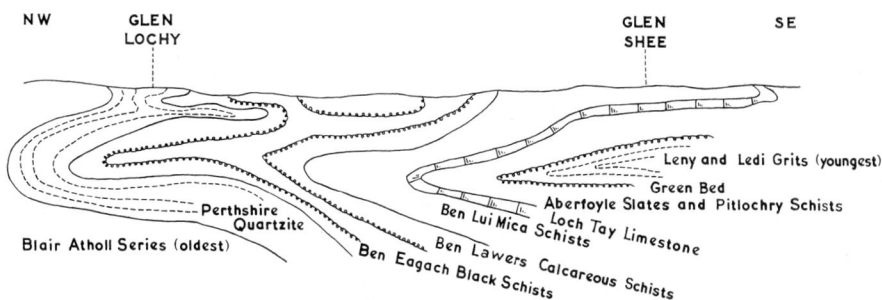

Figure 55. Recumbent folds near Blair Atholl
(Based on Fig. 7, Grampian Highlands Geol. Surv. Handbook)

The Productive Coal Measures, about 1,700 ft. thick, present the usual features of buff sandstones and dark shales with fireclays and coals and some ironstones. They are followed by the Barren Red Measures, mainly of softish massive sandstones, over 1,000 ft. thick.

Volcanic activity accompanied by intrusion is widespread almost throughout the Scottish Carboniferous and Permian strata though outbreaks tend to be localized. Thus, much of the activity in the 'Dundee' area is concentrated into the later or upper part of the Oil Shale Group, though with some recrudescence in Limestone Coal Group times, whereas to the south volcanic outbreaks commenced earlier and in the west occurred later. Most of the lavas are olivine basalts and these in Fife are accompanied by basaltic tuffs. Volcanic necks filled with basaltic agglomerate represent the denuded stumps of the volcanoes; they are fairly common and often form hills, such as Binn Hill of Burntisland and Largo Law in Fife. Sills and dykes akin to the lavas are widespread. Some types common in the earlier Carboniferous rocks do not affect the Coal Measures of Fife but others akin to the Whin Sill of Northern England do so.

REFERENCES

Geological Survey
  Regional Handbooks: Midland Valley of Scotland, ed 2, 1948; *Grampian Highlands*, ed 2, 1948.
Excursions and Field Meetings
  International Geological Congress 1948.
  Long Excursions: C13 Edinburgh and St. Andrews; A16 South-west Highlands; A19 Scotland, General; C16 Vertebrate Palaeontology.

MULL—BEN NEVIS

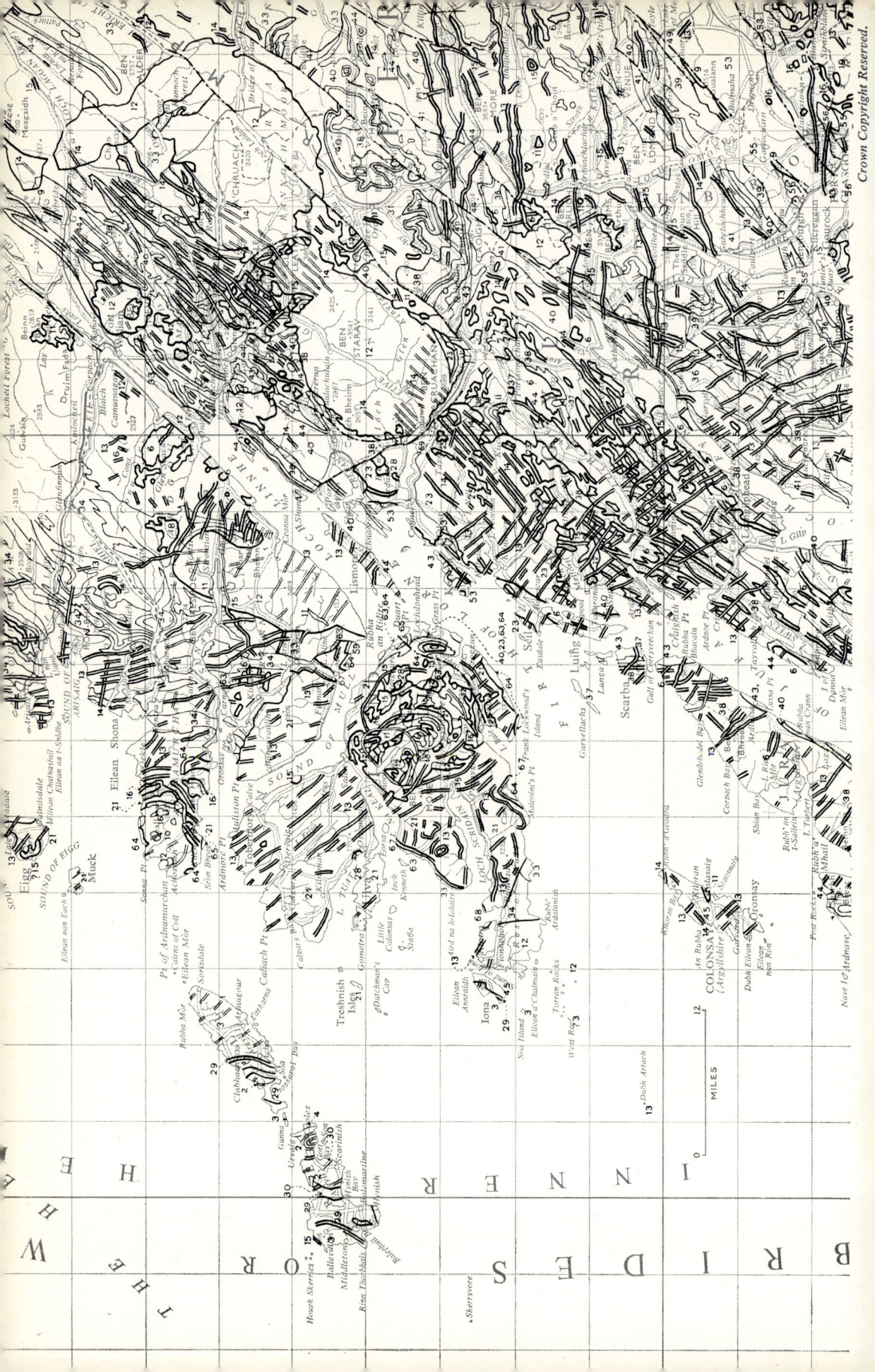

THE INNER HEBRIDES OR WESTERN ISLES

Eigg
Muck
SOUND OF EIGG
Eilean nan Each
Eilean Chathastail
Eilean sa t-Sîdhe
ARISAIG

Lochiel Forest
Druimfada
Camusnagaul
Black

BEN STARAV 3541
BEN CRUACHAN 3689

Eilean Shona
SOUND OF ARISAIG
Pt of Ardnamurchan
Cairns of Coll
Eilean Mòr
Sorisdale
Rubha Mòr
Arinagour
Treshnish Isles
Dutchman's Cap

SOUND OF MULL
Duart
Lismore
Scallastle
Glass Pt
Scridain
LOCH SCRIDAIN
Rubh' Ardalanish
Iona
Eilean Annraidh
Eilean a' Chalmain
Torran Rocks
West Reef
Soa Island

Kilbrennan
Kilfinichen

FIRTH OF LORN
Luing
Scarba
Garvellachs
Corryvreckan
Lunga
Craobh
Rubha Fiola
Eilean Mòr

COLONSAY
(Argyllshire)
Oronsay
Dubh Eilean
Eilean nan Ròn
An Rubha
Scoonaig
Kiloran Bay

Skerryvore
Dubh Artach

Nave Id
Rubh' a' Mhàil

MILES
0

Dubh Artach 13

MULL—BEN NEVIS

THIS sheet includes Tiree on the west, Loch Lomond on the south-east, Arisaig on the north and Oronsay on the south. Ben Nevis (4,406 ft.) is the highest point but there are many heights of over 3,000 ft. including Ben More in Mull. The amount of ground suitable for farming of any kind is therefore limited to the coastal regions and valley margins and further limited by the fact that the lower parts of the valleys are occupied by lochs either sea inlets or as lakes. Population is scanty except in the Clyde area. Oban may be regarded as the focus for it is the port and railhead of the district as well as a tourist centre with magnificent scenery within easy reach. Rocks range from Lewisian to Tertiary in age but the greater part, lying between the Great Glen Fault along Loch Linnhe and the Highland Border Fault from the Clyde to Stonehaven, are of the Moine and Dalradian schists of the south-western part of the Grampian Highlands with large intrusions of granite; apart from tectonic structures, however, greater interest is provided by the Tertiary igneous centres of Mull and Ardnamurchan.

LEWISIAN   The oldest rocks in the district make up much of the islands of Coll and Tiree. They are mostly gneisses formed by the crushing and foliation of granites and other igneous rocks but also include in the western part of Coll and the middle part of Tiree quartzites and schists and near Scarinish in the latter island some limestone. There is also some Lewisian gneiss in Iona.

MOINE SCHISTS   This formation, generally believed to be next in age to Lewisian, occupies considerable areas particularly about Loch Linnhe. Its schists are mostly derived by the metamorphism of sediments and in Ardnamurchan these sediments are but little altered for they are mainly slightly schistose sandstones still showing false bedding and often pebbly. Eastwards they become more crystalline and also include more micaceous and garnetiferous schists derived from shaly rocks; the prevalent strike hereabouts is north–south. Still farther east gneisses are developed by the injection of granitic magma into these schists.

DALRADIAN   This great series of altered rocks is characteristic of the ground between the Highland Boundary Fault and that of the Great Glen from Loch Linnhe north-eastwards. The rocks are mainly of sedimentary origin—sandstones giving various forms of quartzites and siliceous schists, shales and slates producing mica schists, limestones giving calc schists and closely interbedded sediments a great variety of rocks. In other types igneous material has been involved.

The rocks have been bent into folds and overfolds and these further dislocated by thrusts or slides which may themselves be folded or faulted. With such areas of disturbance stratigraphical sequences are difficult to establish and correlation is

often a matter of opinion. It is true that graded and false-bedding provide clues for local successions but the general sequences advocated by various workers have been placed in reverse order wholly or in part by the same workers at a later stage or by other investigators. Of the various sequences proposed a limestone in the middle, that of Loch Tay, appears to be a favoured horizon for correlation. Under one name or another it has been traced through Kintyre and east of Loch Fyne to and well beyond Loch Tay. There are, however, other limestones believed to lie at horizons considerably above and below that of Loch Tay as, for example, two in the Blair Atholl Series (basal series of Dalradian see page 240 and Fig. 55).

Another zone of value for wide correlation is provided by the so-called Green Beds; these are epidote, chlorite and hornblende schists and schistose grits well developed above the Loch Tay Limestone east of Loch Fyne.

The generalized sequence given below may serve the purpose here:

Grits, of Leny and Ben Ledi
Green Beds
Loch Tay Limestone
Pitlochry Schists and Aberfoyle Slates
Schists: garnetiferous mica, of Ben Lui; calcareous, of Ben Lawers; black, of
    Ben Eagach
Quartzites with conglomerates
Blair Atholl Series

The quartzites make up most of Jura and are present in force about Loch Sween and about Loch Awe. There are black slates in north-east Jura and thence along the mainland coast and islands to beyond Oban including the famous slates of Easdale and of Ballachulish (associated with a limestone which also forms the island of Lismore) and alongside the Highland Border Fault (Aberfoyle Slates).

TORRIDONIAN This sandstone group is only present in force in this district in the islands of Rum, Iona and Colonsay. That in Iona is grey rather than the usual red.

OLD RED SANDSTONE Lower Old Red Sandstone makes up much of the island of Kerrera near Oban and part of the adjacent mainland; its shales and sandstones near Oban have yielded fish remains; the basal portion is conglomeratic. Most of the formation, however, is represented by lava flows. Those of the Lorne plateau about Oban are mainly basalts and andesites and exceed 2,000 ft. in thickness. Similar but much shattered basalts intervene between schists and Triassic rocks in the Loch Don anticline of south-east Mull. About five miles N.E. of Connel Ferry there is a small area of tuffs amidst lavas.

At the foot of Loch Lomond both Lower and Upper Old Red Sandstone is present along with some Lower Carboniferous strata (see page 225); in Morvern 300 ft. of sandstones with shales and a poor coal, referred to the Coal Measures, are capped by Tertiary basalt lavas in the cliffs of Inninmore Bay.

MESOZOIC STRATA These rocks are fairly well represented but are nowhere of

great extent. The Trias of pebbly sandstones and red marls occurs in Mull, Ardnamurchan and Morvern; it varies in thickness up to 200 ft. on account of its irregular floor. In western Mull only is it succeeded by Rhaetic (40 ft. of dark sandy limestones) there followed directly by Greensand.

Lias and Inferior Oolite similar to those of Skye and Raasey (page 267) occur in Mull and Ardnamurchan but of the Estuarine Series a few feet only is present in Ardnamurchan and the sequence is not resumed until the Kimmeridge is reached; this is represented by baked shales seen in a stream flowing into Duart Bay in south-east Mull.

In Mull and Morvern the Lower Lias is followed by Greensand; on Beinn Iadain, Morvern, this is glauconitic calcareous sandstone, 40 ft., beneath white quartzose sandstone, 24 ft.; next come 14 ins. of Upper Chalk and the Tertiary basalts. At Loch Aline the white sandstone reaches 40 ft. thick and is of a purity eminently suitable for optical glass making. Tertiary coals ranging from a few inches to 2 ft. but very irregular in thickness and character occur amidst lavas at Carsaig Bay in southern Mull.

IGNEOUS ROCKS OF THE OLD RED SANDSTONE PERIOD There are three large granite masses in the area and several smaller ones. All show interesting characters for they are not simple intrusions. That bisected by Loch Etive may be taken as an example; it consists of several elliptical rings or partial rings of rock centred on Ben Starav and decreasing in age inwards. On the rim just north of Loch Awe is the Quarry Diorite separated by a screen of lavas from the Ben Cruachan granite. Within this on the west is the Meall Odhar granite.

Next comes the Starav granite which has an outer porphyritic type and a non-porphyritic inner core. To the south-west lie the lavas of the Lorne plateau

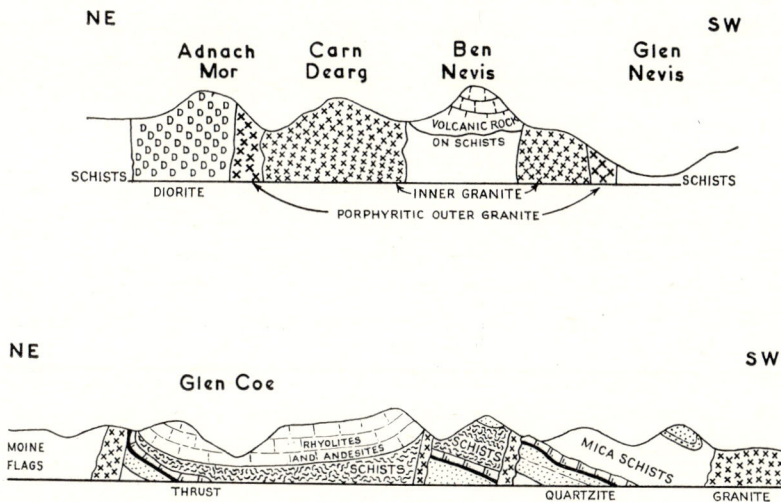

Figure 56. Cauldron subsidences of Ben Nevis and Glen Coe
(Based on Fig. 18, *Grampian Highlands* Geol. Surv. Handbook and on 10 mile Geological Map Sheet 1)

and to the north-east those of Glen Coe. The former are normal lava flows; the latter are associated with an annular fault which is believed to have allowed a cylinder of the crust of Highland schists to sink several thousands of feet but which also provided egress for the andesites and rhyolites.

The granitic types are supposed to have been intruded as the result of successive subsidences of a cylindrical block of country within a ring fault similar to that of Glen Coe save that the block did not reach through to the surface; the granitic magma rose up the fault to occupy the space above the block.

Ben Nevis also has an outer rim of diorite, a porphyritic outer granite and an inner granite of finer grain but the actual summit and core is of lavas, up to 2,000 ft. thick, on schists; the core is believed to represent a final collapse of roof into the still fluid granitic magma.

The Great Moor of Rannoch mass has an outer biotite granite intruded irregularly into the schist country and an inner hornblende biotite granite.

Around all these intrusions there is contact metamorphism of the country rocks usually into hornfelses with various new minerals though lavas give granulites with small biotites etc.

The large mass of Strontian granite on the north side of Loch Linnhe is mainly a biotite granite partially rimmed by granodiorite (hornblende granite) and that by tonalite (a granitic rock with feldspar more basic i.e. calcareous than usual).

The Ross of Mull granite is pink and carries white and black micas; in some portions the place of white mica is taken by hornblende. The granite, however, is remarkable in the way it has permeated and absorbed the schist country rock, and beyond this injection zone has produced one of contact metamorphism with andalusite and sillimanite appearing in the mica schists.

TERTIARY IGNEOUS ROCKS   The London Clay and the soft sediments of southern England are represented in the Inner Hebrides by vast outpourings of lava, even now over 6,000 ft. thick in Mull, and by great masses of plutonic rocks. This igneous activity was widespread; it not only extended to northern Ireland, where it has left the famous Giant's Causeway, but also to Iceland, Greenland, and as proved by dredging far out into what is now the North Atlantic.

The activity took place in two main phases (i) the quiet upwelling of various kinds of basaltic lavas (ii) explosion vents of large size associated with the intrusion of plutonic masses and dykes ranging from acid to basic types.

The basalts are in flat-lying flows generally about 50 ft. thick, slaggy at the top and bottom with the middle part often showing columnar jointing. They give rise to broad flat-topped hills with stepped sides due to the easier erosion of slaggy portions and, on the coast to magnificent cliffs. The almost complete absence of volcanic ash testifies to quiet eruption; the presence of red earth or 'bole' between the flows indicates periods of weathering during the course of eruptions. Lenses of sand, mud, lignite and conglomerate between the flows mark the sites of ponds; these deposits enclose the remains of many plants, including *Ginkgo* the maiden hair tree as well as of trees and plants common in Britain today, and point to Eocene as the period of eruptions. Ardtun (near Bunessan in south-west Mull)

is the best locality for a plant-bed but there is a tree trunk embedded in columnar lava in the cliffs north of the entrance to Loch Scridain (in west Mull); the trunk consists of charred wood round a cast of white bleached basalt 5 ft. in diameter and 40 ft. in height.

The lavas reach their highest development in western Mull. There resting on a few feet of decomposed ash are 3,000 ft. of basalts (mainly rich in olivine) of the Plateau Group—to which the famous one of Fingals Cave, Staffa, belongs. In Morvern the group is 1,500 ft. thick but in Ardnamurchan only 300 ft. remain.

The so-called Central Group (restricted to central and south-east Mull) total 3,000 ft. in thickness; they are poor in olivine and occur in and about great craters or calderas in which pillow-lavas also occur. There are twin calderas in central Mull over six miles in diameter extending from Loch Bà by Beinn Talaidh (2,496 ft.) and Beinn Fhada.

It is assumed from the thickness of lavas that the floor of this wide crater sunk several times and that at a later date it was pierced by explosion vents; these are filled with Tertiary igneous rocks but rarely include the Mesozoic or pre-Cambrian platform rocks though such are common in vents outside the caldera.

In the second or intrusive phase the rocks are arranged concentrically around certain points or intrusion centres. These did not always function at the same time but rather successively and migrating to meet local conditions. One such centre occurs in the great caldera of central Mull and another a few miles to the north-west of it; in Ardnamurchan there are three such centres. There are two main types of concentric intrusions (a) ring dykes, each up to a mile thick, of coarsely crystalline rocks which are postulated as occurring around a sinking cone-shaped block of country rock and 'dip' outwards from the centre; (b) cone sheets, minor intrusions, a few feet thick of fine or medium-grained rocks which dip at about 45° inwards towards a centre supposed to coincide with the top of a magma reservoir at a depth of about three miles.

Volcanic vents with which these intrusions are associated are held to be due to the explosive force of rhyolite or trachyte magma for such contribute largely to the agglomerates.

The rocks of the ring dykes, which range from gabbros to granophyres, may chill against an outer one or may be separated by screens of country rock.

Cone sheets show much less variation; they are usually dolerites.

Ardnamurchan may be considered the show place for these intrusions. Here there are three centres close together.

Centre 3 situated about three miles north of Kilchoan and three miles east of Ardnamurchan Point is perfect in that its ring dykes stand as ridges round a central core; to the south-west of it between Ardnamurchan Point and Kilchoan is Centre 2 whose cone sheets and ring dykes occur on the shores all round the Point; to the east of it lies Centre 1 with cone sheets lying eccentrically with respect to those of No. 2 and visible on north and south coasts and with Ben Hiant marking its major intrusions flanked by volcanic vents.

In addition to the dykes mentioned there are a swarm of others trending north-west—south-east. These are mainly of dolerite and are particularly well shown in Mull although they extend far beyond that island even into North Yorkshire.

REFERENCES

Geological Survey
   Regional Handbooks: Tertiary Volcanic Districts, ed 2, 1948; *Grampian Highlands*, ed 2, 1948.
   Ardnamurchan, Guide to Geological Model.
Excursions and Field Meetings
   International Geological Congress 1948.
   Long Excursions: A12 Mull and Ardnamurchan; A16 South-west Highlands; C11 Ben Nevis,
      Glen Coe, Ballachulish; A19 Scotland, General.
Geologists Association, Proceedings
   1933, Ardnamurchan.

SHEET 23

ABERDEEN

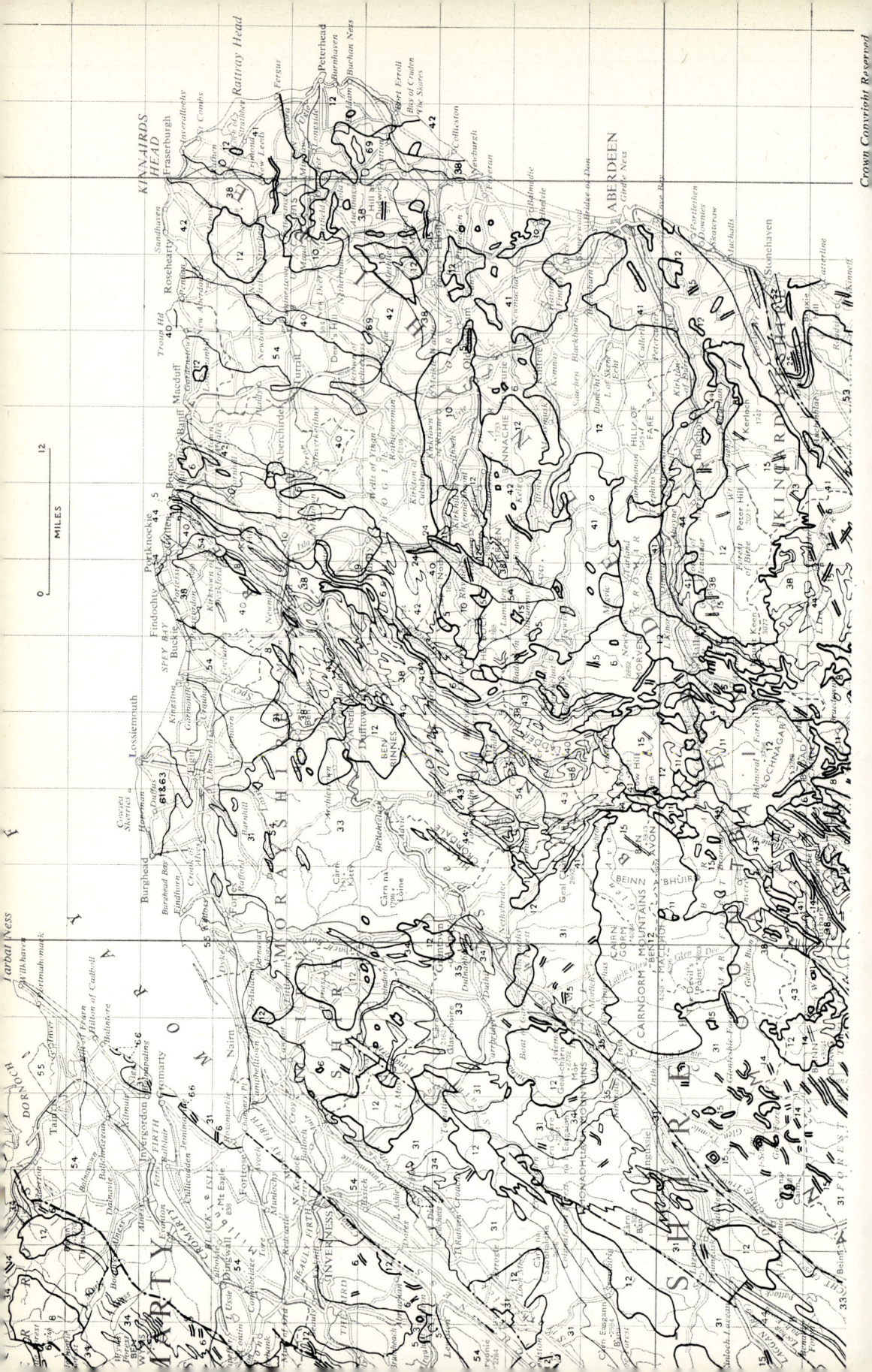

ABERDEEN

THIS district extends from Inverness to just south of Stonehaven; it includes the whole of the counties of Aberdeen, Banff, Moray, Nairn, the eastern part of Inverness, a little of Perth, Angus and Kincardine shires. Heights of 4,000 ft. are exceeded in the Cairngorms in the south-west but these decline to a general level of about 1,000 ft. north-eastwards and less towards the coast. Drainage is mainly north-east and east principally by the Findhorn, Spey, Don and Dee. Agriculture, fishing and quarrying are the principal industries; Aberdeen and Inverness are the chief towns; there are many smaller towns in the coastal tract but the interior is very sparsely populated.

Geologically the district forms the north-eastern part of the Grampian Highlands for it lies between the Great Glen Fault on the north-west through Inverness and the Highland Boundary Fault on the south-east through Stonehaven. Many rock types are represented but granites and schists predominate; more recent rocks include Old Red Sandstone bordering the large faults and some Permo-Trias about Elgin.

ANCIENT ROCKS   The oldest rocks of the district are the schists which are divided into two series of Moine or Central Highland Granulites in the north-western half of the district and the Dalradian in the other half; both are invaded by the granites. The relationships of the two series are obscure and the position of the dividing line between them often appears to be a matter of opinion rather than of fact; about the junction there appears to be a considerable development of markedly siliceous rocks or of quartzites. Both series are the result of the regional metamorphism of rocks chiefly of sedimentary origin—in the case of the Moine mainly of sandstones or of thin alternations of sandstones and shales; in the Dalradian of thick alternations of various sediments.

In the Moine Series or Central Highland Granulites the chief rock types are (a) granulites dominantly of quartz but with varying amounts of feldspars and a little biotite; they occasionally include the remains of pebbles of quartz and feldspar and are derived from sandstones; (b) gneiss with much mica (muscovite and biotite); garnets common; representing metamorphosed shales; (c) a widespread grey, banded and flaggy rock made up of alternations of granulite and gneiss; (d) a granulite with quartz, feldspar, zoisite, hornblende and garnet, derived from marls, which is widespread but not abundant; (e) marbles and calc-silicate rocks made by the alteration of limestones; these are rare and usually associated with hornblende schists; (f) a granulite with aegirine, possibly originally of igneous origin. Of these types the granulites and mica schists with the marbles associated with the latter only are shown on the map.

253

The Dalradian Series includes a great variety of rocks—quartzites and schistose grits, mica schists, black schists and slates and limestones—all representing sediments metamorphosed to varying degrees. Even with the aid of current and graded bedding it is difficult to disentangle the succession of rocks involved in intricate folding and hasty correlation of rock types has not simplified matters. Most workers have put forward their own views as to the sequence and have advanced one or more correlations sometimes involving a complete reversal of the succession.

In the areas to the south-west of the present one the Loch Tay Limestone occurs amidst schists. Downwards these rest on quartzites with boulder beds and these on the Blair Atholl Series with a white and a grey limestone in schists. Upwards the schists above the Loch Tay Limestone are followed by the Green Beds (see page 246) and a series of grits. In this 'Aberdeen' district no Green Beds have been recognized but the Deeside Limestone is equated with the Loch Tay and with the Boyne Limestone of the Banffshire coast.

OLD RED SANDSTONE   The only Lower Old Red Sandstone in the district is that south of the Highland Boundary Fault at Stonehaven. Elsewhere in the district the lowest portion is referred to Middle Old Red Sandstone; it occurs on both sides of the Moray Firth to beyond Elgin with outliers east and west of Banff and to the south at Tomintoul, Cabrach and Rhynie.

In the Inverness–Nairn area the basal conglomerate is followed by flags interrupted at intervals by bands of shale and limestone some of which have been worked for lime and usually yield fish remains as, for example, at Easter Aultlugie, Clava Bridge, Knockloam, at Lethen, Lethen Bar and Clune about six miles S.E. of Nairn, and in Tynet Burn east of Elgin. The Gamrie–Turriff outlier faulted on the west against Highland schists has conglomerates at levels far above the base. The Rhynie outlier, also faulted on the west, is famous for well preserved plant remains belonging to the group psilophytales preserved in fossilized and silicified peat. The Old Red Sandstone here includes a lava flow of vesicular andesite and there are similar lavas in the Fochaber and Cabrach outliers.

Upper Old Red Sandstone occurs as pink and yellow sandstones in a synclinal area bordering the Dornoch Firth. This lies on the north-west side of the Great Glen Fault. On the south-east side of that fault Upper Old Red Sandstone does not come in until the vicinity of Nairn is reached; thence it continues as a coastal strip to Buckie. The beds here rest unconformably on Middle Old Red or, as in the middle part of this tract, on Highland schists. There is usually a basal breccia followed by coarse sandstones with conglomerates and in the Findhorn area a concretionary limestone, 10 ft. thick, succeeded by marls. Fish remains including *Holoptychius* have been got at Findhorn, at Glenshiel and at Boghole and Whitemire.

IGNEOUS ROCKS   Apart from a small patch in the River Blackwater near Ardwell Inn (10 miles S.W. of Huntly) of basic lavas the igneous rocks of the area fall into two intrusive series—an older one which preceded or more or less accompanied regional metamorphism of the original sediments into schists etc. and a younger

series emplaced long after that episode and probably in late Silurian and Devonian times. Both series include basic and acid groups of greenstone or gabbro and granite.

In the older series the basic group forms extensive sills largely converted into hornblende schist but less altered in places as, for example, a thick sill of gabbro at Portsoy. The Loch Tay Limestone horizon appears to have favoured intrusions of this type as, for instance, in the fifty-mile sill from Portsoy to Deeside; this, in places, is accompanied by serpentine derived from ultra-basic intrusions.

Large bodies of the older granites are not common and most of the material is in sills and veins permeating the country rock as, for example, alongside the Dee between Aberdeen and Ballater between two large masses of newer granite.

Included in the newer intrusions are six considerable masses of gabbro—at Huntly, Cabrach, Insch, Maud, Haddo and Belhelvie. They include various kinds of gabbro, some ultrabasic peridotite and some acid rocks including granite; the more acid types invade the basic rocks. In some cases reaction between gabbro magma and country rock has produced contaminated igneous rocks crowded with zenoliths (inclusions of country rock) as, for example, at Cuternack on the western edge of the Huntly mass, in the Deveron below Castle Bridge at Huntly, at Easter Saphook (east end of Insch mass) and at Wood of Schivas near Haddo.

The gabbros also give rise to great aureoles by contact metamorphism of the country rock as, for instance, on the northern margin of the Insch mass where the gabbro slopes gently northwards beneath a roof of Macduff Slates. These usually well cleaved slates first develop spots of andalusite and cordierite and become massive, then, nearer the contact, pass into hornfels.

The newer granites occur in larger and more numerous masses than the gabbros. they are mostly biotite granites but muscovite with microcline is common in some of them—in Moy and Ardclach west of the Findhorn, in Strathbogie in Banffshire, in Kenmay and Coull near Aberdeen, in Rubislaw and Peterhead.

The Kenmay quarries are amongst the deepest in Britain (400 ft.).

Contact metamorphism follows the same pattern as around the gabbros.

PERMO-TRIASSIC AND LATER ROCKS These cover a considerable area around Lossiemouth but are so obscured by superficial deposits that structure and thickness are in doubt. They are mainly of coarse sandstones whose well rounded grains and dreikanter (polished and facetted stones something like a brazil nut in form) indicate aeolian origin though some, believed to occupy the middle third of the sequence, are pebbly and probably water deposited. Interest lies in the fact that they have yielded remains of reptiles ranging from Upper Permian to Upper Trias in age. The chief fossil localities are Cuttie's Hillock and Hopeman for the lower beds and Lossiemouth, Spynie and Findrassie for the upper beds. At Lossiemouth there is the so-called 'Cherty Rock of Stotfield', a chalcedonic deposit comparable with some in deserts, which may succeed the Trias; it and the sandstones are in places impregnated with galena.

There are small patches of Jurassic strata on the western side of the Moray Firth. Those south of Cromarty, near Ethie, range from Corallian (sandstones

N
0 MILES 12
ROSS AND CROMARTY
INVERNESS-SHIRE
NAIRNSHIRE
MORAY
NOT SURVEYED IN DETAIL
Tarbat Ness
DORNOCH
Tain
Invergordon
Cromarty
Dingwall
Fortrose
Nairn
Forres
Burghead
INVERNESS
BEAULY FIRTH
MORAY FIRTH
BLACK ISLE
CROMARTY FIRTH
Grantown
Kingussie
Fort Augustus
Invermoriston
CAIRNGORM MOUNTAINS
MONADHLIATH MOUNTAINS
BEINN DEARG
AN TEALLACH
LOCH TORRIDON
LOCH GAIRLOCH
LOCH CARRON
LOCH ALSH
LOCH DUICH
LOCH HOURN
LOCH NEVIS
LOCH MORAR
LOCH ARKAIG
LOCH LOCHY
LOCH LAGGAN
SOUND OF SLEAT
INNER SOUND
SOUND OF RAASAY
SOUND OF RHUM
SOUND OF EIGG
SOUND OF ARISAIG
SOAY SOUND
RAASAY
Rona
Scalpay
Crowlin Is
Soay
Eigg
Muck
Eilean Shona
Mallaig
Applecross
Plockton
Kyle of Lochalsh
Kyleakin
KNOYDART
Glen Affric
Glen Garry
Loch Mhor
Glen Urquhart
THE AIRD
FIVE SISTERS
The Saddle
Sgurr na Ciche
Meall Dubh
Creag Meagaidh
The Devil's Point
Cairn Gorm
Glen Feshie
Glen Roy
Glen Gloy
Loch Eil
Kinlochewe
Achnasheen
Torridon
Kinloch Laggan

ROSS AND CROMARTY

THE sheet extends from eastern Skye to the Moray Firth and south from a line through Dornoch to between Kingussie and Blair Atholl. In addition to Ross and Cromarty it includes Nairn, much of Inverness as well as portions of other counties. Most of it is wild mountain and moorland penetrated by long sea lochs and deep valleys with fresh water lochs. The Great Glen with its fault separates the North-west Highlands from the Grampian Highlands. Heights between three and four thousand feet are common and arise within a few miles of either coast. Apart from the Great Glen the main drainage is north-east via the Spey. On the west there is a considerable tract of Torridonian Sandstone resting on Lewisian gneisses; to the east of that it is schist country up to the Dornoch–Inverness tract of Old Red Sandstone that supports the main centres of population and provides most of the farm lands. The chief towns there are Dornoch, Tain, Invergordon, Dingwall, Cromarty, Nairn and Inverness; elsewhere the settlements are small. Industries are fishing, farming, forestry, sports and tourists, and whisky.

ANCIENT ROCKS Lewisian gneisses chiefly derived from igneous rocks are present in force about Loch Maree, where they are threaded by belts of north-west trending hornblende schists, and farther south about Loch Carron, Loch Alsh and Loch Mourn. The gneisses are followed by great thick spreads of unconformable Torridonian Sandstone made up of red sandstones and conglomerates. This in its turn is succeeded unconformably by Cambrian strata which form a belt from Loch Broom to the south-east end of Loch Maree and thence to Loch Kishorn. In this tract the Cambrian is represented chiefly by the Basal Quartzite though there is some Serpulite Grit and, in the Kishorn Applecross areas, some of the Durness Limestone (see page 273).

The next formation of consequence is that known as the Moine Series made up of granulites and schists from the metamorphism of sandstones and shales respectively, together with some schists of igneous origin. A general sequence of what was originally sandstones followed by a thick shaly belt and that by more sandstones appears to hold good over much of the country. These rocks may succeed Lewisian more or less normally but are often faulted against those gneisses and may be thrust over the Cambrian and Torridonian by the great Moine Thrust. There are other dislocations notably one ranging north-west along Loch Maree, which appears to displace rocks southwards on its north-east side. Amidst the Moine Series rocks of Lewisian type, and referred to that formation, appear north-west of Loch Fannish and farther south about Loch Monar. In both these tracts they are surrounded by schistose and flaggy quartzitic sandstones and mica schists. A con-siderable tract lying between Loch Carron, Kingussie and Fort William (just

beyond the south-western border) has not yet been surveyed in detail.

OLD RED SANDSTONE   In northern Scotland Lower Old Red Sandstone is absent; moreover, various members of the Middle subdivision overstep others and rest unconformably on Highland schists. It is fairly obvious from the map that the rocks are disposed in a syncline pitching north-east and bringing in Upper Old Red Sandstone along part of the Dornoch Firth; the axis of this syncline runs about midway between Dingwall and Inverness and some Moine rocks appear from beneath the eastern flank on the western side of the Moray Firth. The Great Glen Fault runs through Loch Ness and to the east of these inliers. East of that fault Upper Old Red Sandstone appears to be shifted from Tarbat Ness to Nairn; Middle Old Red is also out of line between Loch Ness and Loch Lochy but is there involved in further faulting.

Although the western margin of the Middle Old Red Sandstone is often faulted a basal conglomerate appears in places; it is present in force on the south and makes the large tongue south of Beauly. Round Dingwall and towards Inverness red and yellow sandstones take the place of some of the conglomerate which in any case thins considerably to the north-east. In places the sandstone–conglomerate group, which reaches 7,000 ft. in thickness in the south-east, includes over a thousand feet of olive and dark fetid shales with flags and thin limestones; these fetid shales give rise to the spa at Strathpeffer. Some of the conglomerates above this shale group contain pebbles of Torridonian and Cambrian strata. The highest subdivision of the Middle Old Red reaches 2,500 ft. thick in the Black Isle; it is mainly of red and yellow sandstones but includes shales red, blue and grey, with plant remains and nodular limestones. There are fish-beds just east of Cromarty, at Ethie south of Cromarty, in Killen Burn about five miles west of Fortrose and at several localities in the coastal tract south of Tarbet Ness. The fish include several species of *Pterichthys*.

IGNEOUS ROCKS   In addition to the many dykes traversing the Moine Series and like those in the Lewisian, now largely altered into schistose rocks, there are numerous masses of granite. Some of these lie west of Dornoch and that situated south-west of Bonarbridge, partly enclosed by mica schists, shows foliation and on its western side includes ribs of epidiorite partly converted to hornblende schists. The other masses of granite lie mainly south-east of the Great Glen. They form the western side of the semicircle of granites stretching southwards from about Inverness to the Cairngorms and thence east towards Aberdeen and north-east to Peterhead. They are classed as Newer Granites and are believed to have been intruded towards if not later than the close of the Silurian Period, i.e. after the main period of Caledonian folding. That considerable movement followed their emplacement is shown by folds in the Old Red Sandstone and the Foyers granite alongside Loch Ness—said to be part of the Strontian mass moved laterally sixty-five miles N.E. by the Great Glen Fault. The small and isolated Cluanie mass north of the Great Glen is a porphyritic hornblende–biotite–granodiorite member of the Newer Granites.

JURASSIC AND TERTIARY   Relatively recent rocks are confined to the margins of the district (see pages 255 and 275). The small patches north and south of Cromarty include Kimmeridge, Corallian and Oxford Clay. In the west there is Lias on Trias at Applecross and on Raasay followed in the latter island and in the neck of Skye by strata of oolite age and these by Tertiary basalts.

REFERENCES

Geological Survey
    Regional Handbooks: Grampian Highlands, ed 2, 1953; *Northern Highlands*, ed 2, 1948.
Excursions and Field Meetings
    International Geological Congress 1948.
    Long Excursions: C12 East Highlands; A19 Scotland, General; C16 Vertebrate Palaeontology.

SHEET 25

SKYE AND WESTERN ISLES

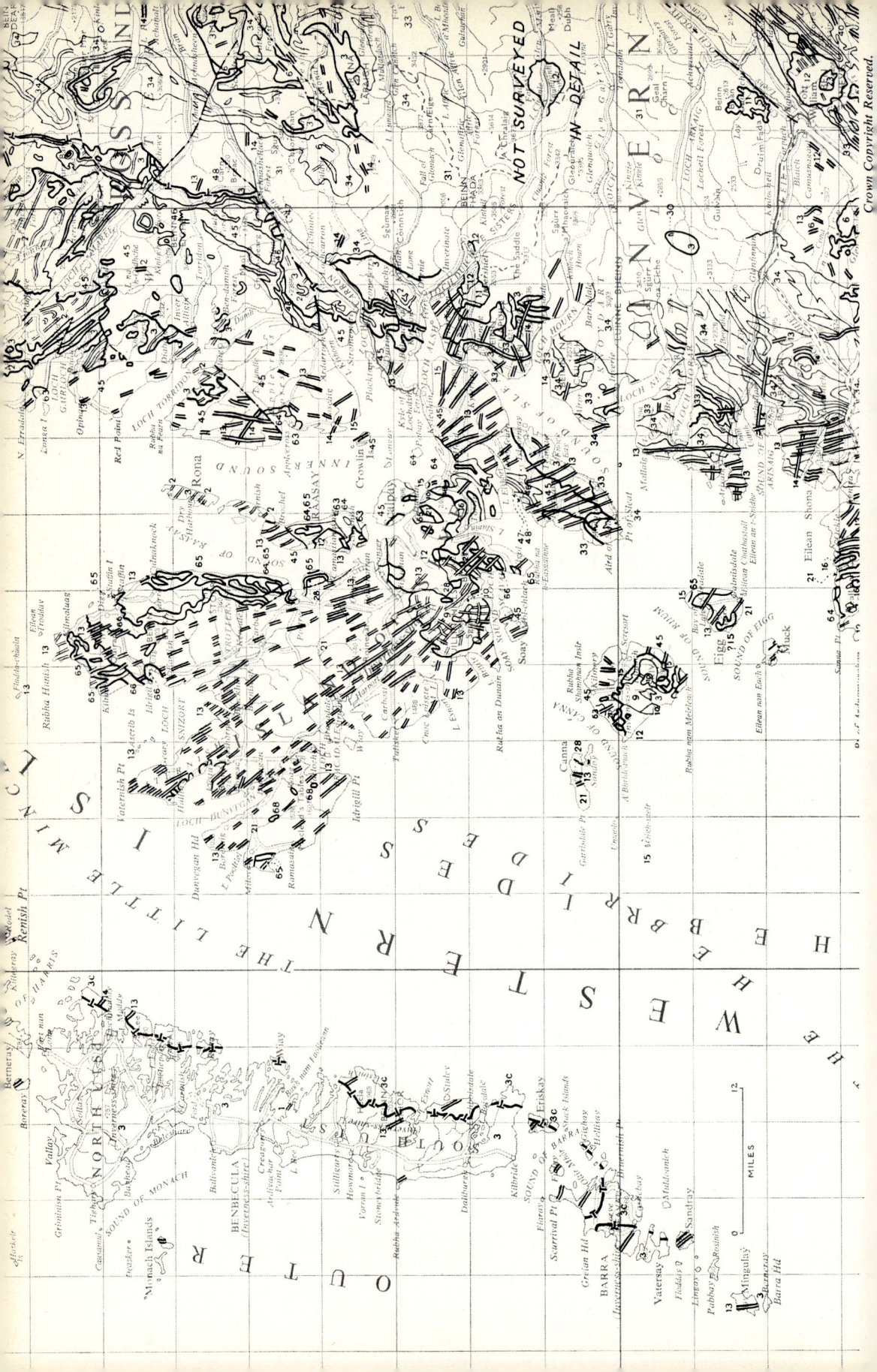

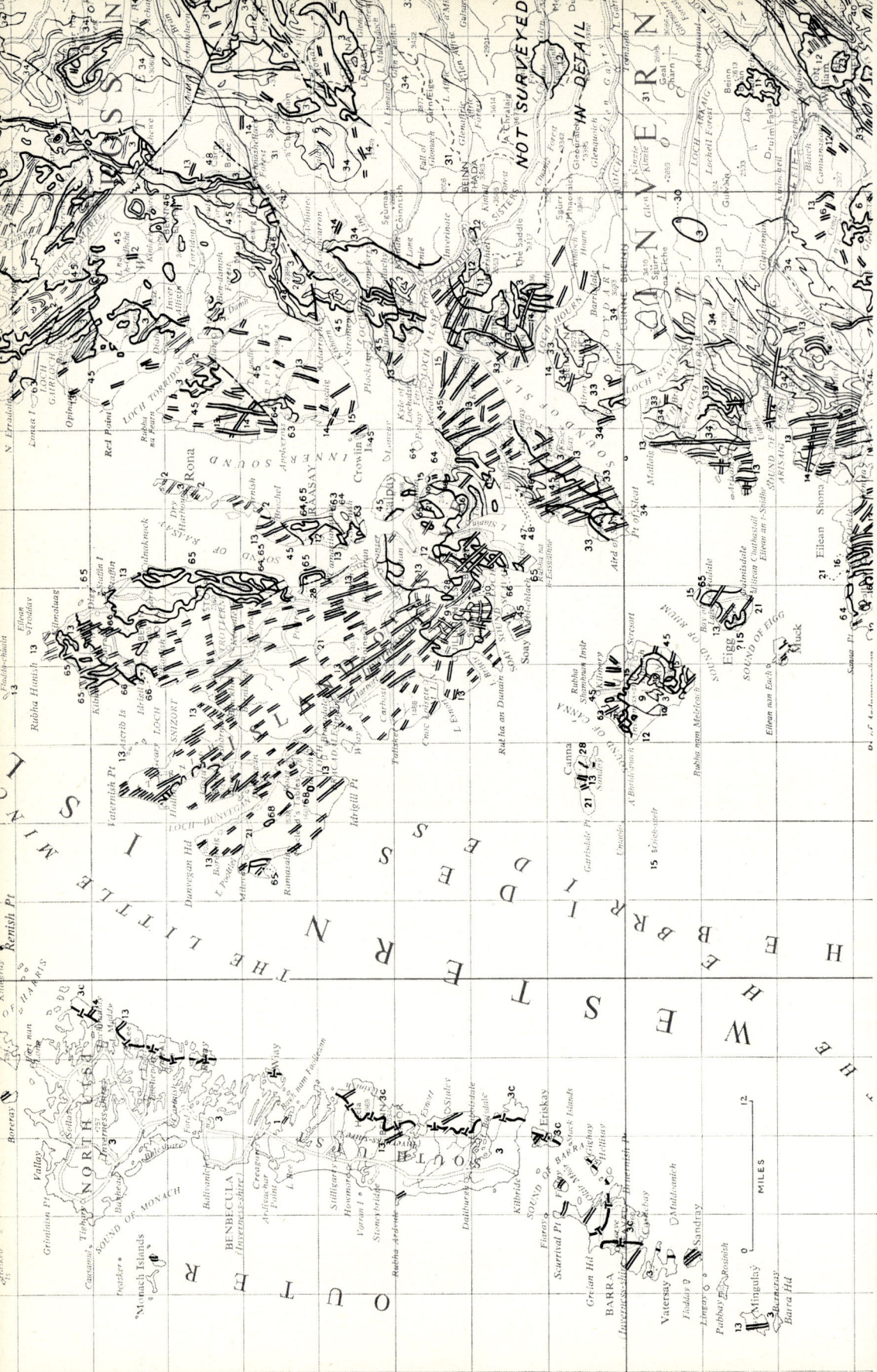

ROSS AND CROMARTY

INVERNESS

NOT SURVEYED IN DETAIL

THE LITTLE MINCH

WESTERN ISLES

OUTER HEBRIDES

INNER SOUND

SOUND OF RAASAY

SOUND OF CANNA

SOUND OF RUM

SOUND OF EIGG

SOUND OF MONACH

SOUND OF BARRA

NORTH UIST (Inverness-shire)

SOUTH UIST

BENBECULA (Inverness-shire)

BARRA (Inverness-shire)

MILES
0   12

SKYE AND WESTERN ISLES

THIS sheet includes the southern half of the Outer Hebrides, Skye and the Inner Hebrides as far south as Muck Island, and the mainland from a little west of Fort William to east of Kinlochewe. It is a sparsely populated picturesque region of mountains and sea lochs and fiords with innumerable freshwater lochs in the deep valleys. The geology is diverse and the rocks range from the ancient gneisses of the Outer Hebrides and the schists of the mainland to the Tertiary lava flows of Skye. Farming, fishing and tourists are the main sources of livelihood.

LEWISIAN ROCKS   The oldest rocks are the pre-Cambrian Lewisian Gneisses of the Outer Hebrides which, however, also occur on the mainland, in Skye and in some of the other islands. The gneisses are mainly derived by the metamorphism of igneous rocks ranging from gabbros to granites though some metamorphosed sediments are included. Differences in the original rock types give rise to belts and bands of gneiss characterized by different minerals in the crystalline foliated products. The strike of the foliation is generally north-west—south-east but there are many exceptions due usually to later movements. Basic dykes intruded after the foliation of the gneiss are crushed into belts of hornblende schist. Such belts are better developed on the mainland about Gairloch and Loch Alsh than in the islands.

A noteworthy feature in the Outer Hebrides is a thrust with a low easterly dip that cuts the gneiss near the east coast and shears it into a flinty crush rock or into shaly mylonite. On the mainland east of the Sound of Sleat there is a considerable development of schists made from Lewisian Gneiss. In places these have not been differentiated from the younger Moine Schists.

TORRIDON SANDSTONE   Resting, often with low dip, on an irregularly sculptured platform of Lewisian Gneiss is a thick development of sandstones known from the type locality between Kinlochewe and Applecross as the Torridon Sandstone. Red and brown are the prevalent colours but some of the intercalated shales are grey, green or black and it may be remarked that the shales are uncleaved. Current bedding is common in the sandstones. The formation has been divided into three main groups. These show marked variations in thickness being thickest in the south and thinner, or in the case of the lowest group, absent, in the north. Thus the lowest or Diabaig Group is 7,200 ft. thick in Skye, 500 ft. in Gairloch and absent farther north; the next or Applecross Group is 6,000 to 8,000 ft. thick around Applecross but thins to 1,000 ft. at Cape Wrath; while the uppermost or Aultbea Group (named from Aultbea on Loch Ewe) diminishes from 4,000 ft. thereabouts to 250 ft. at Cape Wrath. The Diabaig Group is present in eastern Rum, is well developed in south-east Skye and on parts of the mainland up to the top of Loch

Kishorn; then south-east from Gairloch before swinging northwards across Loch Maree to encircle the Lewisian inlier there. The Applecross Group usually lying west of the lower group is present in northern Rum, south-east Skye, on much of the ground west of Kinlochewe and on the north-west side of Raasay. The Aultbea Group in addition to the type locality occurs principally in the coastal tract south of Applecross. The Applecross Group is characterized by red-brown coarse sandstone and arkose with conglomerates; the other groups are less coarse and have shales and calcareous lenses.

CAMBRIAN This formation succeeds the Torridon Sandstone unconformably and in places transgresses on to Lewisian. As in north Scotland (q.v.) the formation comprises over 2,100 ft. of strata of which the lowest 500 ft. is arenaceous while the rest, apart from 70–80 ft. of passage beds is of limestones and dolomites.

The Basal Quartzite of false-bedded grits and quartzites with a conglomerate at the base is about 330 ft. thick in Skye. The next subdivision, the Pipe Rock, is of massive and flaggy fine-grained quartzites characterized by vertical worm casts ('pipes') and is 250 to 300 ft. thick.

In the Passage Beds the lower half is of dolomitic shales known as Fucoid Beds from erroneous naming of markings on the bedding planes now recognized as flattened worm casts. These shales have yielded several species of *Olenellus*—a trilobite diagnostic of Lower Cambrian. The upper half of the Passage Beds is of the Serpulite Grit, part shaly part dolomitic, also with *Olenellus* and with *Salterella* (the tubular shell of a mollusc previously misnamed as the worm *Serpulites*). This shell also occurs in the basal part of the limestone which is therefore referred to Lower Cambrian also.

The lower 1,000 ft. of limestone is poorly fossiliferous but higher portions have yielded fossils, chiefly gastropods and cephalopods, referable to the Upper Cambrian and Lower Ordovician. This fossiliferous group in Skye where it is in contact with a granophyre intruded in Tertiary times is altered to serpentine and marble in concentric rings resembling the pseudofossil *Eozoon canadense*.

On the mainland for some distance north and south of Loch Maree the Durness Limestone and in places the Serpulite Grit is absent owing to denudation.

MOINE From Whitten Head, Loch Eriboll (Sheet 26) to the south-eastern part of Skye the rocks are dislocated by a great thrust fault—the Moine Thrust—accompanied by similar faults which in places make up a broad zone of disturbance as, for example, in Assynt (see page 272). This, in general, forms the eastern boundary of the Cambrian and Torridonian and for much but not all of the Lewisian. To the east of it and in most places carried forward on top of the Moine Thrust there is a great spread of schistose and granulitic rocks known as the Moine Series. They are mainly derived by the metamorphism of sedimentary rocks in which sandstones give rise to quartzites and granulites, and shales to mica schists often with garnets. In places pebbles, graded bedding and false bedding are recognizable. The least altered strata regarded as Moine occur in south-east Skye and there lie west of the main or Moine Thrust-plane though believed to be carried

into that position by a lower thrust—that of Tarskavaig. Shaly and gritty beds are succeeded by thick schistose grits with pebbles of quartz and feldspar obviously stretched by movement.

MESOZOIC ROCKS Permian rocks are absent from this region but the Mesozoic is fairly well represented though there are several gaps in the succession, and even allowing for these the formations are thinner than in England.

There are small patches of Trias in north-west Rum, in south-east Raasay and in south-east Skye. The measures are mixed; they include conglomerates, of which the pebbles vary according to the underlying rocks, and marls and sandstones with some calcareous nodules aggregated into 'cornstones'. They are believed to be of Keuper age. Rhaetic is not recognizable with certainty.

Jurassic strata are more widely distributed than the Trias and are present in Skye, Raasay, Eigg but not in Rum. In places, as in Skye, south-west of Broadford, beds well up in the Lower Lias (Semicostatum Beds) rest directly on older rocks.

In general about 300 ft. of the Lower Lias (Broadford Beds) is of limestones with shales, followed by calcareous sandstones; next comes about 700 ft. of sandy micaceous shales (Pabba Beds). The Middle Lias (250 ft.) and top part of the Lower Lias is of the White Scalpa Sandstone. Shales with jet and the 1 to 8-ft. Raasay Ironstone near the top make up the 80 ft. of Upper Lias. Several zones are absent below and above the ironstone. The Inferior Oolite is usually of sandstone (partly calcareous and up to 650 ft. thick) while the Estuarine Series (representing the Great Oolite and about 600 ft. thick in Skye but down to 460 ft. in Eigg and Muck) comprises dark shales with thin limestones and sandstones; at the base is 7 to 10 ft. of oil shale. The Cornbrash is represented by 23 ft. of gritty limestone in Raasay.

The best exposures of the dark Oxford Clay shales is in Staffin Bay, north-east Skye; the formation is 125 ft. thick. It is followed by 140 ft. of Corallian—at Staffin Bay blue shales but in Strathaird peninsula south-east Skye of shales and sandstones. About 40 ft. of Kimmeridge Clay shales is present in Staffin Bay.

Upper Cretaceous sandstone and glauconitic marl rest on Lower Corallian in Eigg and on the coast of east Skye near Allt Strollamus 15 ft. of altered limestone represents the Chalk which presumably succeeds a grit referred to Greensand on nearby Scalpa Island.

TERTIARY ROCKS Tertiary sediments occupy small hollows in the pre-Tertiary land surface; they are thin, limited to a few localities and consist of sandstones, shales and ashy muds with plant remains, as for example, at the mouth of the River Chracaig near Portree. By contrast there are thick masses of igneous rocks with plutonic types making up the Cuillins and the great sheets of lavas elsewhere which together largely control the topography of Skye. Between the lava flows there are occasional lenses of sandstones, conglomerates and mudstones with leaf beds and lignite suggestive of a Mediterranean climate and Eocene age.

Lavas occupy more than half of the area of Skye and form a great peaty and heather clad plateau north of the Cuillins. For the most part they consist of

olivine basalts but on the northern flank of the Cuillins they are interdigitated with rhyolitic lavas, tuffs and agglomerates and trachytes with porphyritic andesites (see, for example, Bruach na Frith). In general these plateau lavas with tuffs at the base rest on and thereby preserve the softer Jurassic sediments. Their full thickness exceeds 2,000 ft.

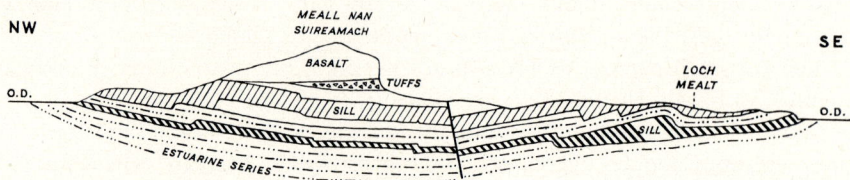

Figure 57. Section across Northern Skye to show Tertiary basalt with basal tuff on Oxford–Kimmeridge Clay, with upper sill, and Estuarine Series with lower sill of olivine dolerite.

(After F. W. Anderson, International Geological Congress 1948, Excursion 14)

The lavas are associated with great plutonic intrusions forming the Cuillins in Skye. The rugged serrated Black Cuillins on the west with twenty peaks over 3,000 ft. high are mainly of gabbro but include the ultrabasic rocks of Sgurr Dubh, whereas the smoother Red Hills to the east are of granophyre and granite. The order of intrusion appears to be one of decreasing basicity i.e. granitic rocks last. Associated with the gabbro mass are a series of dykes and cone sheets mainly of dolerite.

In northern Skye thick sills of dolerite emerge through the Mesozoic sediments and emanating from the Cuillins area is a swarm of dykes of similar material.

Exposures of these various igneous rocks are common in Skye but for plateau basalts see Storr where 1,000 ft. are visible.

Rum may be regarded as a miniature Skye except that the ultra-basic rocks, better developed and more varied, occur in alternating sheets on the hills of Allival and Askival. On the west of the island about Orval Hill is a large mass of horn-blende granophyre.

In Canna, the 400-ft. cliffs of the Compass Hill on the eastern seaboard show alternations of conglomerates and tuffs with columnar dolerites interpreted by various workers as sills or as lava flows.

Attention may also be drawn to Eigg where the great Sgurr of pitchstone rises from the lava plateau.

REFERENCES

Geological Survey
    Regional Handbooks: Tertiary Volcanic Districts, ed 2, 1948; *Northern Highlands*, ed 2, 1948.
    'Geology of the Outer Hebrides', H. J. Jehu and R. M. Craig. *Trans. Roy. Soc. Edin.*, 1923–34,
        vols. 53–55 and 57.
Excursions and Field Meetings
    International Geological Congress 1948.
    Long Excursions: A13 Skye; C14 Skye and Morar.
Geologists Association, Proceedings or Circulars
    1951, Skye and Ardnamurchan.

SHEET 26

NORTHERN SCOTLAND

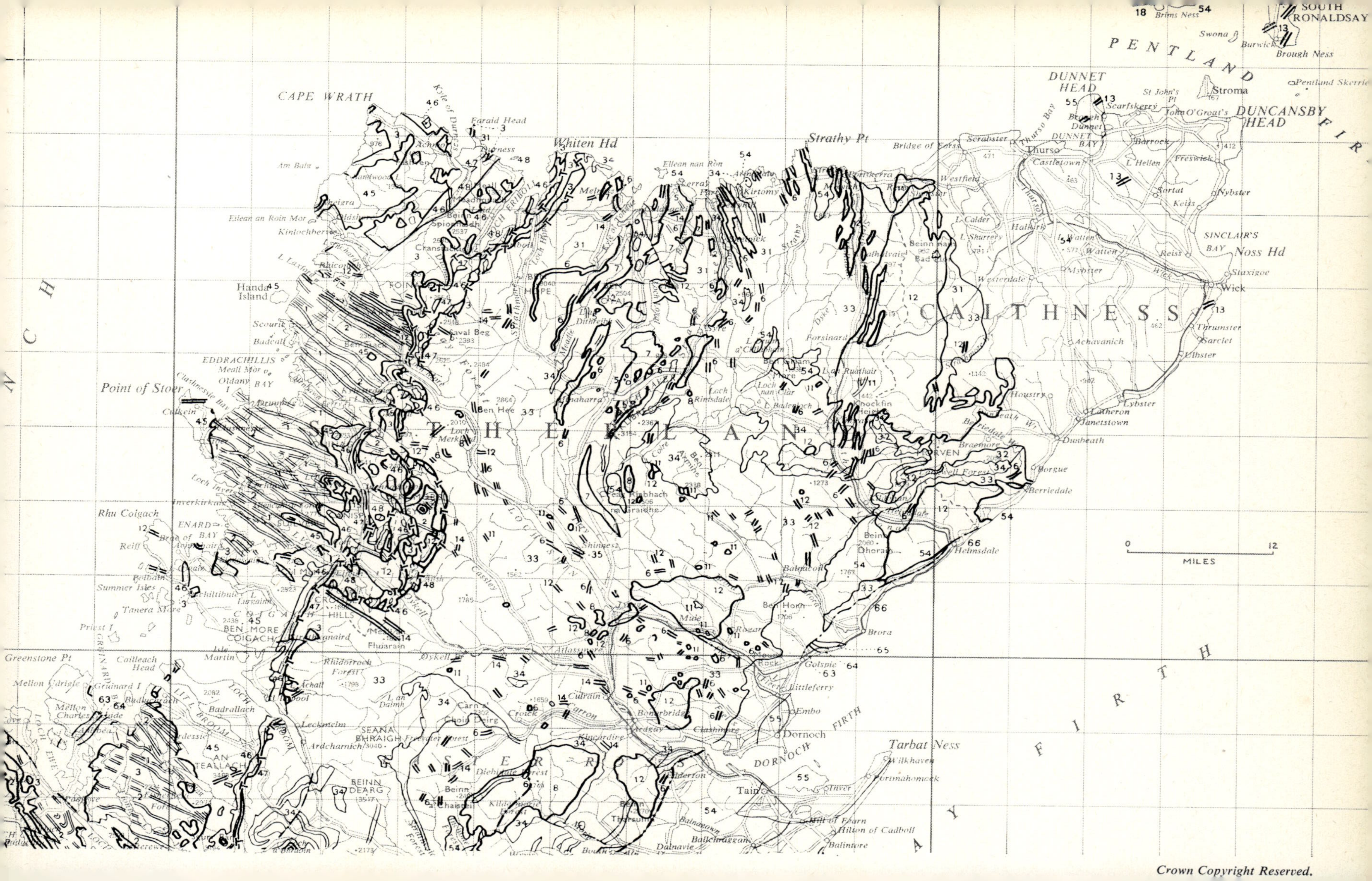
CAPE WRATH
PENTLAND FIRTH
DUNNET HEAD
DUNCANSBY HEAD
SOUTH RONALDSAY
Stroma
Brims Ness
Swona
Burwick
Brough Ness
Pentland Skerries
John O'Groat's
St John's Pt
Scarfskerry
DUNNET BAY
Thurso
Thurso Bay
Castletown
Scrabster
Bridge of Forss
Strathy Pt
Whiten Hd
Faraid Head
Kyle of Durness
Durness
Eilean nan Ròn
Kirtomy
Westfield
Halkirk
L. Calder
L. Shurrery
L. Watten
Watten
Mybster
SINCLAIR'S BAY
Noss Hd
Staxigoe
Wick
Reiss
Keiss
Nybster
Sortat
Freswick
Barrock
L. Heilen
Westerdale
CAITHNESS
SUTHERLAND
Thrumster
Sarclet
Ulbster
Achavanich
Forsinard
Houstry
Lybster
Latheron
Janetstown
Dunbeath
Braemore
Berriedale
Borgue
Helmsdale
Brora
Golspie
Littleferry
Embo
Dornoch
DORNOCH FIRTH
Tarbat Ness
Wilkhaven
Portmahomack
Tain
Inver
Mill of Fearn
Hilton of Cadboll
Balintore
Ballchraggan
Dalnavie
Balnagown
Bonarbridge
Clashmore
Kincardine
Carron
Culrain
Croick
Oykell
Atlassmore
Rogart
Mude
Ben Horn
Balnacoil
Ben Klibreck
Loch Naver
Loch Loyal
Ben Hope
Loch Hope
LOCH ERIBOLL
Ben Hee
Saval Beg
Loch Merkland
Loch Shin
Shinness
Cassley
Handa Island
Scourie
Badcall
EDDRACHILLIS BAY
Meall Mor
Oldany I
Point of Stoer
Clashnessie Bay
Culkein
Drumbeg
Loch Inver
Inverkirkaig
ENARD BAY
Rhu Coigach
Reiff
Summer Isles
Tanera More
Priest I
Achiltibuie
COIGACH
BEN MORE COIGACH
CROMALT HILLS
Isle Martin
Greenstone Pt
Cailleach Head
Gruinard I
Mellon Udrigle
Badrallach
LITTLE LOCH BROOM
LOCH BROOM
Ullapool
Leckmelm
Ardcharnich
Rhidorroch Forest
SEANA BHRAIGH
BEINN DEARG
AN TEALLACH
LOCH EWE
Kinlochbervie
Eilean an Roin Mor
Am Balg
Rhiconich
L. Laxford
Cranstackie
Kinloch
Rhidorroch
Dibidale Forest
Kildermorie Forest
0 MILES 12
Crown Copyright Reserved.

NORTHERN SCOTLAND

THE country included in this sheet extends from Cape Wrath and Duncansby Head to beyond Dornoch and Loch Gairloch and embraces Caithness, Sutherland and much of northern Ross and Cromarty; it is a wild thinly populated country of mountains, ranging up to 3,273 ft. at Ben More Assynt near Inchnadamff, with lochs occupying many of the valleys and sea lochs extending far inland. The watershed ranges roughly west-south-west from Wick then westerly before swinging south-west by Inchnadamff to Loch Broom.

Caithness is mainly of Old Red Sandstone; the rest of the district is mostly of Moine schists with, in the west, Lewisian gneisses, Torridon Sandstone and Cambrian rocks brought into startling juxtaposition by great thrusts. On the east coast there is a narrow downfaulted strip of Jurassic rocks with the workable coal of Brora. The towns are small and are mainly on the coast; they serve as fishing and market centres.

LEWISIAN   The most interesting tract both scenically and geologically is that fringing the western seaboard from Loch Eriboll to Loch Broom. Here the foundation rock is Lewisian gneiss. This is mainly made up of plutonic rocks crushed and recrystallized into foliated small lenses of quartz and feldspar along with various ferromagnesian minerals, such as pyroxenes, hornblende and biotite, which serve to distinguish the various types. There are, however, some gneisses formed by a similar alteration of sandstones, shales and limestone believed to be of marine origin. The original plutonic rocks of the first and dominant group varied from granites to diorites and the resultant acid or more basic gneisses show some regional distribution: thus hornblende and biotite gneisses predominate about Cape Wrath while pyroxene types prevail towards Loch Broom.

The gneisses have been invaded by basic and ultrabasic dykes of considerable breadth and lateral extent which cut across the gneiss foliation. The basic types range from diorites to gabbros; these shear to hornblende schists. The ultrabasic dykes alter to serpentine and are sheared into chlorite- and talc-schists; they trend west-north-west and cut the former which range north-west—south-east, roughly parallel to the main folding. Dykes are particularly abundant in the tract between Loch Laxford and Enard Bay.

MOINE SERIES   This name is given to a great series of sediments and of igneous intrusions into them, which have been metamorphosed into schists and over considerable tracts converted by injection of granitic magma into gneisses. The total thickness of the series is estimated to be of the order of 20,000 ft. but no complete and countrywide stratigraphical or structural succession has been established though one of psammitic (sandy), pelitic (shaly), psammitic types appears to

be fairly general. The rocks have been correlated with Lewisian, Torridonian and post-Cambrian but a date of post-Lewisian and pre-Torridonian is commonly accepted, though the metamorphism may be an early phase of the Caledonian movements which culminated with the great thrusts of which the major one bounds the coastal tract already referred to from Eriboll to Ullapool and thence to the Point of Sleat in Skye.

The commonest rock types are quartz feldspar granulites and mica schists derived largely from sandstones and shales respectively and the interbanding of these types reflects close alternation of the original sediments. The quartz and feldspar are not segregated into folia and though of similar general composition the granulites differ in this respect from the Lewisian gneisses. Garnets from microscopic sizes to an inch in diameter are common in the schists.

There are long belts of hornblendic gneisses in northern and central Sutherland which resemble some of the Lewisian rocks.

There are also some calc-silicate granulites and crystalline limestones as, for example, at Shinness on Loch Shin.

Isoclinal folding is prevalent with axial planes dipping between east and south-east and on these major folds there are parallel subsidiary isoclines. The pre-metamorphic strike of the beds, as shown by the alternation of granulites and schists, is generally N.N.E.—S.S.W.

Sills of dolerite are the commonest of the minor pre-foliation intrusives though there are large granitic intrusions with contact metamorphic aureoles at Carn Chuinneag and Inchbae (about 20 miles W.S.W. of Dornoch) which are now augen gneisses with large 'eyes' of feldspar.

Between the large granite mass on the Caithness–Sutherland boundary and the smaller outcrop of granite to the west and as far south as the granite between Loch Shin and Dornoch there is an extensive tract of Moine Series which by the invasion of granitic magma has been converted into gneisses, mica schists and pegmatite schists. The outcrops, however, are not delimited on the map apart from those of mica schists around Loch Coire and Loch Badenloch though the western limit approximates to the outcrops of hornblende gneiss and schists between Tongue and Loch Shin.

At a later period there was further invasion by granitic and other material which took the more usual form of stocks. Of these attention may be directed to the granites west of Dornoch, that of Helmsdale and to the syenite about Loch Loyal.

TORRIDONIAN In the fifteen-mile broad coastal tract between lochs Eriboll, Broom and Maree the next dominant type to the Lewisian is the Torridon Sandstone which rests unconformably on an old and undulating land surface of Lewisian gneiss. Since it is succeeded by the unconformable Cambrian its pre-Cambrian age is beyond question. Recognizable fossils are unknown but obscure worm tracks and phosphatic nodules suggest some forms of life.

Sandstones and the feldspathic grits known as arkoses, interspersed with conglomerate and shale layers make up the bulk of the formation, and red is the prevalent colour though there are some breccia and boulder beds and some green,

grey and black shales and flags. The sandstones are false-bedded; they show ripple marks, rain pits and sun cracks and the shales are uncleaved so that the formation in spite of its great age is practically unaltered; it has escaped folding and dips are usually low except in the vicinity of faults.

The thickness of the formation in Northern Scotland is about 1,250 ft. but farther south is several times that amount (see page 265).

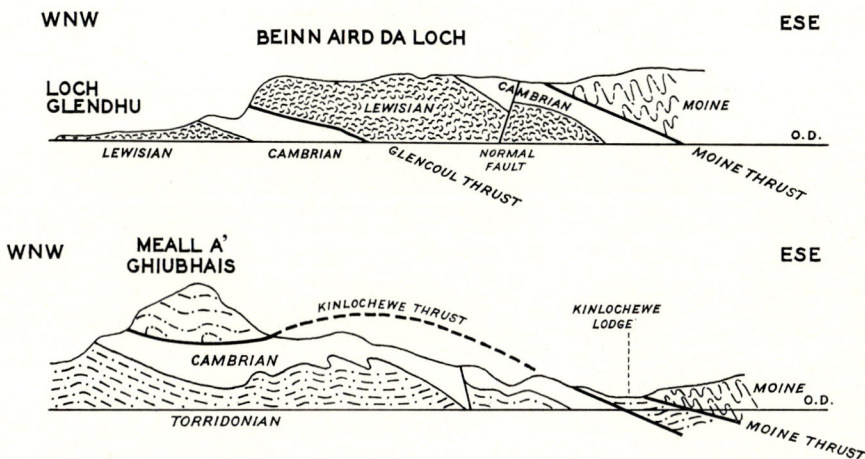

Figure 58. Sections to illustrate the structure of the North West Highlands

Lewisian, Moine and Torridonian thrust over Cambrian (Simplified from Fig. 14, *The Northern Highlands* Geol. Surv. Handbook)

CAMBRIAN As mentioned above the Cambrian succeeds the Torridonian unconformably and since the former where undisturbed by faults dip easterly at 5–20° it is evident that previous to Cambrian sedimentation the now flat Torridon Sandstone should have had a corresponding dip in the opposite direction. It is not surprising, therefore, that the Cambrian transgresses Torridonian and in places rests on Lewisian as, for example, in the Assynt area.

Beginning with a few feet of basal pebbly grit and conglomerate the lower 500 ft. of the Cambrian consists of quartzites—false-bedded in the lower part but alternatively massive and flaggy in the upper part which is also characterized by vertical worm burrows and known as the Pipe Rock. Next come about 50 ft. of dolomitic shales (whose peculiar worm cast markings were mistaken for fucoids hence their name of Fucoid Beds) which yield various species of *Olenellus* a trilobite diagnostic of the Lower Cambrian. These shales are followed by about 30 ft. of the so-called Serpulite Grit rich in *Salterella* a mollusc previously described as the worm *Serpulites maccullochi*.

The sequence is completed by over 1,500 ft. of dolomitic limestone, known as

Durness Limestone, locally rich in gastropods and cephalopods some of which range into the Ordovician of other regions though the greater part of the formation is referable to the Cambrian.

Mention has been made of a great thrust fault separating Moine Series on the east from a coastal belt where Lewisian gneisses, Torridonian sandstones and Cambrian quartzites and limestones occur in upward sequence. The broad effect of this so-called Moine Thrust is to bring Moine schists on top of the Cambrian. The detailed relationships, however, are not quite so simple for the Moine Thrust is usually accompanied by lower thrusts not of such great lateral extent but still of great size and effect. Lenses of displaced rocks between such thrusts are known as 'nappes'. The thrusts though usually of low inclination steepen in places and may locally be bent into folds and overfolds. Minor steep thrusts add to the dislocations and give an imbricate structure. The metamorphism induced by these movements is described as retrograde for instead of shales, for example, being converted into crystalline schists of quartz and mica etc. as is usually the case, dark ferro-magnesian minerals are altered to chlorite and epidote and hard rocks are ground into shaly mylonite.

In the Assynt district the disturbed zone is seven miles wide and sections there have become geological classics. Although these are involved structures recognition of the various members is rendered easier by the fact that they show marked differences in weathering as well as original colour differences of white for Cambrian, red or brown for Torridonian and grey for Lewisian. Attention may be drawn to Loch Eriboll where on the east the Moine Thrust brings schists on to Lewisian gneiss, surmounted by Cambrian, which is shoved westwards over Cambrian by another thrust; or to Ben More of gneiss capped by basal Cambrian which dipping into lower ground on the east is overridden by Moine schists of Sron Lam while towards the west and the river Traligill the Ben More gneiss is carried forward by other thrusts on to Cambrian. These and other examples are figured on page 273.

OLD RED SANDSTONE   This formation covers most of Caithness and much ground bordering the Moray Firth. Apart from such magnificent cliffs as Dunnet Head and Duncansby Head and hills such as Morven it gives rise to rather monotonous country. Lower Old Red Sandstone is not recognized in this region and Upper Old Red Sandstone is confined to Dunnet Head and the Dornoch–Tarbat Ness areas. Fishes are the characteristic fossils and many of these occur in definite beds, which are usually calcareous, but fossil plants are also of interest.

At the base is the Barren Red Series, devoid of fossils, which may reach 3,000 ft. in thickness; it is made up of conglomerates, grits, sandstones and mudstones and its upper members overstep the lower ones and rest with local basal conglomerates on Moine schists. The succeeding Caithness Flagstones, up to 10,000 ft. thick are characterized by repeated sequences of thick beds of sandstones and flags, thin mudstones and thinner calcareous flags and limestones. Ripple-marks, sun-cracks and current-bedding characterize the sandstones which are of pale tint

whereas the flags in the lower part (Wick Group) are dark, or are blue or pale brown in the upper (Thurso) group which has provided much paving stone.

John o'Groats Sandstones complete the Middle Old Red; they are red and yellow friable calcareous sandstones at least 2,000 ft. thick.

Fossils from the Middle Old Red Sandstone include amongst others *Pterichthys* (see page 17).

The Upper Old Red Sandstone consists of 2,000 ft. of pink, yellow and red sandstones and grits strongly false-bedded and with numerous clay galls. Scales of *Holoptychius* occur sparingly.

Fossil Localities Along Allt Muigh-bhlaraidh burn about two miles east of Aultnamain; 10 ft. of greenish shales with sandstones and impure limestone nodules with fish remains. Holborn Head Quarry, top of 300-ft. cliff two miles west of Holborn Head, Thurso. Halkirk five miles south of Thurso: river bank below church and a quarter of a mile upstream. Achanarras Quarry, a quarter of a mile S.S.W. of Archanarras Farm and three miles S.S.E. of Halkirk. Spittle Quarry, one mile east of Achanarras Quarry. Banniskirk Quarry, one and a half miles north of Spittle Quarry. Murkle Bay, three and a half miles east of Thurso, on south-east side not far below John o'Groats Sandstone.

MESOZOIC ROCKS   A narrow strip of Mesozoic strata is faulted down along the east Sutherland coast for twenty miles N.E. of Goldspie. The sequence begins on the south with pale Triassic sandstone followed by red and green marls with a band of cherty limestone. Next comes 250 ft. of pebbly grits referred to the Rhaetic followed by sandstones and clays with two thin limestones with shells indicative of the Lower Lias. Middle and Upper Lias strata are probably cut out by a fault and a 50-ft. sandstone overlain by clays and black shales with the Brora Coal are referred to the Estuarine Series of the Oolites. The coal, somewhat ashy and pyritous, is $3\frac{1}{2}$ ft. thick and is worked at the Brora Colliery. A thin impure limestone (Brora Roof Bed) represents Kellaways Rock followed by shales and these by sandstones which together are equated with the Oxford Clay, topped by limestones and sandstones of the Lower Corallian. With some strata missing the Upper Corallian comprises sandstones, clays and limestones; then come the Kimmeridge with a thick sandstone in the lower part and then mixed measures with boulder beds from 5 to 200 ft. thick. The thickest boulder bed is at Dun Glas and consists of immense blocks of Middle Old Red Sandstone embedded in shelly gritty limestone. Views as to origin range from cliff screes and overturned sea stacks to debris from a submarine fault-scarp shattered by earthquakes and overwhelmed by tidal waves.

In the Jurassic strata fossils are common and include ammonites and plants.

SUPERFICIAL DEPOSITS   Boulder clay is common in Caithness and the most remarkable erratic is an enormous one of Lower Cretaceous sandstone associated with Tertiary clay at Leavad three miles south of Spital. This boulder 240 × 150 yards and 26 feet thick is believed to have been brought by ice from the sea floor off Lybster. Elsewhere boulder clay is restricted to lower ground.

Terraces at Brora and Helmsdale that suggest correlation with the 100-ft. Raised Beach, and submerged peat at Goldspie and Wick point to former oscillations of sea level.

Although coal is worked at Brora the main fuel of the area is peat. Some of the Brora coal is used in a neighbouring brickworks.

REFERENCES

Geological Survey
  Regional Handbook: Northern Highlands, ed 2, 1948.
  Assynt Mountains, Guide to Geological Model.
  Geological Maps. Six-inch maps with geological lines but uncoloured are available for two noteworthy localities—Sheet 5 (in 1 inch 114) Durness, and Sheet 71 (in 1 inch 101 and 107) Inchnadamph, Loch Assynt.
Excursions and Field Meetings
  Geological Excursion Guide to Assynt District of Sutherland, M. Macgregor and J. Phemister, 1937, Edinburgh.
  International Geological Congress 1948.
  Long Excursions: A14 N.W. Highlands; C12 Eastern Highlands; C16 Vertebrate Palaeontology; A19 Scotland, General.
Geologists Association, Proceedings
  1930, East Sutherland.

SHEET 27

NORTHERN HEBRIDES

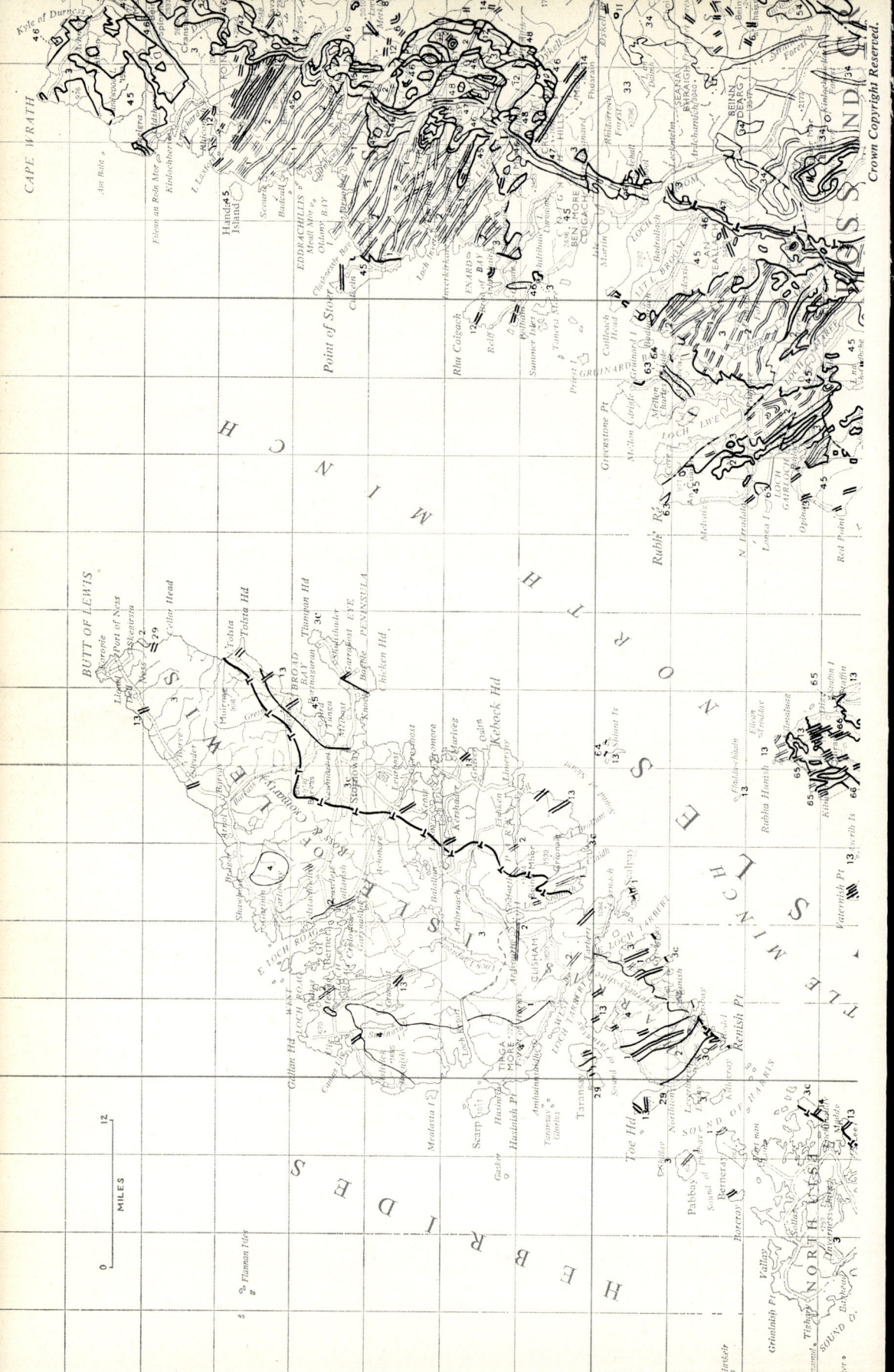

CAPE WRATH

Kyle of Durness

BUTT OF LEWIS
Port of Ness

LEWIS

ROSS & CROMARTY

NORTH MINCH

THE MINCH

LITTLE MINCH

HEBRIDES

ISLE OF SKYE

NORTH UIST

SOUND OF HARRIS

LOCH TARBERT

EDDRACHILLIS

Point of Stoer

Rhu Coigach

BEN MORE
COIGACH

GRUINARD

Geenstone Pt

LOCH EWE

LOCH GAIRLOCH

LOCH TORRIDON

Tolsta

Tolsta Hd

Tiumpan Hd

BROAD BAY

EYE PENINSULA

Chicken Hd

Kebock Hd

Shiant Is

Rubha Hunish

Waternish Pt

Toe Hd

Renish Pt

MILES

0   12

NORTHERN HEBRIDES

THE Outer Hebrides are made up of several islands ranging from the large one of Lewis with its northern tip, the Butt of Lewis, about forty-five miles west of Cape Wrath, to the small Berneray on the south with Barra Head about fifty-five miles west of Ardnamurchan. Together they constitute what is known as the 'Long Island'. Many of the islands are separated by narrow straits. The southern portion, Harris, of the north island is still joined by a narrow isthmus (on which stands Tarbert) to its large neighbour, Lewis, the two arms of the sea being known respectively as East and West Loch Tarbert. All the islands have much in common; none of them reaches any great elevation, gneiss is the prevalent rock, there are many freshwater lochs and innumerable sea lochs. Oddly enough the eastern seaboard is more deeply dissected than that which faces the Atlantic. The presence of peat descending beneath the waves in some of the sea lochs suggests that a relatively modern submergence has drowned the valleys.

The southern half of Long Island is included in Sheet 25 (see also page 265). The present account is concerned with Lewis and Harris and the adjacent isles.

Lewis is largely peat covered and low lying. In the north some of the central belt of hills reach about 900 ft.; in the south the country is more mountainous with elevations of 1,800 ft. Tarbert has already been mentioned but the principal town and port is Stornaway situated at the neck of the Eye Peninsula on the eastern coast of Lewis. The other settlements are small. Cattle are raised but sheep predominate and furnish the basis of the famous product known as Harris Tweed.

Lewis is, as one might expect, the type locality for the Lewisian gneisses. These, as elsewhere, are of two types (a) orthogneisses derived from various igneous rocks and (b) paragneisses which represent extreme alteration of sedimentary rocks such as shales, sandstones and limestones into crystalline, foliated, graphitic, micaceous and quartzose schists and gneisses and schistose limestones with crystals of various minerals due to original impurities. The orthogneiss is chiefly a grey or pink granitic rock with biotite or hornblende. The hornblende gneisses are often richly garnetiferous in pillow-like masses. Veins of pegmatite are fairly common. In both types foliation is dominantly north-west—south-east.

Ranging nearly the whole length of the Long Island on its eastern side is a great disturbance along which the rocks have been crushed into a flinty mylonite. From its form on the map this is evidently a low-angled thrust. In the area under review it courses from Tolsta north-east of Stornoway to Renish Point in south-east Harris. In the latter region it traverses a broad belt of hornblende schist. Farther north to Tarbert it forms the south-eastern boundary of a foliated granite which also has an

outcrop of considerable size in western Lewis as well as smaller ones on each flank of Loch Roag.

Later in age than any of the preceding rocks and structures is a series of red sandstones and conglomerates developed near Stornoway where they form the western shore of Broad Bay and also occupy the neck of the Eye Peninsula, the rest of which is of gneiss. The age of these Stornoway Beds is usually regarded as Torridonian.

Dykes in the above series of gneisses and sandstones range from ultrabasic types, such as are developed in the gneisses of Harris, to the more widespread dolerites.

The Shiant Isles to the east are more akin to Skye than to Lewis. The two western isles, united by a shingle beach, are of a sill at least 500 ft. thick resting on Upper Lias shale; no upper contact is to be seen. The sill is of the peculiar rock type known as crinanite—a basic dolerite with analcime in place of feldspar.

The small islands lying well to the west of the Orkney–Shetland groups are included here for convenience. Sule Skerry and Stack Skerry, situated Lat. 59° W. Long. 4° 30′, and Rona, W. Long. 6°, are of Lewisian gneiss. The St. Kilda group Lat. 57° 50′ W. Long. 8° 30′ show more variety for they are made up of igneous rocks ranging from gabbro to granite.

REFERENCES

Geological Survey
  Regional Handbook: Northern Highlands, ed 2, 1948.
  'Geology of the Outer Hebrides', H. J. Jehu and R. M. Craig. *Trans. Roy. Soc. Edin.*, 1923–34, vols 53–55 and 57.
Edinburgh Geological Society
  1958, Guide to Assynt District.

SHEET 28

ORKNEY ISLANDS

ORKNEY ISLANDS

Fair Isle
N Haven
S Harbour
753

MULL HEAD
Noup Hd
Bow Head
Papa Westray
Papa Sound
WESTRAY
Sacquoy Hd
ROUSAY
THE NORTH SOUND
Stanger Hd
Rapness
Egilsay
Wyre
Gairsay
EDAY SOUND
EDAY
Backaland
Calf of Eday
Fersness
Linga Holm
Mill Holm

North Ronaldsay
Dennis Head
Linklet Bay
Strom Ness
NORTH RONALDSAY FIRTH
Tofts Ness
START POINT
Northwall
Bay of Lopness
SANDAY
Tres Ness
SANDAY SOUND
Bay of Holland
Papa Stronsay
STRONSAY
Lamb Head
Auskerry
AUSKERRY SOUND
Rothiesholm
Ness of Ork

SHAPINSAY SOUND
SHAPINSAY
Rerwick Head
Hall Hd
Mull Hd
Point of Ayre
Rousinay

MAINLAND
FIRTH
LOCH HARRAY
Ward Hill
KIRKWALL
Deerness
Copinsay
Mull Head

BROUGH HEAD
The Barony
L of Boardhouse
Birsay
Costa
Redland
Evie
Finstown

Bay of Skaill
Yescanaby
Stromness
HOY SOUND
Graemsay
St John's Head
RORA HEAD
HOY
Ward Hill
Lyness
Longhope
Melsetter
Flotta
Fara
Cava
Rysa
SCAPA FLOW
SWITHA
Hunda
Barrel of Butter
Burray
Glims Holm
Lamb Holm
St Mary's Hope
Burwick
SOUTH RONALDSAY
Brough Ness
Swona
Stroma
PENTLAND FIRTH
Pentland Skerries
Barth Head

DUNCANSBY HEAD
John O'Groat's
Freswick
Keiss
Duncansby
Canisbay
DUNNET HEAD
Scarfskerry
St John's Pt
Dunnet Bay
Castletown
Murkle Bay
Thurso
E Hellen

MILES
0   12

Sule Skerry
59° N
4° 30′ W
Stack Skerry

Rona
59° 5′ N
6° W
Sula Sgeir

Boreray
57° 50′ N
St Kilda
8° 20′ W
Soay
Dun

ORKNEY ISLANDS

THE Orkneys, separated from northern Scotland by the stormy Pentland Firth, are comprised of ninety islands and islets or skerries of which twenty-eight are inhabited. The chief islands are Pomona or Mainland (which is the largest and occupies a central position) flanked on the south by Hoy and South Ronaldsay (which with others enclose Scapa Flow) while to the north lie Shapinsay, Rousay, Eday, Stronsay, Westray, Sanday and North Ronaldsay. Much of the land lies below 200 ft. but West Mainland is circled by hills up to 800 ft. enclosing low land and several large lochs separated from each other and the sea by narrow barriers. Scapa Flow with its circle of islands resembles a similar topography 'drowned' to a depth of 30 fathoms. Hoy is mainly high ground with heights to 1,563 ft. and St. John's Head reaches 1,100 ft. Most of the coast has steep cliffs often cut by narrow inlets which follow joint planes, faults or dykes and are known as 'goes'. Old Red Sandstone is the dominant formation but some of the basement complex emerges about Stromness. Farming is the chief occupation followed by fishing and trading. Trees survive about Kirkwall the chief town but in general are stunted to wind-blown shrubs.

ANCIENT ROCKS The basement rocks include the pink and grey porphyritic granite of Stromness intruded into schists and gneisses similar to those of Sutherland. These old rocks stood as steep-sided hills when the Old Red Sandstone was laid down.

OLD RED SANDSTONE This formation is estimated to reach a thickness of about 18,000 ft. though Lower Old Red Sandstone is absent; of this great thickness 4,000 ft. is referable to Upper Old Red Sandstone and the rest to Middle Old Red Sandstone. The lowest group of the latter totalling perhaps 4,500 ft. is known as the Stromness Flags. Local basal breccias and conglomerates abut against the old land surface but pass laterally into normal sandstones; they are well exposed about Stromness, at Yescanaby and in Graemsay. Flags, however, predominate and are usually blue, grey or yellow with occasional calcareous bands. One of the latter which forms the dark limy flags of the Sandwich Fish Bed (10 ft. thick) carries *Osteolepis*, *Diploterus* and *Coccosteus* and is believed to lie about 3,500 ft. up in the group; it has been worked to a considerable extent for tilestones for local roofs. The next subdivision, known as the Rousay Beds, amounts to 5,000 ft. of alternating hard and soft flagstones though in Rousay it includes 300 ft. of pebbly sandstone. The succeeding Eday Group is largely of yellow and red false-bedded sandstones but is split by two considerable belts respectively of flags, about 800 ft. up, and of marls (about 2,000 ft. from the top). The flaggy belt includes flows of

dark vesicular basaltic lava of which there are good exposures in Point of Ayre (10 miles E.S.E. of Kirkwall), in the sea stack of Muckle Castle (in south Deerness) and in the Black Holm of Copinsay.

It is believed that a very considerable thickness of sandstones was denuded before a great outburst of vulcanicity ushered in the Upper Old Red Sandstone. This began with an explosive phase, giving ashes, followed by basic lava the total thickness amounting to 450 ft. There is a flow about 300 ft. thick at the Kame of Hoy, with a slaggy base, supporting vertical columns 200 ft. long in cliffs nearly 1,000 ft. high and lava also forms the base of the Old Man of Hoy—a 450-ft. vertical pillar of Hoy Sandstones. These Hoy Sandstones are alternating pink, red and yellow sandstones totalling over 3,500 ft. in thickness and are confined to the island of Hoy.

In addition to the volcanic rocks mentioned there are many volcanic vents filled with a breccia of flagstone in a matrix of lava—particularly in Hoy, South Ronaldsay and in East Mainland—and numerous dykes of dioritic rocks.

Fair Isle, the small island lying between Orkney and Shetland is made up of Old Red Sandstone tentatively referred to the lower subdivision.

The small islands lying well to the west of the Orkney-Shetland group are included here for convenience. Sule Skerry and Stack Skerry, situated Lat. 59° W. Long. 40° 30′ and Rona W. Long. 6°, are of Lewisian greiss. The St. Kilda group Lat. 57° 50′ W. Long. 8° 30′ show more variety for they are made up of igneous rocks ranging from gabbro to granite.

REFERENCES

Geological Survey
    Geology of the Orkney Islands, *Mem. Geol. Surv.*, 1935.
Geologists Association, Proceedings
    1937, Orkney and Shetland.

SHEET 29

SHETLAND ISLANDS

SHETLAND ISLANDS

Muckle Flugga
HERMA NESS
The Neap
Lamba Ness
Norwick
Burrafirth
Haroldswick
The Nev
Balta Sound
Balta
Uney
Gloup Holm
North Neaps
The Vere
Unst

Ramna Stacks
Gravey
Nev of Stuis
Houf Gruney
Point of Fethaland
Fiske Lingey
Uyea
Strandburgh Ness
Hascosay
The Snap
The Faither
Muckle Ossa
Gunzie
Ronas Voe
YELL SOUND
Otterswick
Esha Ness
Stenness
Hillswick
Burravoe
Vidlin Voe
Heoga Ness
Samphrey
ST MAGNUS
BAY
Lunna Ness
Muckle Skerry
Housay
Out Skerries
MUCKLE
ROE
The Gruey
Scatsta
Dury Voe
Skaw Taing
We Skerries
SWARBACKS
WHALSAY
Foula Skerry
Vementry
Papa Stour
The Has
Neap
South Nesting
Bay
Moul of Eswick
Gletness
Watt Ness
Vaila
Score Head
GRUTING VOE
BRESSAY
The Kame
Foula
THE DEEPS
Skelda Ness
Isle of Noss
Kirkabister
Bard Head
Oxna
West Burra
Huddabister
Helli Ness
South Havra
Mousa
Sandwick
St Ninian's Island
Northpunds
No Ness
Fora Ness
L. of Spiggie
Scousburgh
Boddam
Fitful Head
Quendale
Lady's Holm
SUMBURGH HEAD
Horse I
Sumburgh Roost

0   12
MILES

N Haven
Fair Isle
S Harbour

Seal Skerrs
Dennis Head
Linklet
Bay

SHETLAND ISLANDS

THESE islands lie fifty miles N.N.E. of the Orkneys and about 220 miles west of Bergen in Norway; it is not surprising, therefore, that there is a distinct Norse 'flavour' about the names. The largest of the many islands is the much dissected Mainland; to the east lie Bressay and Whalsey and to the north Yell, Fetlar and Unst; these constitute the main islands of the group. While the raising of sheep, cattle and ponies are important there is a greater dependence on fishing than in Orkney for many crops which flourish in Orkney will not grow or often fail in the northern isles. To some extent this may be due to soil as much as climate for unlike Orkney much of Shetland is made up of old schists and gneisses though some Old Red Sandstone is present. The nature of these old rocks and their arrangement into folds mostly of north–south trend determines the shape of islands which are elongated in the same directions. The coasts especially on the west are cut by long narrow and deep inlets known as 'voes'. Much of the land does not exceed 500 ft. in altitude though there are many exceptions especially in Mainland with its central ridge, that reaches nearly 1,000 ft., and Ronas Hill rising to 1,475 ft. in the north-west. Lerwick is the only town of consequence.

The foliated rocks of the Mainland of Shetland fall into two groups. Those of the west are mainly siliceous and hornblendic garnetiferous schists and gneisses with east–west foliation. The other and more extensive group strikes roughly north–south and the highly folded hard schists and gneisses alternating with softer schists, phyllites and limy bands give rise to a system of hills and valleys following narrow echelon folds. These rocks have been heavily impregnated by granitic material at some stage probably anterior to the emplacement of the large intrusions of granite and diorite though these too are foliated.

Foliated granites occupy the central tract and are flanked by impure limestones largely converted into calc silicates by metamorphism, but schists predominate. Limestone may be seen at Vatster (near Laxfirth and 5 miles N.N.W. of Lerwick) and it floors the valley at Sandwater. Siliceous schists, hornblende schists and foliated granites may be seen near the road on the north side of Olna Firth to Brae (18 miles N.N.W. of Lerwick) where a fault which farther south brings in Old Red Sandstone here introduces the granitic and dioritic rocks of the north-west.

Old Red Sandstone occupies the eastern coastal tract from Lerwick to Sumburgh Head, the much dissected peninsula of Walls in the west and again on the north side of St. Magnus Bay where it includes lavas and ashes. It begins with a basal breccia reflecting the rocks on which it rests, for example, with schist pebbles at Loch Brindister (4 miles S.W. of Lerwick) and granite near Spiggie (5 miles N.N.W. of Sumburgh Head). This is followed by the Brindister Flags—brown and purple

sandstones with fish beds at Ness of Sound (near Lerwick) and at Shingly Geo, Exnaboe (near Sumburgh) yielding *Dipterus* etc. Next comes the Rova Head Conglomerate, a coarse feldspathic grit with cobbles of schist, granite and quartzite, well developed between Rova Head and Gulberwick, respectively two miles north and south-west of Lerwick, followed by the grey and purple pebbly Lerwick Sandstones. The Bressay Flags complete the series; these are confined to Noss and Bressay islands; in the latter at Voe of Cullingsburgh they yield fish remains including *Holoptychius* which indicates Upper Old Red Sandstone whereas fishes from lower beds are of Middle Old Red Sandstone age.

In western Mainland most of the sandstones are crushed and indurated but softer beds yield plant and fish fragments at Melby (opposite Papa Stour) where also the intercalated ashes and lavas may be seen. Volcanic rocks are also exposed in Esha Ness the northern headland to St. Magnus Bay.

The island of Yell is mainly of phyllites and mica schists but Fetlar and Unst show more variety. Fetlar has schists on the west thrust against serpentine while the eastern peninsula is of conglomerate with pebbles stretched and sheared. Unst is traversed obliquely by a belt of serpentine flanked on the south-east by greenstone and hornblende schists and to the west by gneisses and schists carrying garnet, tourmaline, staurolite and kyanite and split by a 300-ft. zone of calc-silicate rocks representing an altered limestone. The history of dislocation metamorphism in Unst is too complicated for inclusion here and the reader is referred to papers by Prof. H. H. Read.

In the north-east corner of Unst there is the Skaw Granite with large feldspar crystals distorted into augen (eyes) and with inclusions of schists and granulites.

The small island of Foula, well to the west, is of Upper Old Red Sandstone resting on schists.

REFERENCES

Read, H. H., 1934, Metamorphic Geology of Unst in the Shetland Islands, *Quart. Journ. Geol. Soc.*, vol xc, pp. 637–88.
——— 1936, Metamorphic History of Unst, Shetland, *Proc. Geol. Assoc.*, vol. XLVII, pp. 289–93.
Wilson, G. V. and J. Knox, 1936, Geology of the Orkney and Shetland Islands, *Proc. Geol. Assoc.*, vol. XLVII, pp. 270–282.
——— 1937, Report of Orkney and Shetland Field Meeting (1936), vol XLVIII, pp. 61–76.

Printed in England by Spottiswoode, Ballantyne & Co. Ltd., London and Colchester   QTR

ENGLAND & WALES

INDEX AND EXPLA

SEDIMENTARY FORMATIONS

(All superficial deposits omitted)

Symbol	Formation	Series / System	Era
l	*Norwich & Red Crags & Chillesford Clay*	Pleistocene	QUATERNARY
k^1	*Coralline Crag*	Pliocene	TERTIARY
k	*Lenham & St. Erth Beds*	Pliocene	TERTIARY
i^{8-12}	*Hamstead, Bembridge, Osborne & Headon Series, & Bovey Beds*	Oligocene	TERTIARY
i^{4-7}	*Barton, Bracklesham & Bagshot Beds*	Eocene	TERTIARY
i^3	*London Clay*	Eocene	TERTIARY
i^{1-2}	*Oldhaven, Blackheath, Woolwich & Reading & Thanet Beds*	Eocene	TERTIARY
h^5	*Chalk (including Red Chalk)*	Cretaceous	MESOZOIC
h^{3-4}	*Upper Greensand & Gault*	Cretaceous	MESOZOIC
h^2	*Lower Greensand & Speeton Clay*	Cretaceous	MESOZOIC
h^1	*Weald Clay*	Cretaceous	MESOZOIC
h	*Hastings Beds*	Cretaceous	MESOZOIC
g^{14}	*Purbeck Beds*	Jurassic – Upper	MESOZOIC
g^{13}	*Portland Beds*	Jurassic – Upper	MESOZOIC
g^{12}	*Kimmeridge Clay*	Jurassic – Upper	MESOZOIC
g^{11}	*Corallian*	Jurassic – Upper	MESOZOIC
g^{10}	*Oxford Clay with Kellaways Beds*	Jurassic – Upper	MESOZOIC
g^9	*Cornbrash*	Jurassic – Middle	MESOZOIC
g^{5-8}: g^{6-8}	*Great Oolite Series*	Jurassic – Middle	MESOZOIC
g^{5-8}: g^5	*Inferior Oolite Series*	Jurassic – Middle	MESOZOIC
g^{3-4}	*Upper Lias*	Jurassic – Lower	MESOZOIC
g^2	*Middle Lias (Marlstone)*	Jurassic – Lower	MESOZOIC
g^1	*Lower Lias*	Jurassic – Lower	MESOZOIC
f^6	*Keuper Marl (with Rhaetic & Dolomitic Conglomerate)*	Triassic – New Red Sandstone	MESOZOIC
f^{1-5}: f^{4-5}	*Keuper Sandstone*	Triassic – New Red Sandstone	MESOZOIC
f^{1-5}: f^{1-3}	*Bunter Sandstone, Pebble Beds & basal breccias*	Triassic – New Red Sandstone	MESOZOIC
e	*Sandstones, marls and breccias*	Permian – New Red Sandstone	PALAEOZOIC
e^5	*Upper Permian Marl*	Permian – New Red Sandstone	PALAEOZOIC
e^4	*Magnesian Limestone (Upper)*	Permian – New Red Sandstone	PALAEOZOIC
e^3	*Middle Permian Marl*	Permian – New Red Sandstone	PALAEOZOIC
e^2	*Magnesian Limestone (Lower) & Basal Sands*	Permian – New Red Sandstone	PALAEOZOIC
d^6	*Barren Upper Coal Measures & Pennant Series*	Carboniferous	PALAEOZOIC
d^5	*Productive Coal Measures*	Carboniferous	PALAEOZOIC
d^4	*Millstone Grit & Culm Measures*	Carboniferous	PALAEOZOIC
d^2	*Carboniferous Limestone Series*	Carboniferous	PALAEOZOIC
(stippled)	*Basement Conglomerate*	Carboniferous	PALAEOZOIC
c^3	*Upper Old Red Sandstone & Upper Devonian*	Devonian	PALAEOZOIC
c	*Middle Devonian Limestone*	Devonian	PALAEOZOIC
c^2	*Middle Devonian & Ditton Series* (Lower Old Red Sandstone)	Devonian	PALAEOZOIC
c^1	*Downton Series & Lower Devonian* (Lower Old Red Sandstone)	Devonian	PALAEOZOIC
c	*Probably Devonian*	Devonian	PALAEOZOIC
b^{6-7}: b^7	*Limestones* / *Ludlow*	Silurian	PALAEOZOIC
b^{6-7}: b^6	*Wenlock*	Silurian	PALAEOZOIC
b^5	*Tarannon & Llandovery*	Silurian	PALAEOZOIC
b^{1-3}: b^3	*Ashgill & Caradoc*	Ordovician	PALAEOZOIC
b^{1-3}: b^2	*Llandeilo (partly volcanic)*	Ordovician	PALAEOZOIC
b^1	*Arenig*	Ordovician	PALAEOZOIC
?a	*Manx Slates & Dodman Series*	?	PALAEOZOIC
a: a^3	*Upper Cambrian*	Cambrian	PALAEOZOIC
a: a^{1-2}	*Middle & Lower Cambrian*	Cambrian	PALAEOZOIC
x	*Rocks of Anglesey, Charnwood, Longmynd & ?Ingleton*	Pre-Cambrian	

IGNEOUS ROCKS

Age, where known, indicated by formation letter, e.g.
Ge = *Permian Granite*

Symbol	Rock	Type
T	*Tuffs, Ashes & Agglomerates*	EXTRUSIVE
R	*Rhyolitic & Trachytic Lavas*	EXTRUSIVE
A	*Andesitic Lavas*	EXTRUSIVE
S	*Spilitic Lavas*	EXTRUSIVE
B	*Basaltic Lavas*	EXTRUSIVE
G	*Granite & Granophyre*	INTRUSIVE
F	*Syenite, Felsite, Porphyry*	INTRUSIVE
H	*Diorite, Camptonite, Lamprophyre*	INTRUSIVE
D	*Dolerite, Diabase, Greenstone & intrusive Basalt*	INTRUSIVE
E	*Gabbro*	INTRUSIVE
U	*Serpentine, Picrite*	INTRUSIVE

Metamorphic

Symbol	Rock
𝕲	*Gneiss, Mica Schist*
𝕳	*Hornblende Schists*

GEOLOGICAL BOUNDARIES

between major stratigraphical formations e.g. Devonian and Carboniferous.

between formations within a system, e.g. Millstone Grit and Coal Measures.

Major intrusion, e.g. granites, etc.

Major Thrusts

Major Faults